D0294931

BICTON
COLLEGE
of Agriculture
CULTUS EX MENTIS CULTU
Education Services
Centre

Practical Rare Breeds

Practical Rare Breeds

Valerie Porter

PELHAM BOOKS

First published in Great Britain by
Pelham Books Ltd
27 Wrights Lane
London W8 5TZ
1987

British Library Cataloguing in Publication Data
Porter, Valerie
Practical rare breeds:
a modern approach to the breeding
and farming of minority livestock.
1. Livestock breeds—Great Britain
2. Rare animals—Great Britain
I. Title
636.08′21′0941 SF105

ISBN 0 7207 1746 9

Printed in Great Britain by Butler and Tanner, Frome, Somerset

Contents

Acknowledgements

So many people have helped with this book, generously giving their time, experience, ideas and knowledge, that it is impossible to mention all their names. However, I would particularly like to thank the following for their patience and expertise:

Lawrence Alderson, Rare Breeds Survival Trust
Timothy Ash, Parke Rare Breeds Farm
Dr Christabel Barran
Walter R. Bateman, Dawson International
Dr Maurice Bichard, Pig Improvement Company
Dr John C. Bowman, C.B.E., Natural Environment Research Council
Tim Brigstocke, BOCM Silcock and Open University
Mr and Mrs A. A. Bristor
Brian and Alastair Brooks, Hollanden Rare Farm Animals
Charles Cottrell-Dormer, Rousham Longhorns
Tim Fenton, Agricultural Institute of Canada
Mr and Mrs A. Galloway
Roger Green, B.Vet.Med., M.R.C.V.S., Heath Veterinary Hospital
Joe Henson, Cotswold Farm Park
Professor W. G. Hill, F.R.S., Institute of Animal Genetics
James Hindson, B.V.Sc., M.R.C.V.S.
Mrs Nancy Howard
Ruth Leslie
Christopher Marler, Bolebec Belted Galloways
Donald McLean
Mrs Jean McPhail, Hungerhill Fold
Alan Mowlem, Animal & Grassland Research Institute and Goat Advisory Bureau
Robin Mulholland, Agricultural Development Advisory Service
Niall Osborne, Tilgate Park
Jane Paynter, Knotting Herd of Dexters
Dr Peter Reynolds, M.A., Ph.D., F.S.A., M.I.F.A., Butser Ancient Farm Project
Mrs. M. Rosenberg, British Angora Goat Society
Dr M.L. Ryder, M.S.C., Ph.D., F.I.Biol., Hill Farming Research Organization
Mr and Mrs J.A. Sibley
Kathy Smith
Mrs J. Spooner
David Steane, Meat & Livestock Commission
Richard Straton, Marwell Zoological Park
Lesley Stubbings, Agricultural Development Advisory Service
Geoffrey Tobitt
Richard Wear, Ruslin Ryelands
Mr and Mrs Paul Wilcock, Ashdown Forest Farm
John Wood Roberts, Rare Breeds Survival Trust

Unless otherwise stated, the photographs are provided by the author.

Foreword

This book is intended to be a practical guide to the care of the less common breeds of livestock seen in this country.

It is not restricted solely to the breeds which come under the expert protection of the Rare Breeds Survival Trust (though naturally these are included) nor is it confined to the traditional breeds. There are new breeds, a few foreign breeds, and some unexpected species which might become more popular here in the future.

A general knowledge of livestock management has to be assumed, otherwise this book would be twice as long as it already is. There are many good publications which cover the management of specific farm species such as cattle, pigs, sheep and goats, and this book is more concerned with breeds than with general husbandry. However, the management of minor species, such as deer and lamoids, is looked at in rather more detail.

Further restrictions have had to be made in order to keep the proportions of the book manageable and its scope is therefore limited to four-legged productive livestock, concentrating largely on cattle, sheep, pigs and goats. Horses have regrettably been omitted: they have a special place both on the land and in people's hearts and they deserve a complete book of their own. Feathered livestock of all kinds have been excluded: with their numerous variations and specialist fanciers they, too, merit a separate volume.

★ ★ ★ ★ ★

The book is based on the experiences of a large number of people who have talked generously and enthusiastically about their practical, theoretical and philosophical approaches and experiences. I am deeply indebted to all those farmers, park managers, estate owners, smallholders, geneticists, veterinary surgeons, technical advisers and breeders who have contributed their invaluable knowledge, and in particular to Lawrence Alderson for checking the manuscript.

A note about metrication

Although it is several years since metrication was imposed on the British measuring system, there are still many farmers who continue to 'think imperial'. There is a conversion table in Appendix VI, and in addition metric/imperial equivalents frequently interrupt the main text. However, in many cases a measurement is only intended as a rough guide, and on the whole these are imperial in origin, especially in the historical context of minority breeds (e.g. a yield of about 800 gallons or a fence about six feet high). In such cases metric equivalents are also approximate (e.g. two metres for six feet) and should not be taken as exact conversions.

Valerie Porter

Introduction

'The pedigree breeder is the custodian of one of our national heritages. The duty of maintaining and improving the livestock of Great Britain is his responsibility, and by careful selections and matings, by vigilant attention to matters of detail . . . and finally an infinite patience, it is a duty in which he will not fail.'
(from *A Brief History and Description of the Lincolnshire Red Shorthorn Cattle*, 1943)

The literature of breed societies is peppered with stirring phrases, as much about the fine qualities of breeders as of breeds. There is always abundant optimism — a firm belief that the future is full of promise and that the world will continue to recognize a particular breed's unique qualities, carefully cultivated and promoted by generations of dedicated breeders.

But it is not true. Whatever their contemporary merits, even the most popular breeds fall quickly out of favour when a new bandwagon begins to roll past the thoughtful eyes of the farmer who has a living to make. Some of the breeds that once dominated our landscape are now struggling to survive, and many more regional breeds have become quite extinct, even within the last twenty years. In times of rapid biotechnological development, dodoesque demise is becoming that much more dramatic.

Who cares? Does it matter?

Yes, it matters, to different people for different reasons, some of them practical, some emotional, and more often than not a bit of both.

The geneticist will talk about gene pools, about maintaining genetic variation because of man's present inability to create or to recreate such variation usefully; he will talk about reserves against plateaux in selection response or against the vulnerability of monotype populations, or, in the case of the exceptional geneticist, the aesthetic value of variation (because the day is not far off when identifiable pieces of DNA can be transferred from one strain to another or even from one species to another). A farmer might talk about improving fecundity or maintaining thrift; the owner of an estate might look for a financial return from an attractive collection of animals; a country dweller might long for something a little different in the landscape, a reminder of the past, a regional symbol, and freedom of choice. Some people keep minor breeds because of the particular qualities so many of them offer — their hardiness, their well-flavoured meat or rich milk, their unusual fleece, their suitability for a context. Some keep them for the satisfaction of helping to preserve a precious asset, regardless of whether or not it has any potential use. Others like the shared enjoyment of showing and displaying unusual animals. But perhaps the majority simply happen to like the looks and character of the breeds they choose or chance to care for, and base their decision on affection rather than on any practical or sensible considerations. All the reasons are equally valid; each lends its own dimension to the tapestry.

The concept of purebred livestock is a recent one and it is worth pausing to think, 'What is a breed, anyway?' The question deserves consideration so that the nature of the beast can be understood. To put it into the crudest of nutshells: once upon a time there were wild cows, sheep, pigs, goats, deer and so on, all evolving peacefully in their own sweet way, adapted to the climate and terrain in which they happened to find themselves, and acting out that eternal struggle of survival of the fittest — a term which included suitability in an environment as well as physique, health, agility and the ability to reproduce.

When humans grew weary of the insecurity and physical demands of hunting for meat, trailing hither and yon after migratory herds, they set about taking control of their lives and they became managers of their prey. Domestication was a natural progression, and the most amenable animals were the first to be domesticated.

Domestication is a two-way agreement: the dominant species harvests or makes use of the domesticant, which in turn receives food, shelter, and security from other predators. In a few species, the agreement has gone further and includes mutual respect and companionship, particularly with dogs, cats and horses. Every shepherd and anyone who has kept a house cow, a few goats or a backyard pig will confirm that companionship is also part of the relationship with productive livestock. As a substantial land-owner said recently, 'The cereals pay the bills but the cattle you can come out and talk to on a winter's night.'

The essence of control lay in selecting the type of animal, within a species, which was manageable, adaptable and useful. Initial selection, consciously or not, was for amenability and tameness: it could be said that the animals themselves made the choice in the first place by accepting their erstwhile bipedal predators' proximity without fleeing as far and as fast as they could. So the initial selection was based on temperament. Once man began to manipulate the animals' reproduction, the stage was set for selection based on productivity and, ultimately, appearance leading to the eventual creation of 'breeds'. In theory, a breed is a type, within a species, which consistently reproduces its type in subsequent generations.

But that was a long time coming and the serious business of breeding livestock to type really only came into its own in this country in the last few hundred years — several thousand years after the first tentative steps along the road to domestication. This time perspective needs to be borne in mind: breeding is, so to speak, in its infancy.

Medieval Britain was stocked with mongrels; there was a glorious hotchpotch of genetic material from which to draw. Even then there were regional and local types developing. If you had been dropped blindfolded in any part of the country, you could have guessed where you were by the scenery and by its livestock, and this close identification of the type of animal with its locality is another perspective which needs to be remembered — not so much horses for courses as sheep for the keep.

Once an animal was recognizable on sight as a particular type, and its offspring were also visually of the same type, it became a breed. A breed is essentially recognizable and reproducible; it can exist as a collection of specific inheritable qualities, but it needs to be recognizable by eye for what it is. Appearance matters. With a mongrel, invisible assets and faults are mixed at random and the offspring are hit-and-miss congregations; in a breed, on the other hand, the parental qualities are expected to be reflected within defined limits in the offspring and in subsequent generations. In a local type, there may be a certain degree of similarity in physical appearance but in a pure breed there must be a more positive standard that makes the animal instantly recognizable as a member of the breed and a true representative of that breed's qualities. The standard may change gradually as a breed is developed, but contemporaries are broadly alike. Cosmetic characteristics like colour and markings are the hallmark of a breed.

Traditionally, to be classified as a real breed the type must 'breed true' for six generations, by which time its type can be said to be fixed.

In recent years there has been an alarming trend towards uniformity in all aspects of life, including agriculture. It is a very risky trend indeed. Not only does it dull the senses and depress creativity; it also invites large-scale genetic (or other) catastrophe — the single basket of eggs ripe for crushing. The simile is apt in the context of this book: a breed *is* a basket of eggs, and the more baskets and hiding places for those eggs the more chance there is of avoiding one big omelette. Cooked, smashed or rotted eggs do not hatch. Eggs are packages of genes, and genes are life.

The maintenance of breeds can be good — and bad. On the one hand a breed is a recognizable genetic resource and if a good number of different breeds for any species continue to exist then there is material to hand for adjusting to new circumstances. On the other hand, if there were no mongrels at all within a species an enormous reservoir of genetic soup would disappear and the possibility of future selection would be greatly reduced. In both cases the danger is that if one or two breeds are exceptionally successful they can become popular to the detriment of other breeds (think of Large White and Landrace pigs, or Friesian and Holstein cows for example).

Within a breed the same problem occurs with popular lines. A strongly favoured sire can have far-reaching effects on an entire breed, and there have been recent cases of near disaster, especially with the increasing use of artificial insemination which allows one male to sire thousands of offspring in a very short space of time.

Diversity, then, is important. It might be argued that a mongrel national herd is an ideal diversification, but mongrels breed mongrels and farming becomes a matter of chance. Breeding pure is breeding consistency, and it gives a direction for development. It is vital, therefore, to have breeds, but it is also essential to have plenty of breeds and plenty of differences between them.

Different sections of this book emphasize from different angles the case for retaining a wide range of breeds on a national and international scale. It is likely that anyone who chooses to read it will already be interested enough in the subject to be fairly well convinced in advance, but any doubters would do well to read Lawrence Alderson's classic *The Chance to Survive* and other books which outline the philosophy of rare breed conservation before turning to the more practical considerations of the following chapters. Philosophy forms the skeleton on which practical attitudes are based, and for that reason one of the early sections of this book talks about the context in which unusual breeds might be kept. For example, they do have an important role to play in educating townsfolk who have perhaps lost touch with their distant rural roots and who long to find them again, whether or not they realize it. There is much more to keeping animals than private satisfaction or gain.

1 Breed Conservation

Even now, when governments seem to be trying to eradicate the sense of belonging to a small local area, and when mobility makes the whole country — the whole world — every individual's home, there is still a strong desire to feel a part of a particular place and to identify with a region. In Britain, not only are the Scots proud to be Scottish, the Welsh determined to retain their own tongue and the Irish glad to have their own island, but even the English, so often apparently careless of their Englishness, are loyal to a region, that is an ancient region, not an area randomly bounded and named for the sake of local authorities and post offices. The ancient kingdoms of Wessex and Mercia, for example, are still magnetic.

A breed of farm animal is a living link with a locality and with its past, and seems somehow displaced when it spreads to other parts of the country. It has been bred to suit its special environment and the nature of the people who live there; it is adapted to the local climate, the type of terrain, the soil minerals, the way of life of its region, and the very qualities that made it successful there can be drawbacks if it is transferred to an alien neighbourhood.

There is also the danger that a breed which comes from a tough environment and is said to be able to live on air will in fact be given such minimal feeding and attention that its potential is abused, or, at the other extreme, be given such a life of luxury that its natural hardiness is put at risk. There is always a happy medium to be found between neglect and pampering.

Some breeds have flourished on a much wider scale; others became so introvertedly local that they disappeared. The breeds which spread always had potential, and they owed their moment of glory to particularly energetic, far-sighted and dedicated individuals who knew how to select the good points, breed out the bad, and then did an excellent job in public relations to promote their breed when the time was absolutely right.

The following is an interesting and relevant quote from *The Field* more than sixty years ago (3 January 1920):

> 'The spotted pig of Gloucestershire is fortunate in its supporters. It would be unfair to it, and to them, to suggest that its growing popularity is mainly the result of the pushful policy they pursue, for the root cause of the progress recorded at the annual meeting in Bristol the other day, when Lord Bledisloe and others were sounding its praises, is its own merit as a utility animal of the

> farm. If the Old Spots pig were a new breed it could be predicted that it had come to stay, but, being an old variety newly raised to the dignity of a registered breed, the more correct prophecy is that it will extend its territory and deepen its hold upon popular favour. Hotly pursued by the saddleback pigs of Wessex and Essex, the Old Spots Gloucestershire pig is rapidly making up on the whites, blacks, and reds of older and wider repute. There is room for all, for the result of the development of the territorial breeds on registered lines will be friendly and altogether helpful rivalry, leading to the improvement of all of them worthy of support and the disappearance of the mongrel classes, whose loss there will be no cause to lament.'

There are some classic examples of this successful breed development and promotion which can serve as both an inspiration and a warning to all breeders of livestock. Perhaps the best known are the interlocked fortunes of two of the oldest British breeds, the Longhorn and the Shorthorn. Both had their day, the latter at the expense of the former, but today the Longhorn is struggling back from the brink of extinction and the Shorthorn as a pure breed is dropping rapidly in numbers. Yet there is Shorthorn blood in many other breeds, and by no means just in Britain. Its genes are safe.

★ ★ ★ ★ ★

Table 1 lists some of the many breeds which have either become extinct or have been absorbed into other breeds and lost as recognizable types in their own right, though in some cases these breeds can be 'recreated' by breeding back. Recreation can be deceptive, however: the animal might *look* something like the original phenotype (physical expression of its genotype), but its genotype (genetic structure) is likely to be different, sometimes very different. Once a breed has been lost, it is very difficult indeed to untangle the genes and recover it.

Among farm livestock there is considerably less extreme diversity than there is among dogs — those creatures of immense plasticity which range from the delicate Chihuahua to the monumental Great Dane, a range so extreme that it is difficult to believe they all spring from the same species. It is to be hoped that such extremes will never be pursued in livestock and in particular the travesties of shape wrought upon the dog by fashion. Dog breeding has a much longer history but it takes only a few generations to turn an efficient working or sporting breed of dog into a physically degenerate lap-dog. Take a look one day at the collection of stuffed dogs in

TABLE 1

SOME VANISHED BREEDS

Cattle	**Pigs**	**Sheep**
Alderney	Axford	Bampton Nott
Caithness	Coleshill White	Berkshire Nott
Castlemartin	Cumberland	Limestone
Fifeshire	Dorset Black	Longmynd
Glamorgan	Dorset Gold Tip	Mayo Mountain
Holderness	Lincolnshire Curlycoat	Mendip
Irish Dun	Old English	Morfe Common
Sheeted Somerset	Old Yorkshire	Old Lincoln
Suffolk Dun	Orkney	Old Wiltshire Horn
	Rudgwick	Rhiw
	Small White	Roscommon
	Ulster White	St Rona's Hill
	York Blue and White	Silverdale

And many more named after the counties in which they were bred.

the Natural History Museum at Tring in Hertfordshire. Most of the specimens were donated at the turn of the century, when the breeding boom in all types of animal had already been at full pelt for some time, but some of the dog breeds still had dignity in comparison with their modern descendants.

Fashion did (and still does) have an influence on farm livestock. Today the fashion in beef cattle, for example, is for continental breeds, reaching an almost obscene extreme of double muscling in the Belgian Blue. Breed societies exist to promote their breeds and, it is hoped, to protect them from bandwagon development: they need to tread a very careful path between conservatism and improvement. A breed must be developed to some extent if it is to survive at all as a living breed but it must also retain the qualities that made it special and enough diversity of type within the breed to give it scope for the future.

The British have always been concerned about breeds of domestic animals and the names of our 19th–century master breeders are legendary. It was in that century that so many of the breeds were 'improved', shaken into a more uniform type, and given breed names. The British became aware that it was possible to choose the good points in an animal and to ensure that they were passed on to its progeny, generation after generation. Cattle, sheep, horses and pigs were no longer that familiar patchwork of utility individuals; they became separate identifiable groups, each with its special qualities; they became breeds — lots and lots of breeds.

Selection is a dangerous game. By concentrating on particular characteristics it is all too easy to shed other valuable qualities without really noticing what is happening. Increased productivity is so often accompanied by a decrease in hardiness, thriftiness or longevity — qualities that are difficult to quantify. You can measure milk yield or carcase weight and thickness of backfat, but how do you enumerate the ability to survive in difficult conditions or the quality of good mothering instincts that are so crucial to the successful rearing of the young? They are qualities which affect not only the overall performance of an enterprise but also the profits it can make — the true profits. Margins over concentrates tell you something, but net profits for the whole enterprise, taking into account capital overheads, veterinary bills, man hours spent helping at parturition and so on, give a much more realistic assessment of the situation.

As the new breeds and the 'improved' breeds became fashionable, their numbers grew fast at the expense of other breeds which did not boast such high yields or did not have a fashionable shape or failed to find a niche of their own. The specialist rode roughshod over the generally useful livestock, the Jacks and Jills of all trades, the rent-payers which had served their owners so well in the past.

With increasingly easy communications and increasingly centralized government ('government' in this context includes any powerful group) such fashions spread very quickly. In the past the type of animal developed within a fairly small region was perfectly adapted to that region, meeting the needs of local people and making the best of its native environment. But when the barriers that had existed between communities were breached — barriers based on distance and the time and effort it took to cover that distance, barriers which had enabled local types of animal (and people) to develop at their own pace — then the protective cocoons of locality were ripped open. At first this release of such a variety of local types into the melting–pot gave breeders tremendous choice from which to select a bit of this, a bit of that, a dash of colour from here, a boost in milk yield from there, a quicker growth rate from somewhere else; but in a remarkably short time the mixture became homogenized. Major breeds began to dominate over much wider areas — sometimes nationwide

— and many less fashionable or apparently less profitable (at the time) breeds began to fade into the background and eventually faded right away.

During the second half of the 20th century people began to be seriously worried about the dying breeds. They were already worried about the many endangered species of wild animals and their habitats, and the instincts for conservation spread to include domestic livestock, which were seen not only as farm breeds but also as much a part of the national cultural heritage as were fine old buildings, works of art and beautiful areas of the countryside. The livestock breeds were history on legs.

You know what they say about variety — the spice of life — and it is true. Uniformity within a breed helps to establish its identify as a breed and gives the breeder something to identify with too, something to boast about, a feeling of being a member of the club. But uniformity within a species is something else. The fact that the overwhelming majority of cows in the British dairy herd were (and still are) black and white animals with foreign origins began to worry people. It was not their origins that offended: it was their sheer ubiquity.

During the 1960s groups of people with a common concern for the disappearing breeds began to meet and discuss and think about the future. They included scientists, academics, agriculturalists. As the result of the concern of a group in the Zoological Society (their names are still familiar today) small breeding nuclei of a few rare breeds were set up at Whipsnade Park in the mid sixties. In 1969 most of these animals were transferred to the RASE (Royal Agricultural Society of England) showground at Stoneleigh in Warwickshire.

In the summer of 1970 a survey was put underway to discover just how many individual animals and herds or flocks there were in breeds which were thought to be low in numbers. At the same time the survey team checked on breeds thought to be already extinct. The whole idea came from Dr P.A. Jewell and was generously backed by Mrs Wheatley Hubbard and the RASE. The survey was carried out under the direction of Professor John C. Bowman and his student Charles Aindow of Reading University's Department of Agriculture, and their report in January 1973 was an eye-opener.

They stated the case for conservation quite clearly and included many practical reasons, quite apart from sentimental ones which are powerful enough in themselves. With the permission of Professor Bowman (now Dr Bowman, C.B.E.), here is a long quote from the report: its philosophy holds good today.

'Man "employs" animals in a very wide variety of roles: they are sources of food, transport, fertilizer, fuel for heat and light, clothing materials, power, sport and pleasure. They also act in the roles of pets, guards, religious symbols and of increasing importance as aids in several types of research, including medicine and nutrition. There are various reasons in support of conservation other than purely sentimental ones. These include the need to maintain genetic variation and flexibility to meet quickly man's as yet unforeseen requirements, to maintain genetic diversity to benefit from hybrid vigour for man's current needs, to extend man's understanding of all aspects of animal biology and to maintain the quality of the environment for educational and amenity purposes.

'It is not possible to predict how man in future will wish to use animals. We do not know how much emphasis and importance he will attach to attributes which suit animals for their present roles: present-day livestock may be totally unsuitable for man's future needs. Also known attributes in certain breeds, which are unsuitable for present needs, may be extremely desirable in the future. Even in the short term, because requirements can change so quickly, it may not be possible to meet new needs easily by gradual changes resulting from artificial selection within those breeds of greatest current significance. We must retain flexibility for the future and maintain the substantial amount of genetic variation which has been accumulated, particularly within the domesticated species. If some of the existing genes and gene combinations are allowed to disappear, with the extinction of some breeds, future breeders may be held up in their work until the required gene or gene combination recurs by chance as a result of mutation, or by chance segregation. Genes cannot be created as required by man. He has to select the ones appropriate to his needs from those available which have arisen in the course of evolution and still exist in living populations. Under these circumstances a reservoir of genetic material, in the form of conserved breeds, is a valuable natural resource.

'The maintenance of genetic variation is crucial, not only to the development of new breeds but also to the production of hybrids with various combinations of characters . . . Hybrids, . . . which are making a valuable contribution to livestock production, are derived generally by selection between crosses of non-interbreeding populations with as little common ancestry as possible. There are two reasons for this approach. First, the characters of the progeny of such crosses generally exhibit hybrid vigour; and second, it is frequently possible to obtain progeny which combine the characteristics of more than one breed or strain. The flexibility of this approach is heavily dependent on the existence of a large number of breeds and strains with widely differing origins and characteristics.

'Apart from the need for genetic flexibility and diversity for artificial selection purposes some breeds need to be conserved to further man's knowledge of other aspects of animal biology. The study of the various breeds of livestock is helping towards a better understanding of the evolution and

> domestication of animals, and the effects of natural and artificial selection. Such research is also improving our understanding of the metabolic and physiological processes of domesticated animals . . .
>
> 'In the industrialized countries particularly, conservation is important in maintaining the general quality of the environment and the value of animals as an amenity and for education . . . and to provide urban dwellers with an opportunity of seeing, appreciating and being stimulated by the variety of species and strains.'

The survey immediately found that several breeds had only recently become extinct, including Caithness cattle and four colourful breeds of pig, two of sheep and two of horses. Details were given of populations of seven rare breeds of cattle, five of pigs, and sixteen of sheep, and then the report looked at the histories and qualities of each breed in detail.

Now the facts were known. Next came the action. Some scientists, academic communities and civil servants failed to take up the challenge — they thought that rare breeds had nothing to offer and the geneticists tended to think they could breed anything that the future might require. But more practical men did do something, and later that year the Rare Breeds Survival Trust was established as an outcome of discussions between a variety of concerned people from the Royal Zoological Society, RASE and the Ministry of Agriculture and also private individuals. The survey had identified the breeds most in need of assistance; each was considered separately for appropriate action.

An important priority was to publicize the facts and the need for urgent action. Bowman and Aindow had pointed out, for example, that one of the factors which contributed to the decline of a breed was lack of information on the whereabouts of specimens of that breed; owners who could not locate other herds soon found themselves in difficulties with inbreeding. Secondly, if no one knew that a breed was in trouble, no one would take steps to rescue it. Thirdly, there was a need to 'educate' the public about the importance of breed conservation. The vast majority of consumers in developed countries knew very little (and cared less) about the animals that supplied them with their daily needs. Milk came out of bottles rather than cows, and meat was born as joints. They did not connect the product with the real, living animal, let alone different breeds of animals. It was very different in the developing countries, where most of the population were in close daily contact with livestock.

To meet some of these needs, *The Ark* was launched privately in 1974 by Michael Rosenberg and Lawrence Alderson. It was intended to be an organ for information, liaison and education, and this monthly publication (in more recent years published by the RBST) has become essential reading for anyone who is interested in minor breeds. Its contents spread across a broad spectrum from learned papers on genetics to readers' descriptions of their less serious experiences, and it has an essential role not just as a mouthpiece for the Trust but also as a forum for the exchange of information and controversial points of view.

Concern for minor breeds was already on an international level by the time the Trust was formed. The problem had been discussed in 1969 at Helsinki at a meeting of the European Association for Animal Production, and poultry breeds had been discussed five years earlier in Bologna. In 1971 a private organization similar to the RBST had been set up in France, and likewise in the Netherlands in 1977. Several countries had state-run organizations rather than private bodies and charities.

In 1975 the United Nations Conference on the Environment gave some publicity to the disappearing breeds and an international agency, the UN Environment Programme, included domestic animals in its brief. UNEP combined with the UN's Food and Agriculture Organization (FAO), which had long been concerned with encouraging the conservation and management of animal genetic resources in developing countries, and together the two organizations held a Technical Consultation in Rome in 1980 to identify the problems and to propose solutions. That meeting provided the stimulus: international co-operation was underway.

One outcome was that the Genetics Commission of the EAAP set up a working party to look at the subject of the conservation of animal genetic resources in Europe. Questionnaires were completed by twenty-two countries and on the basis of these responses nearly 1300 'country populations' of cattle, horses, pigs, sheep and goats were identified. ('Country populations' encompass the same breed in several different countries; for example, Shorthorns recorded in, say, Britain, France and Germany represent three country populations.) Sheep were in the majority.

Two hundred and forty breeds were considered to be endangered, and the largest totals of endangered breeds were in France, the United Kingdom and Italy. The working party's report included an interesting comment in its discussions about the practical value of storing frozen semen and embryos as an essential method of conservation: 'Live animals should be maintained for proper breed evaluation and for maintaining interest in the breed.' Geneticists tend to be dismissive of the living whole animal — they claim it can always be recreated from its genes. While it is true that an animal is but the sum of its genes, the EAAP comment should help the geneticist to put matters into better perspective!

The EAAP criteria for considering breeds to be endangered were as follows:

Cattle: Less than 1,000 females, or 1,000–5,000 females but reducing, or less than 20 males.

Sheep: Less than 500 females, or 500–1,000 females but reducing, or less than 20 males.

Pigs: Less than 200 females, or 200–500 females but reducing, or less than 20 males.

Goats: Less than 500 females, or 500–1,000 females but reducing, or less than 20 males.

Table 2 lists the British breeds which met the EAAP criteria in the report.

TABLE 2

ENDANGERED BREEDS IN BRITAIN
EUROPEAN ASSOCIATION FOR ANIMAL PRODUCTION

Cattle	**Pigs**	**Sheep**
Belted Galloway	Berkshire	Cotswold
British White	Gloucester Old Spot	Hebridean
Dexter	Large Black	Leicester Longwool
Gloucester	Middle White	Lincolnshire Longwool
Irish Moiled	British Lop	Manx Loghtan
Kerry	Oxford Sandy & Black	North Ronaldsay
Longhorn	Saddleback	Oxford Down
Shetland	Tamworth	Portland
White Park		Ryeland
	Horses	Shetland
Goats	British Morgan	Shropshire
Bagot	Cleveland Bay	Soay
Golden Guernsey	Clydesdale	Teeswater
	Dales Pony	Wensleydale
	Exmoor Pony	Whitefaced Woodlands
	Fell Pony	Wiltshire Horn
	Shire	
	Suffolk	

Source: *Livestock Production Science*, 11 (1984) 3–22: Conservation of Animal Genetic Resources in Europe – Final Report of an EAAP Working Party (accepted 6 September 1983).

Britain's RBST has slightly different criteria for the acceptance of a breed as 'rare' and also looks at other factors such as dispersal, history and trends:

RARE BREEDS ACCEPTANCE PROCEDURE

Section A: Genetic basis

1. Has there been an accepted Stud/Herd/Flock Book for at least six generations?
2. Have other breeds contributed less than 20% of the genetic make-up of the breed in the last six generations?
3. Are the parent breeds used in the formation of this breed no longer available?
4. Has the breed been known for seventy-five years?

If less than three affirmative answers, the breed is not acceptable unless it possesses a distinct characteristic not found elsewhere.

Section B: Numerical basis

1. A breed will be included in the lists if there are less than the following numbers of breeding females in the breed:

Cattle:	750
Sheep:	1,500
Pigs:	150
Horses:	1,000
Goats:	500

2. Breeds with four or less distinct male lines will be included on the priority lists. A watching brief will be kept on breeds with six or less distinct male lines. (A distinct male line is one which has no common ancestors in the last four generations.)

Section C: Current trends

1. Are the numbers of the breed decreasing significantly?
2. Is the breed found in less than four significant units which are more than fifty miles apart?

Affirmative answers to these questions give the breed a higher priority within the lists, or may even permit a breed which does not qualify otherwise to be included.

Section D: Feral populations

These populations exist in circumstances which limit the action that the Trust is able to take to ensure their conservation.

A watching brief is also kept on other breeds whose numbers are falling.

RBST PRIORITY RATINGS

Priority 1: Critical
Priority 2: Rare
Priority 3: Vulnerable
Priority 4: Below numerical guidelines (watching brief)
Priority 5: Above numberical guidelines (watching brief)
Priority 6: Feral

With the very active co-operation of enthusiastic breeders, the Trust's work has borne considerable fruit in the few years since it was set up in 1973. Several breeds have done so well that they are no longer rated as rare, nor even in need of a watching brief. Nearly all the breeds on the list have improved their situation, and some are on the verge of shedding their rarity — for example Shropshire sheep have doubled their numbers in ten years, and the Belted Galloway and Red Poll cattle breeds achieved the honour of no longer being classified as rare in 1986.

However, an eye is being kept on breeds which are not officially on the list but which are fairly low in numbers — for example one or two south-western sheep breeds. A particularly wary watch is being kept on some breeds which are trying to rescue themselves by a significant degree of cross-breeding. It is feared that the original type may alter to the extent that it no longer really represents the breed, and several red breeds of cattle are included in this category.

The Rare Breeds Survival Trust is much more than an annual census-taker and a publicity machine. It runs several projects which are helping to identify the strengths and weaknesses of different breeds; it is building up a detailed knowledge of bloodlines within breeds; it actively manages certain breeds and provides registration facilities for many more. In fact it acts as an energetic breed society on behalf of a whole range of breeds.

Looking at the ambitious and complex nature of some of those projects, it is clear that fund raising has to be a major activity. There have been very generous benefaction and sponsorship in the past, without which the Trust could not have continued, and it is of course hoped that such generosity will continue. Funds are also raised through subscriptions and through the efforts of a network of local support groups all over the country. The Trust is a registered charity and it needs all the help it can get.

2 Contexts

There is considerable discussion, realistic or otherwise, about 'farm diversification' in the 1980s — making the most of every resource on the farm. Diversification requires a new approach and a fair bit of lateral thinking. It means looking at what you already have, including all those pockets of land which you have always considered worthless, and seeing it all in a new light. There could well be some surprises in store.

Several factors have brought about the need to diversify — some of them economic, some of them social. They say that every crisis is but an opportunity and if circumstances have conspired to make earning a living off the land more difficult than ever then perhaps it is a blessing in disguise. It is too easy to classify land under traditional headings — this is a hill farm, this is prime agricultural land, this is forestry land and so on. The grooves become, if not comfortable, then at least familiar; the restrictions of the ruts become acceptable and almost reassuring. But there is a lot more to land than farming.

Any new enterprises, or mixtures of enterprises, need very careful planning indeed. The first task is to take a detailed inventory of the available resources — a very detailed inventory. Resources include different types of land (soil, geography, vegetation and so on), woodland and copses, bogs and ponds, buildings — all those obvious features of the farm. They also include wildlife, scenery, history, ghosts, peace — assets very easily overlooked. Then there are the human assets — how much labour is already available, what possibilities there are for finding new employees, how many members of the family might help out, how much money can be raised, what skills everyone has (including hidden talents), what training, what interests.

The next question is what to do with all those resources and assets, and this is where imagination comes into it. Of course there are the obvious farming enterprises but there are also possibilities like pick-your-own, farm shops, homemade products of all kinds, a whole range of leisure catering and other services . . . and so much more besides. Somewhere in the midst of all these ideas and dreams there might well be an important place for minor breeds of farm livestock — productive, decorative, educational, emotionally satisfying, or a bit of each.

To make sense of keeping any kind of livestock it is important to look first at the context in which they are to be kept. The context sets the scene for the choice of species and breed but it is surprising how many people make an arbitrary decision without seriously considering environment, assets, aims and personal inclinations. Different livestock suit different situations; indeed as the different breeds were evolved specifically to suit a local context, their historic background needs to be taken into account.

'Context' is best assessed if you break it down into the component parts. Natural environment includes everything from climate to soil types; artificial environment includes the size of the holding, the types of boundaries, the proximity of centres of population and communications, as well as on-farm buildings; aims can include a very wide range of possibilities, and so can inclinations. Take them a step at a time.

NATURAL ENVIRONMENT

It is said that the goat came first, to chew down the forests and create clearings for cultivation, closely followed by the pig to complete the deforestation, ploughing up the land and snouting out the roots of undergrowth so that the grass had space and light and could grow. Then the cattle wrapped their tongues around choice grasses and the sheep cleared up after them, mowing it all down to a uniform sward.

The type of land available to a keeper of livestock should govern the type of livestock kept on it. That may seem an obvious statement but too often animals are expected to thrive in unsuitable environments. Domestication has encouraged versatility and the ability to adapt, but just as there is little point in trying to grow azaleas on chalk so equally there is little point in putting downland sheep on a Welsh mountain or feral goats on lush pasture. It *can* be done but the context is wrong for the stock and the problems will increase. The care of livestock requires plenty of skill, experience, labour, patience and time in the best of environments. Why add to the problems?

The natural environment includes altitude, topography, climate, locality, soil type and other similar factors which are basically unalterable, although at considerable expense artificial environments can be created and maintained. In some cases, if the inclination exists, such expense can be justified in commercial terms. At this stage, however, it is best to look in general terms at the suitability of different stock for different natural environments, regardless of available housing and artifices.

Cattle

Cattle need grass. Some beef breeds can do well enough on the tougher, more meagre swards of the hills where dairy cows could not thrive. No breed can do its best on nothing, though unfortunately some people take too literally a breed's reputation for hardiness and thrift and provide minimum housing or sustenance. The stock will survive, and may look quite good on it, but often their proper potential and size is only achieved when they are treated more generously.

Some 44% of British farmland is hill country, where normal cash crops and dairy herds are out of the question. On that land 65% of this country's breeding sheep and 62% of its beef breeding cows are farmed, and the proportions are even higher in Wales.

There are, of course, certain breeds of cattle which are best able to make use of such land. Normally they are run as single-suckler herds, with a good resilient hillbred cow crossed to a meaty bull to throw a beef calf and raise it economically on her milk. These cows are essentially hardy cattle, growing thick winter coats and thriving on second quality feeds; they are excellent and protective mothers who do not have to be taught how to raise a calf; they tend to be slow-growing breeds. Some were developed particularly for the cold wet western hills, others for the harsher, drier cold of eastern uplands. Many of them are minor breeds.

Regional identity is important. For example, the Welsh Black does well in the teeth of wet Atlantic gales which would make any other cow miserable and rheumatic; Galloways are ideal for their exposed native uplands; Highlands (and the Luing) are just about the only cattle which can shrug off the harshest conditions of northern Scotland and its islands. But they can all do even better in less harsh environments, though too much of the soft life might be deleterious to the hardiness and thriftiness for which they are renowned. Non-hill beef cattle breeds and the dairy breeds are better kept at the lower, lusher altitudes.

Many of the minor breeds are famous for their mothering ability and inclination, and the ease with which they calve — important qualities in a suckler herd or in any low-input enterprise.

Pigs

Pigs' eating habits have always conflicted with humans' taste in food. They are naturally omnivorous. Beechmast, acorns, roots of all kinds, grain and pulses, grass and other plants, and a range of little meaty items like small birds and mice all form part of the diet of wild pigs. The modern pig is rarely given such a choice and only a small percentage of the national herd is kept out of doors, with a very few even of those being truly free-range and able to rootle for their own food where they will.

Outdoor pigs are best kept on light, sandy soils but given the opportunity and enough space they are happy to turn their snouts to woodland clay, bracken-clad hillsides, windfall-strewn orchard grass or any potential backyard vegetable patch.

Climate is important: pigs are sensitive to temperature, and the white-skinned breeds can suffer equally from heat and cold. Darker breeds are much hardier; they are able to withstand greater variations in temperature and seem to be much less prone to sunburn. Many of the minor breeds have pigmented skin (colour prejudice is rife in the pig world!) and nearly all of them have the old-fashioned virtues of hardiness and the ability to look after themselves and their litters.

To a far greater extent than most other species considered in this book, pigs tend to be raised in artificial environments and have indeed been selected for their ability to respond well to intensive management. If the means (and inclination) for housing are available, the natural environment is a less important restriction on choice of stock. In this century very many of the originally diverse local breeds have disappeared — become quite extinct or been absorbed into other breeds — so that the choice of breeds is now fairly limited.

Sheep

There are now more breeds of British sheep than of any other British livestock but there are nevertheless far fewer than there used to be. Each was specially developed for a particulare niche in one of the very many and various natural environments found in this country, and as a species sheep can be farmed anywhere, from the most remote and rocky Scottish islands to the fat, easy lands of southern England. The 'primitive' breeds are ideal on mountain, scrubland and island, and on better pasture they make determined efforts to seek out rough growth along the hedge bottoms and on the banks to supplement a diet which is too soft for them.

With sheep perhaps more than other species, regional background counts. Some are hardy and thrifty for hill farms, others do best on chalk downland and so on. Kept in an untypical environment, some breeds can alter and may deteriorate.

Goats

Goats are essentially browsers rather than grazers. They delight in shrubbery more than grass but can be kept on grazing if it is extensive. They can be divided roughly into three types: the feral animals of the uplands, the dairy and pet breeds derived from Swiss and other imported stock, and the fibre-bearing types which have recently begun to find a niche in this country. The dairy breeds need a certain amount of cosseting:

they originated in dry climates and must have access to housing, particularly in wet weather.

ARTIFICIAL ENVIRONMENTS

The restrictions of a natural environment can to some extent be alleviated by creating artificial environments appropriate to the livestock, but this usually involves considerable capital investment and running costs. The intensification of enclosure of any kind also greatly increases the risk of disease, stress and other adverse factors, particularly where the system has been designed for the convenience of the stockman rather than for the real welfare of the stock.

It makes sense to take a look at existing structures before deciding on suitable livestock. The perimeter boundaries are vital (good fences make good neighbours) and different species and breeds have very different concepts of stockproof fencing! Stone walls invite mountainbred sheep to climb them; very few fences can really seal in a flock of Soay sheep; some deer can leap a boundary as tall as a man; cattle lean on hedges when they browse and find themselves on the other side without really meaning to be there; Highlands and White Park cattle are quite capable of swimming a river; pigs are excellent at working their way under a barrier; goats can be irrepressible. Some animals are determined natural wanderers (no self-respecting Black Welsh mountain sheep will stay in any field by choice) and need endless space; some are simply incurably curious (Tamworth pigs love exploring); some go looking for a mate or in search of lost offspring.

Space is also important for species which are by nature grouped territorially (some deer and primitive sheep) or have a strong social hierarchy (pigs and many cattle). Stocking rate depends as much on these social factors as on the amount of food available from the acreage. Different breeds have different habits too: some prefer to graze close together in a bunch, while others spread well out and ignore each other.

There are breeds that never bother to go anywhere. Lop-eared pigs are said to be more home-loving because their vision is obscured for example. But it is not necessarily true that a well-fed animal will be content to stay within bounds. There is more to life than food.

Perimeter protection may be expensive but it is essential to peace of mind. Paddock and yard fencing within the perimeter is part of good management, and here again some species and some breeds require more elaborate enclosures than others.

Housing can be a very expensive investment. Hardy hill breeds make minimum demands in this respect but for many enterprises housing to varying degrees is essential, especially in any kind of dairying (cows, milksheep or goats), most kinds of goat keeping, pigs to a greater or lesser extent, non-suckling calves and, increasingly, early lambing flocks.

Housing for livestock breeding has advantages and disadvantages. It enables better supervision at the time of birth, for example, (and keeps the observer out of the weather) but it can also encourage the spread of disease. Ample space is vital to avoid the stress of overcrowding and bullying. Wintered beef cattle seem happy enough jostling together in an airy barn or yard, but dairy cows risk trodden teats, while pigs react badly (and sometimes savagely) to overcrowding or boredom.

There is a worrying trend in livestock farming towards breeding specially for very intensive systems. It has been taken to an extreme with poultry: when laying cages were first introduced enormous numbers of stock were culled because they could not cope with such intense confinement and since then hens have been increasingly selected for even better tolerance of caged environments to such an extent that they are quite incapable of surviving in any other situation. That is a very frightening thought, and pig breeding is beginning to head in a similar direction. If there is no other reason for keeping some of the old minor pig breeds, they will be needed against the day when the modern white pig has atrophied legs.

AIMS AND INCLINATIONS

Details of markets and outlets are considered in the next chapter but first it is important to have some idea of why the livestock are being kept. Are the main aims commercial or for self-sufficiency, altruistic or purely for personal satisfaction? Will you employ regular or casual labour or none at all? Once you have assessed your natural and potential artificial environment, to see the extent of your choice of livestock, you should then look very closely at your motives and aims and decide right from the start the *raison d'être* for the whole scheme. Keep those aims constantly in mind and constantly under review.

Commercial production

The straightforward commercial farmer might consider some of the following enterprises, or a combination of them, on whatever scale.

Cattle can be run as a dairy herd (that lovely regular milk cheque does wonders for your cash flow), beef single or multiple sucklers, store and finishing cattle. You could raise heifers as dairy herd replacements for other people, or calves on the bucket or bottle. Among the minor breeds there could be an interest in building up a herd by grading up to a breed. Dairy farms might want to specialize in their own dairy produce such as cream, cheeses, yoghurts and ice-cream.

In pigs the commercial choice is really limited to a breeding herd producing piglets for other people to feed on, or taking on weaners and stores to finish up to porkers, baconers and heavy hogs. There could be a very limited commercial outlet in supplying the big hybridizing companies with purebred parental stock.

With sheep, the industry in Britain is 'stratified' and the main end product is meat, wool being almost incidental. The stratification system is described fully in the Sheep chapter.

Goats have several possible commercial roles, and are really in their infancy as farm animals. There are some very good commercial goat dairy herds; there are the newly established fibre herds, and there are herds in both categories which produce meat as a second cash crop. A triple goat enterprise would be combining land improvement with fibre and meat production.

There are other possible livestock, such a deer, and these are discussed separately at the end of the book.

Public display

It may be a cliché but it is none the less true that leisure is a fast growing area ripe for commercial exploitation by those with a few new ideas. Many of the minor breeds find a useful niche in this context and many will probably owe their continued existence to breeders who are prepared to display their livestock to the public in various situations. The possibilities are restricted by practicalities like suitability of access, local authority requirements, location near centres of population or in tourist areas etc., and very careful planning is essential. Suggestions and problems are looked at in more detail in the chapter on Showing and Displaying, but here are some ideas:

Farms parks and approved rare breed centres
Farm schools/holidays for deprived children
Urban farms (council, private, community, co-operative)
Education centres
Heritage centres
Theme centres (period farms etc.)
Open-air museums (livestock in the context of historical architecture, farming methods and equipment)

Children's corners
On-school farms

Research
Government and private organizations continuously undertake breed research projects but there is plenty of room for individual breeders to investigate minor breeds and particularly the rare ones. Such investigations could be crucial to such a breed's continued existence. They involve experimental breeding for its own sake, followed up by progeny or performance testing to discover and record the merits or drawbacks of a breed or of a line within a breed. They might include, say, breeding for a particular fleece colour (plenty of scope here) or a type within a breed (which could lead to a new breed) or crossbreeding for lean meat or other qualities. These are dedicated, long-term enterprises which are costly and unlikely to offer much in the way of returns, if any — labours of love in fact. Outside support and encouragement are vital and co-operative ventures might be appropriate. Performance recording among minor breeds is very important indeed, whatever the context: if performance is not monitored the breeds tend to fall out of favour even faster because commercial enterprises like to know exactly what qualities they can expect from their stock. And the lower the numbers, the less meaningful are the statistics — a chicken-and-egg situation which can lead rapidly down the dreaded plughole of extinction. If every owner of a minor breed kept comprehensive records and submitted them regularly to a central point for co-ordination and assessment, the future of the breeds would be a great deal more secure. The computer technology is available but perhaps the overall organization is lacking. Paperwork has always alarmed farmers but those who do record reap immediate dividends for their own businesses and contribute vitally to the good of the breeds.

Work
There is a certain amount of scope for the older breeds in film and television work, particularly for period settings, but income from such sources will be sporadic and limited. The animals may need to be properly trained (though normally they are just part of the scenery) and good temperament is important. Lack of curiosity is an asset: cameramen only want close-ups when the director demands them but cattle, goats and pigs in particular seem to be fascinated by filming equipment and have backed many a cameraman into the nearest thorn hedge or muddy ditch. A sense of humour, perhaps?

Cattle can be trained for draught work and 'oxen' are popular for shows and pageants. Llamas have always been pack animals and are readily trained to a light children's saddle or a small cart.

Pigs are very intelligent animals and can be trained in several ways. They can be used as draught animals — indeed it used to be said that a sow drew better than a cow or a horse. The best working role for a pig, however, is as nature intended — as a cultivator. A couple of hired-out Tamworths or Old Spots will earn their keep nicely by turning over potential vegetable patches or clearing out a scrubby copse.

Wasteland management and pasture improvement

Flocks of primitive sheep breeds are used to reclaim wasteland such as china clay tips and other spoil heaps, and they also do a good job of keeping reservoir embankments looking tidy. Many people buy in a handful of primitives to keep their grass down, which they can do well enough if adequately fenced. Feral goats are being used to improve pasture by grazing out the coarser stuff before sheep are run through. Soay sheep are deerlike in appearance as well as agility and grace any setting in which they care to linger. The aesthetic appeal of most of the minor breeds is an important point in their favour and should not be dismissed as irrelevant. Productivity and financial returns are not all one asks of livestock.

Conservation

The desire of individual breeders past and present to ensure the future of a breed is the saving of the many unfashionable or less than commercial breeds whose disappearance would be at the least a visual deprivation. Conservation for its own sake is just as worthwhile as conservation for practical considerations. A certain well-known geneticist feels that conservation of livestock has to be considered mostly for aesthetic value and for exhibition, rather than because of any long term practical value in animal improvement. He points out that, as a consequence of genetic improvement, modern strains have become far removed in performance from their ancestors or other old strains, to such an extent that it would become impossible to find useful genetic material in the old strains that could be brought into the modern strains without sacrificing performance. If conservation is to be practised, it should be aimed largely at maintaining population or types as examples of diversity and for the historical record, rather than as likely sources of useful material.

Some will disagree with that point of view and it highlights several areas of contention among those who are interested in rare breeds. There are those who believe that a breed is only worth saving if it has a potential *use*, now or in the future, if only as a contributor to the genetic pool. There are others who conserve for the sake of doing so and have problems in deciding whether it is ethical to improve the type in any way, however minor, at the risk of losing the original. Well, there are no real originals, are there? A breed comes about by chance as much as anything else — a type happens to appeal to a breeder for reasons which may be practical, aesthetic, sentimental, or simply because the animal reminds him of his Aunt Gertrude! And at that point in the development of the type he decides to fix it as a breed. Who is to say that his taste should prevail ever more?

3 Outlets

Without their altruistic supporters, many breeds would soon die out. It may be controversial whether any breed of livestock should be conserved for its own sake if it has little commercial value or potential (and who can cast a judgement on potential when the needs and fashions of future generations are unknown?) but it is fair to say that a breed stands a far better chance of surviving if outlets can be found for its produce. Some people declare that conservation is too important to be tainted by commerce. Some protest at slaughtering a rare breed for meat and express concern at the thought of eating something precious enough to be identified as rare. In fact, although it may seem to be a contradiction, eating a rare breed *increases* its chance of survival because it encourages breeders to produce more of that breed in order to meet a market demand.

Realities must be faced. Some breeds seem to have no commercial future at all, but again, who can tell? In the meantime it is possible to make use of whatever qualities can be recognized and to make full use of careful publicity to promote those qualities. The success of groups like the Jacob Sheep Society, the Black Welsh Mountain Sheep Breeders' Association and the Dexter Cattle Society in rescuing their breeds from the status of rarity and establishing them firmly on their own four feet in a commercial context could be the inspiration for all minor breeds. In each case those who had faith in the breed had a good, hard look at its qualities, backed their boasts with facts and figures, and then went out and told the world about their breed. The Jacobs had the advantage of unusual looks and links with the Bible (at the beginning of this century the breed was called the Piebald — not nearly as interesting as the Jacob); the Dexter breeders emphasized the value of their small cattle as house cows but also proved that they could succeed in recorded dairy herds; the Black Welsh turned the disadvantages of being a black sheep into a major selling point (fleeces for home spinners) but also pointed out the excellent mothering abilities of the ewes and the breed's special virtues of resistance to fly attack and foot infections as well as self reliance and sweet meat. In each of these cases, the breed was instantly recognizable even to the layman and, in the sheep world in particular, such 'brand identification' can be difficult to achieve. Sheep are sheep, unless they have remarkable horns or colours. Black and white cattle are Friesians even if they are Gloucesters or Shetlands. The Tamworth is an eye-catching pig because of its ginger colour but the British Lop, however good a pig it is, tends to be classed with all the other white pigs that exist in their millions. Longhorns fascinate people, but

White Park and British White are often (and historically) seen as a single breed of white cattle with pretty markings.

Quite apart from creating a strong identity for a breed, there is the vital question of potential outlets. Market research is essential and for those debating a choice of breeds it should be a preliminary exercise rather than a vague afterthought.

MILK

Cows

Cows' milk is sold through the various Milk Marketing Boards in this country, a fact which both protects and restricts the producer. Health regulations are necessarily strict, and the imposition of quotas has discouraged many dairy farmers. Most minor breeds are quite capable of holding their own on the milk market in this context: their yields may not reach the high levels of Holsteins and Friesians but they can compensate with quality or even lactation or attractive margins of milk income over inputs such as feed and veterinary bills. It is a mistake to look only at yields — any farm accountant can tell you that there is a lot more to profits. For example, outgoings on the concentrates needed to get the best out of high-yielding breeds can be alarming, but some of the minor breeds are much more efficient at producing good milk on less expensive feeding. Good feed conversion rates (FCR) — whether for milk, meat or fibre — will become increasingly important and it could be that some of the minors will be able to succeed in the future because of their thriftiness and high FCR. Once again the main problem is that not enough records have been kept to show exactly what margins are possible for minor breeds, nor have enough herds of any size been recorded to demonstrate breed averages.

Another reducible input is the capital cost of housing. A hardy minor will often make do with less elaborate winter housing and still produce adequate yields, and some of the smaller breeds have the added advantage of being less likely to poach winter fields.

Milk can, of course, be converted into butter, cheese, yoghurt, cream and ice-cream, and in these products there is considerable scope for marketing minor breed specialities. The milk of black-and-whites can have a mediocre butterfat content but several of the minors do well in this respect. Although the current trend is for low-fat diets, butterfat is valuable in itself and there is a ready slimmers' market for the skim!

If you are a producer of cows' milk or any product from it for human consumption, you need to register with the Ministry of Agriculture. If you want to sell untreated or farm-treated milk direct to the public you need a special licence as well. You will also have to comply with the Food Hygiene regulations, enforced by local Environmental Health officers, and all sorts of other regulations such as food labelling etc. enforced by your local authority's Trading Standards department.

If you sell raw cream, be careful how you describe it. For example, 'double' cream must contain at least 48% butterfat, 'whipping' cream 36% and 'single' cream 18%. However, very few people have on-farm facilities for testing their cream for fat content, but if you call it 'farm' cream you are not misleading anybody, and quite often farm cream is in fact richer than double cream — perhaps 60% butterfat.

There are also all sorts of regulations governing buttermaking, cheese, skimmed milk and ice-cream. For example, dairy ice-cream must contain a minimum of 5% milk fat and 7.5% solids-not-fat, and there are various strictures regarding heat treatment, cooling temperatures and storage temperatures. Your local Agricultural Development Advisory Service (ADAS) office will be able to give you a pile of leaflets on different kinds of farmhouse produce.

The cheese potential is exciting. Cheeses can be associated not only with regions but also with different breeds. Several of the minors produce milk with very small fat globules (Gloucester, Red Poll and Kerry, for example) which are not only better for butter but are also excellent for cheese-making. Some Gloucester keepers are making the once famous Double Gloucester cheese, and there is a new Red Poll 'Llanboidy' cheese finding great favour with specialists, which is as it should be from a descendant of the Suffolk Dun, once Britain's most remarkable dairy cow.

A well planned marketing strategy is important. First perfect the cheese, then make sure supplies are reliable, then spread the reputation. A strong link with an attractive looking breed is definitely a bonus. The instantly recognizable image of a British White head makes an ideal packaging logo and there is increasing public awareness (thanks to shows and general publicity) of the older British breeds as a valuable part of the national heritage — an awareness which can be exploited. If that sounds too commercial, bear in mind that it could save a breed.

Yoghurt and ice-cream are also interesting possibilities. They are flavoured products and that gives endless scope for individual flair and imagination. ADAS milk product advisers will give useful advice on production and marketing. It is worth noting, incidentally, that ice-cream is not included within quotas: it is a good outlet for over-quota milk.

All these products, it should again be stressed, need good marketing and a professional approach. On a very small scale they might be sold in a farm shop, especially if it is linked with some other public-access enterprise like a farm park or children's corner. Once members of the public have been attracted to a location, they are likely to spend money on everything from souvenirs and plants to cream teas and homemade jams. There are several farms which have become more than locally well-known for their own special ice-cream flavours: people come from quite a few miles away to buy them, and the farms have been able to extend their enterprises to cater for these 'captive' markets.

It is important to be up to date with health and retailing regulations in the planning stages.

Goats

Goats' milk has several advantages. It is ideal for those who are allergic to cows' milk (and there are many more than are aware of the fact) or who have delicate stomachs; it is good for young children, invalids, and orphaned young animals being reared on the bottle; it can be frozen whole (which cows' milk cannot be). It is also outside the embrace of the milk marketing boards and you can sell untreated goats' milk straight from the udder. Apart from normal public health regulations, there is very little red tape about selling other goats' milk products like yoghurts and herb-flavoured cheeses — on a market stall, perhaps, or down the lane or in a health food shop. In the case of the latter, consistency of supply all year round is essential and well designed, attractive packaging is decidedly an asset. You can already buy Capricorn English Goat cheese, Threeshires Dairy Castle Ashby, and Round Oak cheeses as well as various French Chevres and Chevrots.

There is a minor outlet in goats' milk cosmetics etc. but check whether or not such products have already been registered by someone else.

Sheep

There was a time when sheep-milking was a common practice, even in Britain. Then wool, and later lamb, became more important. Now there is a gradual return to milking sheep and there are several commercial herds which have very definitely found a good specialist market.

Breeds of particular interest are the hugely productive British Milk-sheep (specifically bred by Lawrence Alderson for prolificacy and high milk yields) and the British Friesland. The latter have a long history as milking animals and are therefore docile and easy to handle in the parlour. No doubt other breeds, too, could be bred with milk in mind. For example, the Portland gives far too much milk for its single lamb, and even the Soay has a very reasonable yield — though trying to milk the latter could be challenging, to say the least! Yet Soay ewes were still being milked by islanders on St Kilda when they were evacuated in 1930.

Outlets for sheep milk are in gourmet food halls and health food shops, which are often interested in sheepmilk yoghurts and cheeses. The French have their Roquefort and the British already have cheeses like Sheviok, Ladywell, Sleight Farm Fetta, Wackley Farm Ewes' cheese and Furzehill Garlic and Herbs cheese. There is a promising commercial future in sheepmilk and it could be worth experimenting among the minor breeds to see what potential they have.

Other milk animals

In theory any mammal can be milked. Cleopatra is said to have bathed in asses' milk but horses and asses do not take kindly to being milked! Llamas are also milkable in theory, and so are water buffalo — more about them in Chapter 12.

MEAT

The meat market has always reflected social changes and today tastes are changing too rapidly for the breeders. There was a time, it is said, when every man in the country ate at least three or four pounds of beef a week. There was a time when mutton was a prized meat and the first taste of new English lamb was a joyous confirmation that the long winter was over. There was a time when every country family raised its own backyard pigs and knew how to slaughter them and how to dress and preserve the carcases to see them through the coldest weather, making a meal out of every edible part and a use out of all the rest. The habit of backyard pig-keeping continued even when the population began to become urbanized. Today, however, there are laws against home slaughtering and there is also a marked and increasing prejudice against pig meat in many of the European countries which traditionally depended on the domestic pig. Bacon sales in Britain have dropped sharply because cereals have replaced cooked breakfasts. Pork is no longer the staple winter diet of the majority; folk memories of tapeworm and pig 'measles' still linger, but perhaps the greatest disadvantage of all is the association of pigs with that bogey of our time, fat.

Lamb, too, is suffering a decline — quite possibly because the farmers have not yet caught up with public taste and are still producing over-fat lambs. (The Chernobyl disaster has not helped either.) Mutton is but a juicy, tasty, fatty memory. It should be noted that some of the 'primitive' breeds of sheep naturally produce a much leaner carcase of good, small joints.

Beef suffered from fast rising prices a few years ago and is now susceptible to a general trend against red meat and fat. Venison, on the other hand, another red meat, is selling well on its leanness, taste and lack of yield-boosting hormones.

Goats' meat, long ignored in Britain, is welcomed by Asian and Mediterranean communities living in this country and there is potential for considerable expansion in the goats' meat industry.

Mocked though it might be, vegetarianism does strike a chord with an increasing number of consumers. It is worth considering why this should be and how minor breeds might be able to escape the general condemnation. The common breeds are associated, rightly or wrongly, with dark doings like hormone implants, factory farming and abattoir stress. They also end up as bland supermarket packaged products. But people who promise to sell 'real' meat are doing well — no additives, no cruelty, plenty of taste. Minor breeds, farmed on a smaller scale and on less intensive systems, could well find a 'real' image and thus a better market for their meat.

There is already ample scope for the specialist. For example, Aberdeen Angus beef is universally acknowledged as the best and, at the time of writing, it is top of the menu at the London Hilton. The Hilton, after considerable research, decided to open a British Harvest restaurant in which every food was genuinely British and seasonally fresh — meat, vegetables, fish and shellfish, fruit, cheeses, wines, butter and so on (though obtaining supplies of unsalted British butter has been a problem). Foreign clients have enjoyed eating British: perhaps it is a way for the jet-lagged businessman and whirling tourist to recognize which country they are in. The menu is based on top-quality food, beautifully presented and simply cooked so that its natural flavour is enhanced. Quality is very carefully controlled by the purchasing manager Danny Radovanovic and the executive chef Oswald Mair, and strict specifications are enforced on carcase size and conformation. Aberdeen Angus beef is very popular for huge weekly banquets and the hotel is adamant that no beef is as good as Angus. Other 'Scotch' beef (which in honesty is often stock from Ireland that has briefly touched down in Scotland for killing) does not have the same appeal, though the upland Scottish breeds are favoured. It seems that the fact of grazing on upland pastures is a bonus to the quality of the meat, whether beef or lamb, and the Hilton claims to be able to tell a hardy upland carcase at a glance. No doubt other breeds would be given a fair chance on the British Harvest menu but proof of excellence must be given — *consistent* excellence — and here again minor breeds have suffered from lack of regular and careful testing of the product.

The Hilton has linked itself with the Rare Breeds Survival Trust for the lamb section of the menu and they have a regular contract through Richard Wear, the Bristol breeder of the Ruslin Ryelands, who supplies exactly the type of joints required on a weekly basis. Breeds sent at various times include Portland, Shropshire, Norfolk Horn, Wiltshire Horn, Ryeland, Southdown, Cotswold and Oxford Down. With seventeen rare breeds of sheep to choose from, Wear finds no difficulty in keeping to the exacting specifications. The lambs are slaughtered by FMC (Bristol) and ear-tag numbers appear on the Meat and Livestock Commission (MLC) grading certificates (so far 89% of the carcases have been in the 3 classification bracket, which is ideal for the home market). Wear supplies tickets giving details of the breed of each carcase so that customers at the Hilton can be told just what they are eating if they wish to know.

Richard Wear points out that one of the reasons for a breed becoming rare today is that the modern trend is for hybrid sheep bred for prolificacy and fast growth to meet the supermarket trade. Rare breeds tend to be slower growing, eating more natural food, and their meat is therefore much tastier.

In such a professional environment there is no room for the smallholder offering the occasional excess Soay ram lamb, but a regular supply of different breeds at different seasons, all to specification and of uniformly high quality and correct size, could be an interesting marketing venture. In a world which is growing too homogenous there is a strong attraction in regionality and a potential enterprise might well emphasize a breed's identification with a locality rather than its rarity. 'Heritage' is an overused word but it remains emotive and, with good marketing and a blatant appeal to sentimental longings for the past, every minor breed could find a niche on the gourmet tourist menu.

Some breeds do offer distinctive meats — the primitives really do taste different. The Portland is claimed to produce the sweetest, most tender mutton, but every breed makes its own claims. The type of grazing makes a difference — I have never tried it but surely seaweed-eating North Ronaldsays taste different from pasture-fed Southdowns or hill-grazing Black Welsh? Yet again it is a question of good marketing: find an image, build it up and sell it. Mutton could make a comeback and smoked sheep meats have untapped potential.

In the general beef market, several minor breeds have begun to prove their worth — for example the Longhorn. Some breed societies are eyeing the beef market more closely and are beginning to develop their breeds accordingly — for example the British White, once more a dairy or dual-purpose animal, is now being selected for beefier qualities. This is a case of a breed society making positive efforts to 'improve' their breed to meet contemporary and (it is hoped) furture demands, but it does raise what might be called ethical points. If the breed is altered too radically, is it still the same breed?

In pigs there are excellent examples of market-minded enterprises which are succeeding very well indeed. Heal Farm Traditional Meats have specialized in minor breeds and have developed an imaginative range of smoked, cured and fresh products. Their marketing is very professional and they are also taking the trouble to look much more closely into carcase quality, especially polyunsaturated fats.

The Real Meat Company has tackled marketing from a different angle, concentrating on extensive rearing methods rather than on minor breeds, but yet again the key to their success is careful market research, which has kept them alert to what the public wants, supported by good publicity which lets the public know where to get what it wants!

An increasing outlet for meat is to ethnic minorities in this country and if an enterprise is suitably located there is scope for supplying, say, goats' meat to the Gurkhas or to curry houses. Look around in your own area for ideas and openings. Go and talk to the local abattoir: they will know a great deal about local possibilities and demands and will also be able to advise on the type of carcase which sells best.

In an age when supermarkets dominate, it may be difficult for the small-scale producer to find a comfortable cuddle in the embrace of giants like Tesco or Marks & Spencer, whose specifications are very exacting and extend to every detail of how the livestock are raised and cared for. It *is* worth investigating, again on the gourmet side, and Marks & Spencer has flirted with the possibility of minor breeds. But a co-operative approach might be better, simply because of the volume of produce required, and here again consistency of supply and of quality are absolutely essential.

Conformation and carcase evaluation

Lean meat is the taste of today and it also makes better margins for the producer because lean animals tend to make more efficient use of their food. Fat is an energy-dense tissue containing a high proportion of water (about 750g per kg) and its creation uses up four times as much feed energy as does the creation of lean tissue.

As an animal's weight increases from the day it is born, the body's proportion of bone falls and that of fat increases, while the proportion of lean remains fairly constant up to slaughter weight, after which the proportion of lean begins to fall as fat is deposited more rapidly. The ideal slaughter weight, of course, is just before that lean proportion begins to decline in comparison with the fat.

Slaughtering at lower weights is one way of producing leaner carcases. Another way is to judge just the right level of nutrition for a particular breed (and it has to be adjusted for strains within breeds and for the sex of the animal) to meet the requirements for the deposition of lean meat without giving excess nutrition which is simply converted to fat. Fatness increases with development: breeds with low mature weights will be fatter at a particular slaughter weight because they are more developed at that weight than are breeds with higher mature weights. In the past there has been positive selection for animals which fatten easily, i.e. mature at low weights, and this trend is now rebounding against some of the traditional breeds.

This association between carcase composition and mature weight holds true for cattle, sheep and, to some extent, pigs (though a pig like the Pietrain, which does not have a high mature weight, produces a carcase with a high proportion of lean). Dairy breeds of cattle, incidentally, tend to have low ratios of lean to bone compared with beef breeds and they also have lower ratios of subcutaneous to intermuscular fat, tending to deposit fat in the body cavity.

Uncastrated males grow faster to a particular weight (and are therefore leaner at that weight) than females or castrated males.

The MLC carcase classification schemes for cattle, sheep and pigs take into account conformation as well as carcase weight and the proportion of fat. Poor conformation often produces butcher cuts which lack visual appeal and therefore do not sell well. Full details of methods of assessing conformation in a living animal are given in the Appendix, along with details of the MLC classification schemes for different species.

FIBRE

Sheep's wool

In most commercial flocks the income from wool is only a small percentage of total income: meat is far more important. To many, wool is merely a nuisance, something which has to be dagged and shorn, a haven for a host of pests and diseases which have to be controlled by the traumatic ritual of dipping. The Wiltshire Horn is a breed which is proud of its lack of fleece — a concept which would have shocked the monasteries and wool barons of earlier centuries. Britain grew great on wool.

Among the minor breeds, however, fleece is often a major asset and the name of the breed is strongly linked with its wool. The Shetland is an obvious example, and more recently other breeds are being credited for their fleeces. The British Wool Marketing Board has been promoting in particular the Black Welsh, Herdwick and Jacob as 'breeds of British sheep whose fleece is often spun and woven in its undyed form, to give a look that is both unique and natural'. In giving support to the work of the respective breed societies, the Board is proud of the definite effect of its marketing. The Herdwick is a good example: through the Board's efforts its wool has risen from being a coarse carpet wool to occupy a good place in the market for apparel yarns used in sweaters and cloth for the 'natural look'. The Jacob Sheep Society has done a magnificent marketing job too (with the Board's support), likewise the Black Welsh.

These success stories are perhaps ironic in that for centuries sheep breeders have been trying to breed the colour out of their fleeces, because white takes dyes better. Certainly the island Shetland flock has been biased towards the whiter fleece and it is only recently, with the growth in the number of hand spinners and weavers who prefer the natural colours of undyed fleeces, that Shetland breeders have begun to lose their colour prejudice. Fortunately the Shetland still has a wide range of evocatively named colours.

The once rejected black sheep is now recognized as an acceptable member of the family in some circles. Coloured long-wools like the Lincoln and Wensleydale add lustre and staple to the increasing range of colours in other breeds — the browns and creams of the Jacob, the greys of the Herdwick, the surprising potential range of the Soay and the North Ronaldsay, for example. As an enterprise, breeding sheep specifically for coloured wool is on the increase in this country and a good example has been set in Australia. However, there can be problems and these are discussed in Chapter 4.

Fibre from goats

There are several interesting developments concerning enterprises making use of fibre from goats and, although it is early days yet, the initial successes are very promising. There are three fibres — cashmere, cashgora and mohair — and the Goats chapter gives full details of the possibilities.

LIVESTOCK

It is almost fair to say that the market in supplying pure rare breeds to new breeders has already been cornered by a handful of breeders with considerable experience and excellent reputations. Rare breeds (a more precise term than 'minor' breeds) are by definition limited in numbers — indeed breeders are sometimes asked to supply animals from 'the rarest breed there is', regardless of whether the breed is suitable to the potential purchaser's land, enterprise or management techniques. This smacks of the old-style zoological gardens or the dilettante collections of oddities, animate or otherwise.

It is of course important that breeding stock are of the best quality, bred by people who know what they are doing and who are more concerned for the breed than for commercial gain. Reputation is vital: you are unlikely to make much of a living out of selling pure minor breed livestock until you have proved yourself and become well established. It takes years to gain a good reputation and you need to show your stock whenever and wherever you can in the meantime. You will also be at an advantage if you keep very careful records, not just of pedigrees but also of performance.

Supplying crossbreds is a little different: performance tends to be more important than appearance or pedigree. Good reputations are being made by some breeders who have found a useful cross, persisted with it and promoted it — for example the Fishwick Longhorn × Welsh Black as a suckler dam, the Luing (West Highland × Welsh Black) and the classic Masham (Teeswater × hill ewes). The challenge of crossbreeding (which ultimately creates a new breed like the Luing) is to decide firmly on the aims of a programme and then select the best mixture of breeds and of lines within those breeds to meet those aims. The British Milksheep, for example, which is now a breed in its own right, was created from a carefully chosen mixture of several breeds with the specific aim of producing a ewe with very high prolificacy and also a high yield so that she can raise the large number of lambs she bears in each gestation.

An obvious enterprise is purebred replacements for milking herds of, say, Dexters or Red Polls, or for export. The latter is fraught with frustration and red tape. The possibility of gaining the necessary licence to export depends on the destination and on precedence, and if you are hoping to export a few Tamworths to Iran, perhaps, which has never been attempted, it will take months or even years to set up all the necessary arrangements. The veterinary profession in this country and the target country have to come to mutual agreements about health restrictions and so on. For example, Israel and China are difficult if you want to import from there, because British health regulations are aimed at keeping a host of African and Asian diseases out of this country. It is now simple to export to America, but importing is a different matter because of the risk of importing something like 'blue tongue'. Import and export are more straightforward with, say, Denmark, Holland and New Zealand, but with several countries there are still no arrangements and you have to start from scratch. Ask your District Veterinary Officer for advice in the first place, and be prepared to take a long time over the whole business.

Once your overseas link is established, exporting becomes a little simpler, as long as your stock puts up with lengthy periods of quarantine at either end of the voyage, passes all the health tests, avoids dock strikes, and is not flown in bumpy weather. Regulations regarding crating and other confinement in transport are naturally strict, all in the interests of the welfare of the animal, which you will of course already have at heart.

With minor breeds, most purebred livestock will be sold privately or at specialist events like the annual RBST Show and Sale at Stoneleigh, Warwickshire. It makes sense to sell where specialist buyers are most likely to congregate. In the ordinary market–place the qualities of a minor breed are less likely to be be appreciated, and the breed itself will probably not be recognized by the majority of bidders. If it is not black and white, or if it has not got a white face or double muscling, who will buy? Yet again instant recognition is important — that is why breeds exist. The Hereford's dominant white face indicates beef potential in its crossbred offspring; the Ayrshire's shapely udder promises reliable milking; the Saddleback's characteristic belt offers outdoor hardiness and a good maternal temperament without blue meat. The drawback to performance breeds like the British Milksheep which do not necessarily have such distinctive phenotypes is that they are not recognized by eye, and stockmen tend to trust their eyes first and foremost, detecting the trace of an undesirable outcross generations back simply from the set of an ear. Appearance does matter: phenotype has always won more acclaim than the genotype which determines it.

RECORDING

No, do not skip this section! Deskwork (or diskwork) is often deemed irrelevant — most farmers would rather be knee-deep in muck and mud than in paper — but, as already mentioned several times and without apology for the repetition, record-keeping is vital in any livestock enterprise, however small, and particularly with minor breeds, for the sake of the breed and for the sake of the enterprise. A simple card-index system is easy enough to set up and maintain manually or on computer. Computers can be of great assistance: they encourage more detailed record keeping and give instant access to all kinds of reports, cross references and useful extractions which you never knew you needed but which can highlight trends otherwise easily overlooked. Farmers took a while to accept the telephone, remember, and now where would they be without one? Computers (home or business models) are becoming increasingly common in farm offices, though they are still crying out for really reliable and relevant software. Your children can probably write an appropriate programme for your needs.

The most important records, depending on type of livestock and enterprise, are based on individual animals, though herd-based recording has its place. Pedigree recording is obviously of prime importance and should go as far back as possible, well beyond dam and sire, or at least quickly cross-referenced so that you can easily discover whether or not potential partners have ancestors in common. Ideally you need performance figures for as many of an animal's predecessors as possible so that you can spot trends. You also need details of how those predecessors were managed, because that will affect performance and you cannot have a true picture of performance unless all animals are treated in exactly the same way — a near impossibility except with contemporaries. (Remember the drought of 1976? What did that do to performance figures?)

Individual records should have details of everything that has ever happened to the animal — date of birth, ease of birth, identification number, name, pedigree, dates of weaning, disbudding and other juvenile events, detailed breeding records (age of first heat, date of first and subsequent services, details of sire used and whether successful, dates due to give birth and due to be served after birth, actual dates of parturitions with comments on any problems and details of offspring), dates for steaming up or drying off, length of lactation, yields and lactation curves, rations fed, whether housed or not and when, fleece or coat colouring (individual, parents and progeny), fleece/meat yields and quality, whether or not horns are present, milk quality (solids, TBC counts etc.), prices for outputs . . . Yes, the list could go on forever, and the more you can record the better.

Recording is not the end of it. There is no point in records unless you make good use of them and that includes not only calculating margins and breeding potential or whatever but also contributing to the pool of knowledge about the breed.

Please, for the sake of the breed, keep records!

4 Hoof and Horn, Hide and Hair

HOOF

All the livestock described in this book are ungulates (hoofed animals). All of them are even-toed ungulates — their hooves are split. The world's modern ungulates share certain other features in common: they have reasonably good hearing through small rotatable ears, a good sense of smell and, in nearly all cases, very good eyesight; they are generally herbivorous (though pigs are a little wider in their tastes if they fail to obtain enough protein in their foraging); their muzzles are long and held horizontally; their forelegs are roughly the same length as their hindlegs; their thickish skins tend to be hairy rather than furry, and their weight, be it the three tons of a hippo or the few pounds of a delicate dik-dik, is all balanced on tiptoe. The hoof, therefore, has a lot to put up with.

Hooves are formed of thick keratin with a hard edge. The tissue is renewable, constantly being worn down in use and constantly growing to compensate. In domesticated animals the tissue often grows faster than it is worn away and it needs to be pared or rasped. Untreated foot problems can cause all sorts of difficulties, some of them not perhaps so obviously connected with feet. For example, during mating the female needs to stand firm and take the weight of the male on her back, which she will not be able to do if her feet are killing her. The male needs to be surefooted on his hindlegs while he works. Good, strong legs and sound feet make for more successful mating.

Sheep are particularly prone to foot ailments, typically footrot, but most of the primitive breeds and many of the mountain and hill breeds are much better heeled than their softer lowland cousins, especially if they remain in their native habitat. The sheep's weight is carried on the outside edge of the front part of the hoof and this should be remembered when its feet are trimmed.

Domestic goats often develop overgrown hooves, because they were originally rock scramblers and it seems that their hooves still grow in anticipation of constant erosion by unforgiving terrain. It is important to pare their feet regularly and to give them concreted yard areas. Indeed a regular walk on concrete is useful for all the ungulates.

HORN

Keratin also outcrops as horn, and horns have always found a human use

— implements, weapons, instruments, decoration. In his article in *The Ark* (March, 1986) John L. Jones described the craft of the horner and the outlets for his product — lampshades, drinking vessels, spoons, combs, boxes, flasks, handles, toys, ornaments, manure ('hoof and horn'), glue, soap, walking sticks and shepherds' crooks for example. Horn has some useful qualities. It does not bend or warp; it is waterproof and non-flammable, yet it is malleable for working after it has been carefully heated, and it can be split into thin layers which are almost as transparent as glass if they are treated with oil. In the 18th and 19th centuries the British horn trade was flourishing, and there is still scope for the modern horner, particularly as so many of the minor breeds bear a wonderful variety of horns.

Horns among ungulates come in all shapes and sizes. The Kaffirs of the 19th century were passionate about their cows and did some amazing things with their horns, transforming them into elaborate ornaments on the living animal, persuading them into all sorts of shapes and directions. One might be trained forwards and the other back, or one upright and the other pointing groundwards, or both bent with their points nearly touching the shoulders or their tips almost meeting in an arch above the head. A particularly elaborate technique was to train a young animal's horns over its forehead as they grew until the points met and they were then manipulated so that they coalesced and thereafter grew straight up from the middle of the forehead, unicorn style. Another contortion was encouraged with the aid of a small vertical incision sawn into the horn buds at an early age: each horn was thus divided into two parts and would then grow separately so that the Kaffirs had the world's only multi-horned milking cows!

In our own domestic species the range of horns is impressive enough without such tortuous training. Among cattle the old British breeds were exuberantly horned and, oddly, the breeds with really impressive horns seem to be very docile. The Longhorn, for example, is a most amenable animal whether bull or cow, and the West Highland is notoriously low in the pecking order within a group of mixed breeds (though with a new calf at heel the cows are pretty belligerent to all comers). But sweeping cattle horns went out of fashion: they were a nuisance when the stock was housed, and unwitting turns of the head could accidentally jab a horntip at the stockman's arm; they sometimes broke and bled, or grew inwards like toenails, and they took up too much space in a tightly packed cattle wagon. The Shorthorn breed replaced the Longhorn (for reasons other than its horns, it must be admitted – see Cattle chapter). At the beginning of this century many of the breeds were still proud of their horns. Today, however, most dairy animals are automatically disbudded for practical reasons, and certainly a horned dairy cow in a polled herd can make her presence uncomfortably felt.

In the 18th century long-horned breeds were concentrated in Yorkshire, Derbyshire, Lancashire, Staffordshire and the north west of England, with middle-sized horns in the south and west of England and in Wales and Scotland, and short-horned types in the north east of England.

Horns can also be an asset in cattle. They were, for example, essential in draught animals. Ropes could be tied to them for binding the yoke (though the horns tended to break under the strain) or for guidance reins, and they could prevent the yoke from slipping off over the head.

Horns can be a fine sight. Polished for a show they really set an animal off well, but in a more natural environment they are equally effective. Take a look at the Rousham Longhorns gracing the parkland, or the silhouette of a West Highland against a Scottish skyline. The Ayrshire's lyre horns and the Jersey's neat little curves add character to the cow, giving it a kind of face-lift. If polling is considered necessary for practical reasons (though who would dare to deprive a Longhorn of its trademark?) it must be done as soon as the buds can be recognized, within weeks of birth.

If horns show any tendency to grow back into the skin, use a cheesewire or a sharp razor blade and gradually pare them back, a sliver at a time, to avoid bleeding. Horns are very much living tissue and can eject an alarming amount of blood if the quick is reached.

Cattle are either horned, polled or disbudded. Horned cattle are born with horn buds which develop fully into horns unless the calf is disbudded, i.e. has the buds cauterized to destroy future growth. Polled cattle are born without any potential to develop horns and this feature can be bred into a horned breed by crossing; the polled factor is normally dominant to the horned factor. Some people claim that polled animals feed better than horned ones and therefore grow better.

Sometimes a calf is born with 'scurs', which are an indication of the recessive horned factor retained in its genotype. Scurs do not develop into proper horns but in some supposedly pure polled breeds they can be an indication of outcrossing to another breed in the past, maybe many generations back.

Among sheep, horns become much more fanciful — they sweep, they spiral, they convolute, and in some breeds they multiply twice or even threefold. Many breeds of goat are also naturally horned but are often disbudded as early as a week old. The buds can be detected during the first twenty-four hours of life. If the hair curls where you would expect to find horns, the goat is likely to grow horns, but if there are a couple of chunky knobs it is likely to be polled. It is sometimes possible to feel the prick of potential horns just under a little bare patch of skin in the centre of each curl.

TABLE 3

HORNS IN SHEEP AND CATTLE

SHEEP	*Ram*	*Ewe*	**CATTLE**
Black Welsh	+		Ayrshire
Boreray	+	+	Dexter
Dartmoor	(+)		Gloucester
Dorset Horn	+	+	Highland
Exmoor Horn	+	+	Kerry
Herdwick	+		Longhorn
Jacob	+*	+*	Red Ruby Devon
Hebridean	+*	+*	Shetland
Manx Loghtan	+*	+*	Shorthorn
N. Ronaldsay	+	+	South Devon
Portland	+	+	Sussex
Shetland	+		Welsh
Soay	+	+	White Park
Torddu etc.	+		
Whitefaced Woodlands	+	+	
Wiltshire Horn	+	+	

Key: + = horned
(+) = sometimes horned
* = multihorned

Note that, especially among ewes, some animals may not grow horns in a horned breed.

Note that many of these breeds, especially cows, are often disbudded.

Pigs? Well, pigs have tusks rather than horns but they are just as effective as weapons and as digging tools.

HIDES AND SKINS

Hide comes from cattle (and horses), skin comes from sheep and pigs. The heavier hides are from steers, the lighter from dairy cows, and the breed, its health and its diet can also make a difference to the thickness of the hide.

Britain exports more than half its five million hides, which are often worth 5–10% of the total return on the carcase, a fact which beef farmers sometimes overlook. Hide value can be substantially reduced by damage from warble fly and other parasites, or minor wounds from horns, wire and other hazards.

Hides can be cured to preserve the hair intact or tanned for leather and suede. It is possible to set up your own curing and tannery enterprises but the processes require considerable expertise, patience and quality control, and they stink.

Sheepskins, with their range of colours, patterns and textures, perhaps have more potential for an on-farm enterprise. A carefully cured sheepskin rug sells readily, and several home industries produce other sheepskin products like moccasins, jackets, gloves, underblankets and linings. It could be worth talking to the Council for Small Industries in Rural Areas (CoSIRA).

HAIR AND WOOL

Mammalian hair usually grows as a double coat, with long, coarser 'guard' hairs forming the outer protective layer and undergrown by a soft, fine insulation coat. Guard hairs can be as coarse as pig bristles, horses' tails and kemp, and undercoats can be as fine as cashmere and vicuña.

There are some uses for actual hair. Cow hair can be mixed into wall plaster, mattresses and underfelts; pig bristles and horse-hair are used for brushes. From the British farmer's point of view these are only incidental outlets for what might almost be called waste materials, but in other lands the hair of animals like the yak (which is imported into Britain) and the American bison has found many an important use.

It is only among the sheep and goats of Britain (and the new lamoids) that pluckings and shearings from the coat become valuable commodities. Sheep fleece has evolved over the long ages of domestication; the wild sheep has the coarse/fine double coat (the outer-coat hairs being kemp and the undercoat wool) but with many domesticated sheep the kemp hair has gradually become finer, the undercoat fibres in some cases a little coarser, and an intermediary third type of hair has also been selectively bred for. These three types of fibre all add up to wool and it is the quality, combination and proportion of them which gives each breed its typical fleece. The wild goat has a much longer outer coat than the wild sheep, but the fleece of goats bred specifically for fibre has characteristic differences.

Wild sheep shed their fleece in spring but this process has gradually been bred out of most domesticated breeds, though many still lose quite a proportion of fibres in spring, shedding them individually rather than in great handfuls. However, primitive and island breeds like the Soay, Hebridean, North Ronaldsay and Shetland still have a natural moult and traditionally their wool has been hand-plucked or 'rooed'. This harvesting is carefully timed to coincide with the moult so that the majority of the loose wool can be gleaned from the sheep before it is strewn all over the landscape. Although most Shetlands are now shorn like any other sheep, rooing has the advantage of leaving the sheep's coat with uncut fibre tips so that it remains waterproof.

There will never be a manmade product as good as wool, and the damp, temperate climate of Britain has always produced the best wool. Thirty-four million British sheep and lambs are shorn or skinned every year, producing fifty million kilograms of fleece and skin wool. Skins are sold through fellmongers but the bulk of British wool is bought by the British Wool Marketing Board and then sold by auction. Anybody who has more than four adult sheep is required to register with the Board and sell their wool through it, with a few exceptions among the rare breeds. Once registered, the producer is allocated a local wool merchant who grades the clip and sends it through to the Board so that payments to the producer can be calculated and made promptly, irrespective of when the fortnightly auctions are held. The Board also runs a free ram-fleece assessment service, which is very useful for breeders wanting to select the best sires for wool production.

Very recently the Board has supported the work of the RBST by granting exemption to breeders of nine rare breeds: Boreray, Castlemilk Moorit, Hebridean, Manx Loghtan, New Norfolk Horn, North Ronaldsay, Portland, Soay and Whitefaced Woodlands. Fleeces from these breeds can be sold privately, which makes a great deal of sense as they are all appreciated by home spinners.

Most British wool has a uniquely high degree of 'crimp' and a fairly thick fibre diameter, and these factors combine to make a very springy, elastic wool which is ideal for items that look bulky but are light. It also gives elasticity and shape-retaining qualities to knitted and woven fabrics. The wool is very hard-wearing, and wool from rain-soaked mountain-bred sheep has inbuilt weatherproofing which can protect the outdoor activist as snugly as it did the sheep. If the yarn is twisted too much, however, it can feel a bit scratchy.

The large number of sheep breeds in Britain means that there is a wide variety of wools — lustrous, kempy, soft and so on — and also a good range of natural colours, especially among the minor breeds which have resisted generations of selective breeding for white, dye-taking fleeces.

Colour apart, British fleeces are divided by the Board into four main categories:

Short-wool and down
Longwool and lustre
Mountain and hill
Medium

Table 4 shows how the minor breeds in this book fit into these categories and gives the Board's figures for fleeces. It should be noted, however, that breed society figures and classifications are often at variance with those of the Board. The table also gives Dr Ryder's classifications which take into account the correlation between face colour and wool type. He points out that the black-faced, horned breeds tend to produce carpet wool while the white-faced, horned breeds have shorter, finer, less hairy fleeces which can be kempy. The polled breeds, whatever the face colour, have shorter and moderately fine wool; the longwools are divided into the medium length demi-lustres and the longer true lustres.

The local merchants grade wool clips into any of some two hundred grades specified by the Board, each of which is separately priced per kilogram net graded weight. The wool cheque will show the grade and maximum price, and will give reasons for any reduction from that price if condition or quality earn forfeits. The price schedule is revised and published annually.

TABLE 4

SHEEP CLASSIFIED BY WOOL

Notes

British Wool Marketing Board classifications:

L & L = Longwool and Lustre
Med = Medium
M & H = Mountain and Hill
S & D = Shortwool and Down

Dr Ryder's classifications:

BFSW = Black-faced Shortwool
LL = Lustre Longwool
Misc = Miscellaneous
WFHH = White-faced Horned Hill
WFSW = White-faced Shortwool

Other symbols

* = rare breeds exempted from the BWMB scheme
C = naturally coloured fleeces

Breed	*BWMB Wool Classification*	*Ryder Classification*	*Staple Length (cm)*	*Fleece Weight (kg)*	*Bradford Count (fibre diameter)*	
Black Welsh	M & H	Misc	8–10	1.25–1.5	52–54	C
Boreray	M & H					*C
British Friesland	Med		10–15	4–6	52–54	
British Milksheep	S & D		10–15	2–3		
Cotswold	L & L	LL	15–25	4–7	38–48	
Dartmoor Grey faced	L & L	LL	15–20	6.5–8	36–40	
Dartmoor White faced	L & L	LL	15–20	5.5–7	36–40	
Devon Closewool	Med	WFSW	8–10	2.25–3	46–54	
Devon & Cornwall Longwool	L & L	LL	20–25	7–10	32–40	
Dorset Down	S & D	BFSW	5–8	2.25–3	56–58	
Dorset Horn	S & D	WFSW	8–10	2.25–3	54–58	
Exmoor Horn	M & H	WFSW	8–12	2.25–3	48–56	
Hebridean	M & H	Misc	5–15	1.5–2.25	48–50	*C
Herdwick	M & H	WFHH	15–20	1.5–2	Coarse	C
Jacob	Med	Misc	8–17	2–2.5	44–56	C
Leicester Longwool	L & L	LL	20–25	5–6	40–46	
Lincoln Longwool	L & L	LL	15–35	7–10	36–40	
Llanwenog	S & D	BFSW	6–10	2–2.5	56–58	
Lleyn	Med		8–12	2–3	50–54	
Manx Loghtan	M & H	Misc	7–10	1.5–2	44–54	C
Norfolk Horn	Med		7–10	1.5–2	54–56	*
North Ronaldsay	M & H	Misc	4–8	1.5–2.5	50–56	*C
Oxford Down	S & D	BFSW	10–15	3–4	50–54	
Portland	S & D	WFSW	6–9	2–3	50–56	*
Ryeland	S & D	WFSW	8–10	2.25–3	56–68	
Shetland	S & D	WFHH	5–12	1–1.5	50–60	C
Shropshire	S & D	BFSW	10–15	2–3	54–56	
Soay	M & H	Misc	5–15	1.5–2.25	44–50	*C
Southdown	S & D	BFSW	4–6	1.5–2.25	56–60	
Teeswater	L & L	LL	15–30	3.5–7	40–48	
Torddu and Torwen	M & H		7–10	1.5–2	46–56	C
Wensleydale	L & L	LL	20–30	3.5–7	44–48	
Whitefaced Woodlands	M & H	WFHH	10–15	2–3	50–54	*
Wiltshire Horn		WFSW	0.5	Negligible	50–56	
Castlemilk Moorit	Not included in BWMB classifications					*C

The merchant first sorts fleeces into major categories (fine, medium etc.) then separates hogg (first shearing) fleeces from 'ewe and wether' fleeces. Hoggs have longer staples (fibre lengths) with curliness at the tip. The final stage is the actual grading and this can be confusing to the producer because it is based on wool types but given breed names to epitomize the type, and that name may have nothing to do with the actual breed of sheep which produced the fleece! Forget the name: stick to the grade number.

There are special grades for several minor breeds, notably the Jacob (two grades), the Shetland (white, moorit and cross), the Orkney (three colours), the 'super' Black Welsh, the Herdwick (light and dark) and various Devon and other lustre wools. The Coloured Sheep Breeders' Association is currently in negotiation with the Board for coloured fleeces from other breeds, so that they can be sold direct to the home-spinners who really appreciate them rather than having to be sold to the Board. It is a complex situation because, while the Board has no wish to dampen the enthusiasm of sheep breeders and craft outlets, it is none the less governed by Statute and is bound to inform producers that they cannot sell any wool, either in the United Kingdom or elsewhere, unless they are registered with the Board or have special exemption (as in the case of the nine rare breeds). In considering possible exemptions the Board must also ensure that these do not harm in any way the service offered to the majority of its ninety thousand producers for whom sheep-keeping provides a living rather than a hobby, and this seems to be the sticking point at the moment with coloured varieties of breeds which are normally white.

As can be seen from Table 4, wool is typified by the diameter and length of its fibres; in general, longer fibres are thicker. *Staple* is the fibre length and British staples vary from about 5cm to about 30cm. Fibre diameter is measured by the *Bradford Count* quality system which in theory indicates the number of hanks of yarn, each 560 yards long, which could be spun from one pound of the wool. The coarsest, thickest fibres are rated as 28s, and the very finest go up to 90s or more. British wools tend to range between 28s and 58s. Those in the 28–44 range are used in carpets, heavy tweeds etc., and those from 46s upwards are made into woollen and worsted cloths, hosiery, handknitting wools etc.

There is no magic mathematical formula for relating Bradford Count numbers to fibre diameters, nor does the original definition really hold good any more — it is only a guide. For example, very few (if any) wools described as 64s could actually be spun to 64 × 560 yards of yarn per pound of fibre under modern processing conditions. A 64s wool with an average diameter of 22.5 microns and a mean fibre length of 64mm will spin to finer counts than a wool of similar diameter but with a mean fibre length of 50mm. So the Bradford Count figures are slightly vague but, taking UK averages, they can be compared loosely with fibre diameter measurements: the chart below gives some examples for higher counts.

Microns	**UK Average Bradford Count**	
	Greasy Wool	*Tops*
25.2	58/60s	60s
26.3	58s	
27.2		58s
27.5	56/58s	
29.5	56s	56s
31.2		54s
31.5	54s	
32.5	52s	
33.0		52s
33.5	50s	
34.5		50s

Except in the case of the very uniform Merino, each fleece tends to contain a range of wool quality on different parts of the body: it is often finer on the shoulder than on the back and flank, and least fine of all on the breech. Michael Ryder's publications (see Bibliography) describe all you will ever need to know about wool and hair, and they are essential reading, especially for home spinners who are interested in the difference in quality of fleeces in different seasons, different environments and under different management regimes. Many factors affect the quality of a fleece.

The fibre from certain goats and from llamas is for a different market altogether, and a growing one for the specialist producer. The products are considered in the chapters on Goats and on Other Livestock.

5 Breeding

For the sake of their posterity, this is the most important chapter for minor breeds. Those who opt to care for them take on a precious responsibility and they should not do so too lightly. If you make a hundred mistakes breeding Friesians, the breed as a whole will hardly notice, but just a few mistakes could be crucial to a breed which is already fragile in numbers. I would make a strong plea to all breeders, on however small a scale, to take a basic course in genetics and animal breeding, or at least to read as many texts on the subject as possible. Some very readable books are listed in the Bibliography.

Man has been controlling the breeding of livestock for eight or nine thousand years, attempting to fashion animals to suit human needs, and, because those needs are so diverse and the methods (until recently) so haphazard, there is now a glorious variety among domesticated animals. Wild species tend towards uniformity — an eland is an eland (though it is being eyed for domestication even now) — but cattle and pigs, sheep and goats, horses, dogs, cats and poultry come in all sorts of shapes, sizes and colours and with a wide range of productivity, vigour and adaptability. Controlled breeding separates the domesticated from the wild; controlled breeding gives the greatest scope for artificial selection and the perpetuation of control over the development of a species.

It is a paradox that, while breeding has encouraged such diversity, the more scientific breeding of the last two hundred years has led to greater uniformity within the breeds and, by commercial selection, fewer breeds. Breed societies exist to promote and encourage their own breeds, and some of them do so with imagination but some, sadly, have become so rigid in their specifications for phenotypic characteristics (i.e. outward appearances) that ultimately the breeds suffer. A misplaced dab of white can result in the culling of an animal which might well harbour immensely useful genes for, say, prolificacy or hardiness, and excessive fussiness about superficial factors like colour patterns can deprive a breed of important genetic reserves.

Of course, breed societies want to ensure that their breeds are visually distinctive and so they continue to tighten their standards. When a farm breed's fashionable looks become more important than its performance it is on the downward path — literally going to the dogs and ending up as a show-ring curiosity. Some of the minor breeds already have a tentative toe on the top of that slope.

Domestication enabled man to alter animals to suit his practical needs first and foremost. The important attributes were temperament, productivity, hardiness, fertility, mothering instincts . . . how many breed societies list those qualities in their breed standards? They may boast them in their literature but they do not demand them as conditions of registration.

However, if one accepts that a breed should be recognizably a breed and that a particular breed has enough good qualities as well as being pleasing to the eye, then it is important to know enough about basic genetics to be able to retain those good qualities, within the framework of the outward appearance. It is also important to *improve* its qualities. Some would argue otherwise and prefer to retain a breed, particularly a rare one, exactly as it was when they first knew it — conservative conservation, so to speak. But is that for the ultimate good of the breed? More often than not it has become rare because it has too few qualities to offer, or has too many disadvantages, or because its qualities have either not been recognized or have no value in contemporary markets. Conservation should preserve those qualities against the time when they might be valued, but museums and zoos are not the best places for farm livestock. There is a real risk of rare breeds going the way of pet Pomeranians, a dog which was originally capable of hunting a bear but which was prettified and cosseted and miniaturized into a lapdog which is now scarcely capable of hunting a mouse. If a breed loses its usefulness, it loses its point and it loses its dignity. And there are not enough gracious parks or gracious park owners around to give a setting to the picturesque simply for the sake of their looks or novelty value. Nor can any animal retain its dignity in a zoo.

BASIC GENETICS

(See Genetics Glossary for full explanation of terms used.)

When Mendel the monk began studying his pea plants he also began a revolution. By very detailed observation, measurement, recording and analysis over a long period and over a wide range of conditions, he was able to discern and quantify generational patterns and to work out why different combinations of parents produced different results. Once he knew why, he was able to predict outcomes. He had proved the value of careful recording!

The basic facts revealed by Mendel's work were that each characteristic in a living organism is controlled by pairs of genes, that each parent contributes one of each of those pairs to the offspring, and that within each pair there is a system of dominance which determines the expression of the characteristic.

Very broadly, a gene can be dominant or recessive for a specific characteristic. Say, for the sake of a grossly simplified example, an animal's nose can be either pink or purple, and that purple is the expression of a dominant gene for nose colour while pink is that of a recessive gene. If both parents contribute a purple gene, the offspring will have a purple nose. If one parent contributes purple and the other pink, the dominant gene overrides the recessive and again the offspring has a purple nose. If both parents contribute a pink gene, the offspring's nose is pink.

However (and this is where Mendel's work comes in) the offspring in the second case, although to outward appearances having a purple nose, still retains a pink gene in its genetic structure, and it can pass on that pink gene to the next generation where, if it pairs with another pink gene, the second generation will have a pink nose. So it is quite possible for two purple-nosed parents to produce pink-nosed offspring. The recessive gene is, if you like, dormant or masked until it pairs with another of its kind in a subsequent generation, and it can be passed through many generations masked by dominant genes until one day, as chance would have it, it pairs with another similar recessive and expresses itself.

Each everyday cell in an animal's body contains paired genes for every characteristic of that animal, linked together on chromosomes like two parallel strings of beads. But the reproductive cells — sperm in the male and ovum in the female — are different. They each contain only one gene for each characteristic. If, say, the sire's normal cells have one purple and one pink gene for nose colour, some of his sperm will only contain one dominant purple gene and the rest will contain only one recessive pink gene. The same is true for the dam's ova. So when a sperm and an ovum meet and join, the resulting embryonic cell has a pair of genes (one from each parent) which may be both purple, both pink, or one of each, and the offspring which develops from that cell will express the characteristic according to the combination.

It is customary to annotate dominant and recessive alleles (alternative forms of the same gene) by the use of a capital letter for the dominant one, using lower case for the recessive, and the use of such annotation can demonstrate the likely outcome of a mating when a single simple characteristic controlled by a single pair of genes is considered. Take horns, for example: in cattle, sheep and goats the gene for lack of horns (the 'polled' allele) is normally dominant to the gene for the presence of horns (the 'horned' allelle). If the polled allele is **P** and the horned allele **p**, here are some possible outcomes of crossing a horned animal with a polled one (the latter, of course, being an animal born without horns, not one which was subsequently disbudded). Remember that, as it is recessive, the horned characteristic will only be expressed if two **p** alleles combine in the offspring, and that an animal with one **P** and one **p** allele will be polled but will still be able to pass on the horned allele to its own offspring.

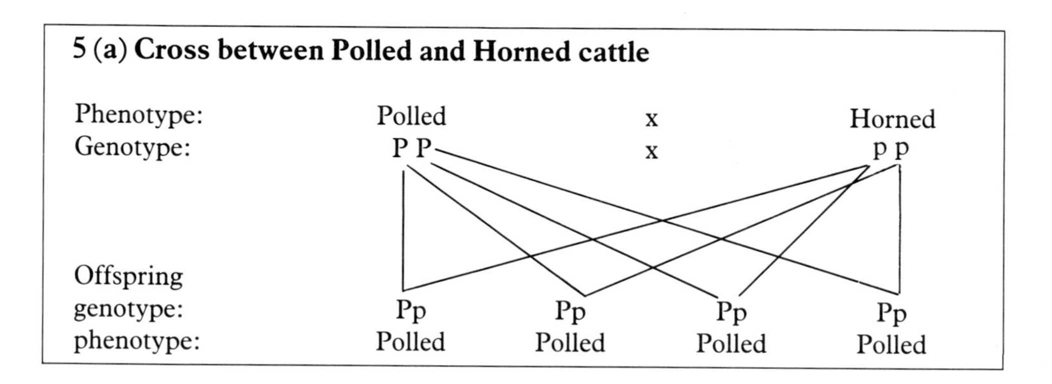

An animal which has two similar alleles (e.g. **PP** or **pp**) is termed *homozygous* for that gene and one with two different alleles (e.g. **Pp**) is termed *heterozygous*. The only cases in which the offspring always 'breed true' for a characteristic are those in which both parents are homozygous for the same recessive allele, or both for the same dominant allele. Heterozygotes mask the recessive allele.

If you are interested in a *combination* of characteristics, the sums naturally become more complicated. For example, take horns and coat colour. Black is often dominant to red in cattle and you could therefore annotate the black allele as **B** and the red allele as **b**. If you cross a black polled animal with a red horned one, your possible results will be:

5 (b) Black Polled × Red Horned

The Black Polled parent may have any one of four different genotypes: BBPP, BBPp, BbPP or BbPp. The Red Horned parent, showing two recessive traits, is homozygous for both: bbpp. There are therefore four different possible combinations:

BBPP × bbpp
BBPp × bbpp
BbPP × bbpp
BbPp × bbpp

Each combination has different results:

Genotype:	BBPP × bbpp
	Black Polled BP
Red Horned bp	BbPp
Offspring phenotype:	Black Polled (all)

Genotype:	BBPp × bbpp	
	Black Polled	
	BP	or Bp
Red Horned bp	BbPp	Bbpp
Offspring phenotype:	Black Polled	Black Horned

Genotype:	BbPP × bbpp	
	Black Polled	
	BP	or bP
Red Horned bp	BbPp	bbPp
Offspring phenotype:	Black Polled	Red Polled

Genotype:	BbPp × bbpp			
	Black Polled			
	BP	or Bp	or bP	or bp
Red Horned bp	BbPp	Bbpp	bbPp	bbpp
Offspring phenotype:	Black Polled	Black Horned	Red Polled	Red Horned

If you now cross the heterozygous generation **BbPp** which resulted from mating the two homozygotes **BBPP** and **bbpp**, you will get 9 black polled progeny, 3 red polled, 3 black horned and 1 red horned:

5 (c) Cross between first generation offspring with genotype BbPp

Parent 1 × Parent 2
BbPp × BbPp

		Parent 1			
		BP	or Bp	or bP	or bp
Parent 2	BP	BBPP (1)	BBPp (1)	BbPP (1)	BbPp (1)
	or Bp	BBPp (1)	BBpp (2)	BbPp (1)	Bbpp (2)
	or bP	BbPP (1)	BbPp (1)	bbPP (3)	bbPp (3)
	or bp	BbPp (1)	Bbpp (2)	bbPp (3)	bbpp (4)

Second generations offspring phenotypes are:
(1) Black Polled
(2) Black Horned
(3) Red Polled
(4) Red Horned

The chart shows that the proportions between these four phenotypes are:
9 Black Polled
3 Black Horned
3 Red Polled
1 Red Horned

Note, however, that there are four different genotypes for the Black Polled phenotypes, two different genotypes for the Black Horned phenotypes and for the Red Polled phenotypes, and only one genotype for the double recessive Red Horned phenotype.

This is a classic Mendelian ratio and it can be expressed for larger numbers of gene combinations. For example, with four genes the ratio of different phenotypes will be 27:9:9:9:3:3:3:1 and will include 81 different genotypes.

Even then it is not as simple as Mendel implies. For a start, some characteristics are affected by more than one pair of genes and the results depend on the combinations of all the relevant genes. Also, many events can occur during the formation and division of cells. Clive Dalton's excellent and very readable book on this subject is listed in the Bibliography.

As a practical breeder, here are some facts you need to know.

Heritability

Studies have shown the degree to which certain characteristics seem to be heritable but the figures are affected by so many factors that it is difficult to be precise. There are marked differences between species, between breeds, between populations within breeds (e.g. British or Australian) and between lines within breeds. *Heritability* defines the 'additive genetic proportion of phenotypic variance' and if heritability is very low for a characteristic there is little scope for improving it by selection.

In general it seems that factors affecting morphological characteristics, adult weights and carcase are fairly well up on the heritability scale but those concerned with reproductive function (including the ability of the young to survive) are the least heritable. Natural selection has worked hard in this vital area and has reduced the potential for genetic variation by eliminating all but the fittest reproducers.

Correlation

Certain characteristics are strongly correlated with each other so that selective breeding for one affects or is based on the other. It is important to bear this in mind. You might do more harm to one characteristic than good to another.

However, it is commonly necessary to improve more than one characteristic at a time, particularly in cattle: a cow produces on average only one calf a year and it is another two or two and a half years before the next generation is born, let alone can be judged. Progress is therefore slow, especially compared with pigs which can produce two or even three litters a year with a dozen young in each litter and can be grandparents the following year. There are sensible ways of achieving wider improvements, some more time-consuming than others.

You can select in tandem, i.e. select for one characteristic first, fix it over several generations, and only then go for a second one. But that will take years and you may very well find that altering the second factor upsets the one you have already fixed.

You can select by culling. Decide on acceptable levels for each chosen characteristic, then cull any animal below any of those levels and retain those above them for breeding stock. Adjust culling levels as necessary according to the importance you place on each characteristic.

You can adjust this method by combining desirable traits and setting a combined culling/breeding level. This is more efficient than having different levels for different traits but it is also more complicated. You need to find a formula which takes into account heritability and potential for good economic margins as well as productivity and looks, and you may well find that improvement in some characteristics works against the others. For example, some of the most productive pig breeds used in intensive systems are so averse to stress that they keel over and die if an unkind word is spoken(!), or they will betray their stress at slaughter by producing soft fat or very pale meat in the carcase.

Environment

In seeking to maintain or improve a breed, bear in mind the type of environment in which it will be managed. For example, there seems to be a promising outlet for blue-skinned breeds, like British White cattle, in hotter climates. The blue pigment protects the animal from sunburn and heat stress, and, no doubt, a white coat colour helps by reflecting away the sun's rays, adding to the animal's ability to withstand subtropical conditions. With limited numbers in minor breeds it is not yet practical to breed specific lines for overseas markets but the possibilities can be borne in mind. Other foreign conditions, such as day length, disease, available feeding and management techniques, will also affect the aims of any export breeding programme and it must be remembered that theoretical and actual performance in a different environment are not necessarily the same. Sometimes it is easier and more practical to adapt the environment or system to suit the animal, rather than vice versa.

Selecting the parents

The age-old breeding maxim has always been, as Bakewell put it, 'Breed the best to the best.' It still holds good, with reservations. Yes, breed only from good animals, but make sure that the *line* is good as well; look further back than the parents, and look sideways too at their siblings and the offspring of those siblings, to check for any trends, problems or, more positively, for desirable traits. Never breed from an animal with a genetic fault, however good it is otherwise: it will only perpetuate the fault in future generations.

Check, too, the pedigrees of potential parents as far back as possible to try and ascertain the extent of relatedness. *Inbreeding* is the mating of individuals which are ancestrally more closely related than the average individuals in a population and the most extreme examples of inbreeding are offspring to parent or sibling to sibling. Inbreeding increases the chance of masked recessive genes common to related individuals pairing and giving expression to a phenotype which may be undesirable or even abnormal. It also tends to lead to 'inbreeding depression' in which fertility and general vigour are progressively reduced. On the other hand, inbreeding was used quite often in the past, to 'concentrate' desirable genes, when a particularly good bull was mated to his own daughters and granddaughters.

In 1931 the well known John Hammond, working at Cambridge on solving animal breeding problems, made a strong plea for the advantages of close inbreeding 'as a means of fixing desirable strains in heavy milking cattle'. He pointed out that the pioneers of British livestock improvement had used this method extensively but that by the 1930s the frequent introduction of fresh blood was preferred by dairy stock breeders — with the exception of Friesian breeders in Holland. Hammond reminded his readers that, provided the stock were sound, there was nothing to be feared from inbreeding.

However, inbreeding is risky and is not practised so much now except by those who really do know what they are doing. When it is successful, say the cynics, it is called *line breeding* — which is much more an approved practice! The problem with rare breeds is that the population is so small that its members are more likely to have common ancestors not too far back in their pedigrees, and the chances of a degree of inbreeding are greatly increased. The RBST has made a careful study of several breeds and can calculate the *coefficient of inbreeding* for animals registered in their Combined Flock Book and also for several breeds of cattle. For a small charge their Technical Consultant will report on the coefficients in potential breeding programmes and give advice on the best selection.

The coefficient of inbreeding evaluates the probability that two genes at any locus in an individual are alike by descent, and it can give guidance on the likelihood of an individual being homozygous at a locus because the same gene has come through both parents from a common ancestor. The term is a relative one, referring to a particular generation within a population. A high coefficient sounds a warning, and it is important (for the sake of the breed and breeder's stock) to be very judicious about using inbreeding techniques.

SELECTING FOR BREEDING

When considering a breeding programme, check the following:

Performance

For characteristics of high heritability look at the potential parent's own performance within its contemporary group, particularly in pigs, sheep and beef cattle. Take the best individual from a group of animals which have received the same management, so that its performance reflects its own merits rather than the treatment it has received or the environment in which it has performed. For preference, the records of its performance should give details over several seasons (to prove trends rather than flukes or setbacks) and must always be in comparison with the performances of other animals. It is usually true, incidentally, that you can tell a good milking cow from her very first lactation: if she yields well as a first-calf heifer she will yield well as a cow. But, if you can afford to wait for an accumulated record, do so. Check the performances of the animal's siblings as well.

Pedigree

For traits of less high heritability, check the ancestors. Pedigrees often give only the name and registration number of an animal's ancestors and that might help a little if those ancestors can be remembered accurately for their performance and appearance. Pedigrees become invaluable to the breeder if they actually *record* such details, with as much comment as possible on elusive 'qualities'. For the sake of future breeding, *always* record every detail you can find space for. It might be important for a future breeder to know that Daisy, whose yields and butterfat were excellent, was a real bitch in the parlour — even more important if her daughters or sisters showed traces of a similar temperament. In an ideal world you could call up comparative computer reports on every aspect of every registered animal which has contributed its genes to your potential breeding stock. Unfortunately, defective animals are often not registered at all and a pedigree could well hide a few genetic skeletons in the cupboard.

Progeny testing

This technique is valuable for the good of the breed but it can be costly and by its nature it has to be spread over quite a long period if the results are to be of use. It is carried out by organizations like the Milk Marketing Board, who monitor the offspring of sires used for AI on the basis that the qualities of the offspring reflect those of the parent. But in order to avoid statistical unreliability a large number of progeny must be assessed before a judgement can be made on the parent. (Usually it is the sire rather than the dam which is evaluated because normally he passes his genes on to many more progeny than any female can produce in a lifetime.) A good number of parents need to be involved before the results are of real value to the breed as a whole. With rare breeds it is that old vicious circle again: there may be too few potential parents (or lines or herds) to produce a wide enough sample for statistical purposes, with the result that the performance of the breed cannot be properly assessed nor its production figures enumerated, which means no figures to encourage the interest of new breeders, which means that breed numbers remain static or fall, and so on.

You can undertake limited progeny testing within a herd or group of herds but the results will not be statistically significant and you also run the risk of confusing environmental effects with genetic traits. For realistic statistics on a breed you need to test *all* offspring, good and bad, which means no culling, and you need to mate at random. But it is difficult to ask a conscientious breeder *not* to use the best sire on the best dams!

This leads to another problem with low-number breeds. Naturally every breeder wants to use the best breeding stock, and with AI in cattle this can easily lead to a particularly favoured bull being used for a very high percentage of inseminations throughout the breed, thus reducing the genetic spread in future generations and increasing the risk that a masked genetic default in the bull may become very widely spread in the national herd before it is recognized. It has happened, and if it happens in a rare breed it is potentially disastrous for the breed. A quick way of highlighting this kind of problem is to breed a bull to his daughters.

BREEDING FOR SPECIFIC TRAITS

There are so many possible characteristics on which different breeders might place different emphases that it is far beyond the scope of a general book such as this one to look at them in any detail, especially those that are affected by a combination of genes. However, some important characteristics are controlled by only one or two loci, which makes breeding for those characteristics much simpler. Genetic correlations have already been mentioned but the following paragraphs deal with single, easily visible physical characteristics such as colour and horns.

Colour

In 1815 Thomas Quayle said that colours in one breed of cattle ran from cream, to cream mixed with white, to red, and red and white, and from these colours to black, and black and white. Some were black with a dingy brown-red ridge on the back and about the nostrils and they 'all have a good pile, and generally are thin-skinned and fatten soon.'

He was talking about Jerseys! No wonder Jersey breeders claim that no good cow can be a bad colour.

But colour often ostracizes a minor breed. Some of them are seen merely as coloured deviations in a more widespread breed and they may or may not be acceptable to the main breed society or may be exiled into a separate section of the Herd or Flock Book, left lingering on the sidelines like unwanted aunts. Some would say, for example, that the Belted Galloway and White Galloway are simply black Galloways in different coats, though others point out that they breed true and also have slightly different qualities. Likewise some say that the Bolian Gwynion is just a belted version of the standard Welsh Black (and there are plenty more colours in that breed). Red and white Friesians have been barred from the Friesian Herd Book; coloured Wensleydale and Leicester Longwools are only just beginning to be acceptable. As many as 20% of Wensleydale lambs may be black (most of the longwools carry a recessive gene for black wool) and in this breed the black gene is associated with the blue skin colour. Among the Welsh Mountain sheep there are several different and very recognizable colourings, for example the Black Welsh, the Torddu or Badger-faced, the Torwen and the Baalwen. The Torddu pattern has also been seen in other breeds such as the Ryeland and is very similar to the Shetland 'catmogit'.

It all goes back to the defintion of 'breed' and to the prejudices of breed societies in favour of uniformity of appearance, often at the expense of performance. In some cases there is a real difference between coloured and standard versions of a breed, apart from the colour; for example, fawn self-coloured Soay sheep are thought to be less viable than the typical chocolate-and-beige *mouflon* pattern Soay. On the other hand it is claimed that black sheep in a selectively white breed often give a better carcase and are also more prolific. Colour prejudice works both ways.

In some sheep breeds there is a noticeable difference in fleece colour between lambs and adults. For example, Herdwicks start life almost black and generally become greyer with maturity (progressing sometimes through a brownish stage), their final colour varying from dark grey to almost white and often continuing to pale with age. Portland lambs have a foxy-red fleece but the adults are creamy white with a very slight tan tinge.

Many of the primitive sheep breeds still retain a range of fleece colours within the flock. Shetlands have been selectively bred for white for many generations on the islands but the original range of colours can still be found, from white through grey to black and 'moorit' (a reddish brown), and even in that range there are several mixtures and patterns. The North Ronaldsay's range includes white, various greys, black, blue or red roan, moorit and fawn. The Hebridean is normally black or dark brown in the fleece, sometimes greying with age, and there can be a small white spot on the head. The Manx Loghtan, which fades to light brown from its early chocolate-coloured lambswool, sometimes shows similar white markings not only on the head but also about the tail and legs. The Soay, as has been shown at the Butser Iron Age farm in Hampshire, can be selectively bred for an increasing amount of white in the coat, and no doubt the Hebridean and Manx Loghtan also have that potential. This 'spotting' gene is much stronger in the Jacob, with its splodges of black and dark brown in a creamy fleece.

Colour inheritance is quite straightforward in sheep. There are four important loci for colour which affect the species in Britain and they control not just colour but combination of colour and pattern. For example, grey is often a mixture of black and white hairs in different proportions for different degrees of greyness, and some grey fleeces include tan fibres as well. There is some parallel here with roan cattle, whose coats are a mixture of blue or red hairs with white hairs. In the Jacob, however, the dark fibres and the white fibres are not mixed: they occur separately, creating the characteristic piebald pattern, and quite often the dark fibres are coarser, longer and straighter than the white part of the fleece and, because of their lack of crimp, the black fibres stand up above the general level of the rest of the fleece.

Colour is also affected to some extent by the time of year. A black sheep looks quite brown in some seasons, and this is because the staple tips fade during the year. The base of the staple tends to become paler as well by the end of the winter and the new spring wool beginning to push its way through the fleece is noticeably more intense in colour. Several breeds also become greyer with age, particularly the Herdwick (which can end up almost white) and the Hebridean (which often looks quite silvery as the number of white hairs in the dark fleece increase.).

In most breeds of sheep, white is dominant to all other colours but in the Black Welsh and Jacob black is dominant. Grey mixtures are recessive to white but dominant to other colours. Black (apart from the exceptions just mentioned) is recessive to both white and grey, and moorit is recessive to all other colours.

The *mouflon* pattern, seen typically in the Soay and the Torwen, and the badger-faced pattern of the Torddu and the catmogit Shetland, are dominant to black and moorit but recessive to white and grey. In the Soay, some animals show the mouflon pattern but others are self-coloured (i.e. the same colour all over): mouflon is dominant to self-colour and the typical chocolate brown of the Soay is dominant to the light brown or fawn.

The 'spotting' factor which is so fully expressed in the Jacob, and to a lesser degree in the Manx Loghtan, Herdwick, Hebridean and Soay, is controlled by interactions between genes on two different loci, which makes matters a little more complicated. If a Jacob is crossed with other breeds, its dominant black gene generally suppresses the spotting factor and the lambs will be black, not spotted, except in the case of a cross to a pink-nosed white breed.

The genetics of the interesting mixtures of colours seen in breeds like the Shetland, North Ronaldsay and Herdwick are less than straightforward. Michael Ryder's paper *Coat Colour inheritance in Soay, Orkney and Shetland sheep* will help breeders who would like to know more. Herdwick breeders will be interested in the results of experiments with crossbred lamb colours carried out by Dr Marca Burns and published in *The Ark* (September 1985).

If you want to breed for specific colours, your first priority is detailed and accurate recording of results. Make a note of the fleece colour, pattern and quality of every lamb born and any alterations as it matures. The picture will soon build up. If several breeders co-operate, so much the better. If you can identify an animal as homozygous for a dominant colour you can proceed much more scientifically.

Sometimes it is possible to detect the presence of a hidden recessive for colour in a heterozygote. For example, a white Wensleydale which is homozygous for white has a coppery tinge inside the ears whereas its ears will be blue if it is heterozygous and is carrying the black recessive. White sheep carrying a red recessive have pale eyes, and black sheep carrying a red recessive have orange eyelids.

Horns

As already stated by way of example, in cattle the polled factor is dominant to the horned factor and it is quite simple to introduce polling into a breed. A heterozygote can sometimes be recognized by a visibly heavier crown, or possibly the presence of scurs (anathema to the British White!). The heterozygote of course carries a recessive gene for horns and if your breed is supposed to be a polled one watch out!

In sheep the situation becomes more complicated especially where the multi-horned breeds are concerned. Some people think that the four-horned factor is dominant to the two-horned, and some people also think that the split-eyelid problem is associated with the multi-horned factor. Far more data is needed before categoric statements can be made.

Sex

The sex of the offspring is controlled by the sire and no one has yet come up with a practical method of ensuring a crop of heifers in the dairy herd. They have tried turntables, phases of the moon, douching with acid or alkali, holding one or other testicle, blowing into the left ear for a female and the right for a male, and all sorts of tricks with nettles, herbs and magnets! The problem is that only one sperm is needed to fertilize an ovum and an awful lot of sperm fight for the privilege. The solution is to control which one gets there first. Some people say that such and such a cow nearly always throws heifers when she is put to such and such a bull, or that everybody is getting males this year, but if such trends were studied over a long enough period it would be found that the distribution was in fact random and would even out eventually. There is another theory that in a small population of any animal (e.g. in a zoo or a small herd or flock) a greater percentage of males will be born, particularly in zoos where the females become sexually mature at an earlier age than they would in the wild (because they are better fed, like the Americans), and that younger females tend to have more male offspring.

Prolificacy

On the other hand, the eggs, as they say, is in the daughters and if you want to select for prolificacy you should look at the records of the females. A twin does not necessarily beget a twin. In some cattle, twins are conceived but one of the pair is not viable and may be reabsorbed (quite common in the Gloucester) and the resulting single calf, if female, will be an infertile freemartin. In all species, some strains tend to produce more eggs than others, or at least more eggs are fertilized and remain viable. In pigs, for example, Chinese breeds seem to have very much larger litters than British breeds but it is not clear whether they are more fecund or whether fewer foetuses are reabsorbed before parturition.

Lethal recessives

In several breeds of cattle, but more often in the Dexter, homozygosity for a certain recessive allele results in death. The problem is the 'bulldog' factor, and it is discussed in more detail in the Cattle chapter. There are other lethal genes, some of which are dominant and some recessive. For a dominant lethal allele, animals homozygous for the recessive allele will live but all other genotypes will die. For a recessive allele, only those homozygous for the lethal recessive will die and those which are heterozygous carry the lethal recessive into the next generation. Lethal or semi-lethal genes can result in cleft palates, hairlessness or amputated limbs in various species, imperforated anus in pigs and sheep, hydrocephalus in cattle, sheep and pigs, as well as bulldog or dropsical calves in cattle. Sometimes the lethality is expressed long before parturition and may therefore be quite unsuspected.

Congenital defects

The RBST keeps a register of congenital defects seen in different breeds and for the sake of the breeds it encourages breeders to notify all such defects. Culling is usually advised but some breeders are concerned that automatic culling may risk the loss of desirable genes as well.

A congenital defect is one which is present in the newborn animal. Usually it is inherited but sometimes it can be the result of mechanical damage during the pregnancy and the main aim of the RBST register is to identify *inherited* defects, such as in-turned eyelids, bulldog calves, split eyelids, cryptorchidism etc. and to confirm that they are in fact inherited rather than due to environmental factors. Some examples of defects found in certain breeds (not necessarily characteristic of the breed but possibly characteristic of a line within a breed) are listed below. The fact that many of the breeds are sheep does not necessarily mean that sheep cause more problems but may only prove that sheep breeders are more co-operative!

Entropion in Cotswold sheep
Wrytail in Portland sheep
Monorchidism and cryptorchidism in North Ronaldsay sheep
Split eyelid in multi-horned sheep
Bulldog calves in Dexter cattle.

BREEDING METHODS

While the debate will never end about whether any breed, particularly a rare one, should be systematically 'improved' and possibly in the process lose valuable genetic material, or whether breed society standards should be more relaxed to ensure flexibility for future needs or tightened to preserve the type, individual breeders will always want to experiment with their own ideas to their own ends. As long as they are careful not to breed from animals with deformities or congenital defects (expressed, or masked by recession) and as long as one all-powerful breeder does not take charge of an entire breed and shape it to his own taste regardless of the consequences, there cannot be too much harm in such experiments. In any event, you will never deter breeders from expressing their creativity.

Here are the main types of breeding programme:

Close breeding or the mating of relatives

Inbreeding, as has already been discussed, is the mating of animals more closely related to each other than the average in the population, i.e. they have at least one ancestor in common. This technique should only be used with caution and insight.

Line breeding could be described as cautious inbreeding which stops before it has gone too far.

Outbreeding (mating non-relatives)

Outbreeding is, of course, the opposite of inbreeding. It is the mating of animals *less* closely related than the average in the population. It is used to 'bring in new blood', which in genetic terms means that it increases heterozygosity and, usually, the fitness of the offspring. The result is increased variation in the breed, both genetically and phenotypically.

Crossbreeding is mating between two different breeds (which, in freedom-of-choice dogs, produces mongrels). It can also be mating between different species (e.g. the Beefalo, Yakmac etc. mentioned in Chapter 12) or between lines or strains within a breed. Interbreed crossing is very commonly and methodically used in the British national sheep flock; indeed it is the essence of the industry's stratification system. It is also used in dairy herds to produce beef calves, and it has been used to an extreme in the national pig herd to produce hybrids.

The advantage of crossbreeding is that the first generation progeny tend to perform very well, i.e. they exhibit *hybrid vigour* and perform better than the mean of their parents (but not better than the best parent) in a similar environment. Hybrid vigour is not, however, a guaranteed result of crossbreeding, nor does it get better in subsequent generations.

Every now and again, as often as not quite by chance, the old breeders would find an animal or a strain which seemed to give results (though not necessarily hybrid vigour) whatever it was crossed with, within or outside its own breed or strain. The popular term for such a successful match was *nickability*.

In any description of crossbreeding, the sire is given first. For example, Hereford × Friesian indicates that a Hereford bull was put on a Friesian cow, a very common cross. The order of listing is important because a reverse cross can produce quite a different result.

Back-crossing is mating a crossbred animal back to the breed of one of its parents. (Mating it to the actual parent is inbreeding). Back-crossing is one method of grading up (see below) and it is also a way of trying to fix the benefits of crossbreeding or testing for recessive traits.

Outcrossing is a technique used to introduce new blood into a herd or flock by importing a sire from another herd or flock (physically, or by means of AI), particularly when inbreeding levels are undesirably high. It is very valuable in the rare breeds as long as enough is known about the pedigree of the introduced sire.

Topcrossing tends to be an international affair. Many British breeds have been exported all over the world for many years. When, say, a Canadian breeder of West Highland cattle returns to the old country for a new Scottish bull for his herd, he is topcrossing — going back to source to re-tap the original genetic fount of his breed. It is common to find that overseas populations diverge considerably from the original native stock, and indeed the technique works both ways: some of our minor breeds are now being refreshed by the import of American and antipodean lines. This may well save the breeds from continuing degeneration in this country. A worldwide survey of a breed which is minor in Britain will sometimes show that there are considerable numbers abroad. The ark is a global ship.

Grading up is an important technique for building up numbers to pedigree status as quickly as possible. It is rapidly increasing the stock of Angora goats in Britain. Using the Angora as an example of the technique, any old nanny (feral or otherwise) is taken as the first dam and is crossed to a registered pure Angora billy. The first generation females are again crossed to registered pure billies, and this continues for several generations gradually increasing the percentage of Angora blood in the herd. The fourth generation of offspring will be 93.75% Angora. Most breed societies accept such a percentage in the female offspring as being eligible for registration as purebred though some (including the Angora) prefer to wait until the sixth generation.

Maintaining variability

In 1971 Dr Michael Ryder obtained three pairs of Hebridean (Boreray) Blackfaces from St Kilda and set in train a simple exercise in genetics. He initially mated the pairs once or twice to create a basis for families, and thereafter all matings took place between individuals from different families. He feels that, since the aim with numerically small populations should be to maintain genetic variability, the ideal situation is to use as many rams as possible — even on a one-to-one basis if that is possible.

SELECTION FOR TRAITS

With rare breeds it is often a case of 'breed at any price' just to keep the numbers up: a dangerous policy, but an understandable one. Sometimes the RBST Sale and Show betrays the results — any old sheep as long as it is a Manx and never mind that it is scraggy or has rotten feet and split eyelids: you cannot ask for *quality* as well. . . .

Oh dear! You most certainly should ask for quality as well.

6 Showing and Displaying

The exhibition of a minor breed is important, whether at the big shows, local shows and markets, in farm or country parks or city farms, in the Press, or to invited guests at private premises. It publicizes the existence of the breed, stimulates interest in its future, demonstrates its desirable phenotypes, provides a meeting place for like-minded people, trains the eye of potential breeders, gives an opportunity to look for fresh lines, enhances reputations, and sells the qualities of the breed as well as selling actual livestock.

The RBST has recognized the vital need for keeping endangered breeds in the public eye and is increasingly successful in attracting the attention of a wide range of people, from landowners and stockmen to corporate organizations and individual members of the general public whose interest may be emotional or sensual but whose financial support is essential. Every tenpenny piece dropped into one of the distinctive Trust collecting boxes helps towards the practical everyday work of caring for the breeds, carrying out research into their genetic make-up and potential, finding niches for them in commercial farming, and generally ensuring that their future is more secure. The Trust's own annual Show and Sale attracts very large crowds; its membership is increasing at about a thousand newcomers a year, and more and more county and local shows are featuring classes for rare breeds.

There are those who say that if rare breeds have no contemporary commercial worth their genes can be preserved in the deepfreeze for future use, stored as semen and embryos, and that there is no need at all to keep fully-grown animals which need feeding, space, veterinary attention, housing and other expensive care. They argue that frozen germinals are all we need.

In theory, perhaps, there is a degree of truth in that idea, but the drawbacks (so obvious they hardly need stating) far outweigh the tidiness and economic savings of the proposal. All other considerations apart, the moment something is hidden from view the public memory begins to fade, and then — who cares?

Not every livestock owner wants to go to the considerable trouble and expense of showing, nor has stock good enough to be paraded as an example of a breed, nor, perhaps, agrees with the tight standards demanded by breed societies. Many prefer to let the public see their animals in their own setting, all year round or on occasional open days, living everyday lives with weatherbeaten coats and muddy feet rather than dressed up and on their best behaviour. There are ways of displaying breeds to suit every inclination and aim.

SHOWS AND SHOWING

Showing livestock is addictive, and it can become an expensive addiction at that. It can also be immensely satisfying or frustrating, always stimulating, usually most enjoyable, and full of good humour however serious the competition. In the arena all is formality and gamesmanship, but back in the sheds the most serious opponents are friendly and mutually helpful. Newcomers are given every encouragement by the experienced, and those who are prepared to watch, absorb and ask questions are usually made welcome.

Selection of stock

Preparations for showing begin months before the season, and years before the first show. For a start there must be the inclination, and it must be shared by everyone involved — owners, stockmen (where they are not one and the same person), and the families who will have to tolerate someone who spends far more time with the livestock than at home and who is much more concerned for an off-colour animal than a 'flu-ridden spouse.

Potential show animals must be selected at a very early age and then given special attention to bring out the best in them. Naturally it takes experience to be able to judge which calf, lamb, piglet or kid has show potential, but to succeed in serious showing an eye for that potential is essential. Beginners can strike it lucky — sometimes — but the real competitors, to whom second place is failure, start with stock from a top breeder with generations of good breeding in the herd or flock, and are off to a head start when the time comes to choose the show animals.

Have a look at schedules for some of the bigger shows (obtainable from show secretaries) to decide the kinds of classes you might want to aim for. There will usually be classes for specific breeds, different ages, different sexes, animals in milk or pregnant, dams with young at foot, matched pairs and trios, progeny groups, shorn or in-wool sheep, crossbreds and so on. There will be classes based on milk yield, interbreed championships, supreme championships; there will be awards for presentation, tidy cattle lines, herd promotion, stockmanship and showmanship, young handlers, carcases, fleeces and so on.

Try and decide what you are aiming for, then select your animals (reserves, too, in case of disasters) and plan a timetable that brings them to a peak of perfection for the most important show. Select according to breed society specifications for a start, and if you are aiming for the RBST Show and Sale ask for details of the newly devised card system which has been introduced to improve the general standard of stock on display at Stoneleigh.

On the day, presentation is all important. If the most superb animal in the world is not immaculately turned out, it can lose to the second best which caught everyone's eye by being beautifully presented. Unjust and impractical and even immoral though that may seem, first impressions count in the show-ring.

The run-up

Feeding, coat care and health care are obviously important. The feeding regime should aim to bring the animals to very slightly above ideal condition on the day because the stress of travelling and strange surroundings at the show will no doubt set them back a little.

Most important of all, whatever the species, breed, sex or age, is handling and training (see Chapter 7). It is essential that the stock behaves well in the ring, and the animals need to know and respect their handler. Kindness, a quiet voice and unhurried movements should be used at all stages of training and showing. As one very successful cattle showman puts it: 'I want them to know that I'm their best friend.' This breeder chooses his show animals long before they are weaned, then at weaning they are introduced to restraint on a rope and handled frequently from then on. He spends plenty of time in their company so that they get to know him and his voice. Six months before the first major annual show the young bulls are already walking well to the lead and are regularly exercised near a main road to get them used to loud and unexpected noises. Five months before the show, preparations start in earnest: the suckler cows, which have been outside all winter, and the in-calf heifers are brought in for handling two or three times a week. By the time of the show all the animals are looking their best, leading beautifully, and are fresh and ready for the ring. They enjoy the shows as much as their owner does, and they take the top prizes time and time again.

As Tony Carr points out in his notes on preparing beef cattle for shows (*The Ark*, March 1984), correct feeding is important for making the most of a good beef animal. In general, feed little and often for maximum food conversion and an even distribution of flesh. Limit the amount of hay fed at weaning and do not allow too much grazing later on. Regular grooming from the very first time the animal is introduced to restraint will not only keep its coat in good order but will also accustom it to being handled. Grooming stimulates the circulation, which helps muscle development and coat growth. Regular attention to feet and horns is not only good for the tissues but, again, helps the animal to get used to handling so that the judge will have not problems in the ring.

The same long-term preparation has been used for show pigs by that master stockman, Donald McLean, who is well known now as a judge. The show season begins in May but the breeder's planning begins long before then. First of all, scan the schedules. In the old days sows were farrowed in January and July; offspring classes were for the January litters, yearlings from the previous July, 18-month-olds from the previous January, and older boars and sows — four classes for males and four for females. Today the pig classes vary and there may be, for example, yearling gilts from last July and also perhaps September-born gilts. So planning goes even further back, to the extent of ensuring that the sow goes to the boar at the right time of year.

Apart from being brought to absolutely the right condition for a show by sensible management and proper feeding, some preliminary work needs to be done on the pig's coat and skin. Give it a weekly massage with vegetable oil and a dusting with flowers of sulphur. About a week before the show give the animal an all-over wash with *warm* water (avoid getting inside the ears) using a soft brush and soft soap. Rinse carefully with more warm water, sluicing the animal from the tail end first, and finally dry it off by rubbing it with fine sawdust. Do a second wash the day before the show. Apart from improving the pig's looks, such intimate attention will also improve its relationship with the handler.

Training is important — frequent handling, regular exercise, practising your skill and authority with boar boards and pig bats, constant conversation with the pig, and generally getting acquainted with your animals and they with you.

Some of the pig classes are for individual animals but some are for matched groups and for these selection has to be made even more carefully. Whichever class is entered, different judges have different ideas as to what they look for in a pig (or any other livestock) and you can only breed carefully, develop an eye for an animal when it comes to choosing one for the ring, and then present it at its best, in top condition and as well turned out as you can make it. Never show the second-rate: it is bad for your own reputation and can damage that of the breed as well.

Unfortunately it seems to be among the sheep that standards slip most often, probably because minor-breed flocks tend to be very small in numbers so that the breeder's choice is limited anyway, and also because more often than not the small-flock owner really does not know enough about what the best of the breed should look like or how it should be presented. The stockman's eye is a precious asset and if newcomers do not have time to visit plenty of flocks and shows to get their eye in, they can at least take the trouble to look at photographs of good animals — not as useful as in the flesh but the pictures will show a better range of phenotypes then will be found in a one-paddock flock.

Of course, it is important to know what the breed standards are for sheep, as with all purebred show animals, but it should also be borne in mind that sometimes the demands of the show-ring are not necessarily the same as those of the practical stockman or the commercial farmer. That trend has not yet gone too far, though one day it might if it is allowed to. Then the breeds will really begin to deteriorate.

THE SHOW

Before they attempt to show any animal, first-timers would do well to attend several shows to observe what goes on — to learn something about formalities, techniques, etiquette, niceties and the strength of the opposition. Study the form. Ask polite questions at convenient moments. Get to know the faces, and get to know what the different judges look for. Judges of minor breeds, particularly at smaller shows, are usually very helpful with their comments.

Notice that the appearance and behaviour of the handler are as important as those of the animal. Handlers look neat and clean; they are quiet and unobtrusive (well, most of the time); they know how to present their animals' best features to the judges. They give no hint of the fact that they have slept pretty rough, sometimes even with their animals or on the back seat of a vehicle, or that they were up before dawn exercising, feeding, washing and grooming (their animals as well as themselves). They never argue with a judge's choice; they lose gracefully, always congratulate the winners, and learn from the experience. And novices can learn far more by watching the experts at work, both in the ring and in the sheds, than they will ever glean from books, even such excellent and detailed ones as Edward Hart's *Showing Livestock*.

When you are ready for your first show, submit your entry forms well before the deadline and make due note of the showground's arrangements for exhibitors and their employees. Read all the show regulations carefully;

it would be a shame to be disqualified on a technicality. Accustom your livestock to loading, travelling and unloading with a few dummy runs and then, when the time comes, transport them as comfortably as possible, giving them five-star treatment so that they arrive in good shape and not unduly stressed.

Make a checklist to ensure you take everything you need. For the animals that includes something to heat water on and in, plenty of clean sweet straw (unless it is provided at the ground), fodder and feed, rugs and protective sheets, tool-kit with hammers, nails, screws, strings etc., plenty of cleaning equipment, first-aid kits, water and feed containers, halters and ropes (and spares), footcare equipment, shears and trimmers, grooming and coat-care equipment. The environment is nearly always too warm for the animals: bear this in mind and take the necessary precautions.

For yourself you need to be completely self-sufficient: camping tables and chairs, bedding (and bed), Calor-gas stove, cooking equipment, crockery and cutlery, food, a change of white overalls — and train your animals not to think that anyone in a white overall is the vet. Make a show-box for all the equipment you need with you by the pens: the pen is as much a showcase as the show-ring is, and is sometimes judged on its tidiness. It is also the place where many of the public will come and see your animals, and it should be a good advertisement.

Final touches

Cattle

For many weeks before the show, cattle should have a thorough monthly shampooing. Brush and comb the coat regularly too, and you can gradually train the hair if you brush it wet. Clip the coat a week before show day. Make sure there are no vermin anywhere — check the ears in particular and other hiding places. Keep the feet carefully pared; work on the horns by gradually sandpapering them to a very smooth finish (you can use a piece of broken glass for the first rough patches). The day before the show give a final shampooing and use a little Vim or Brillo on the horns. Plait the tail switch and wrap it up in bandaging to keep it clean, then when you unwrap it the following day it will be nicely waved.

Be careful about feeding for two or three days before the show. (At all costs you want to avoid loose dung!) Hay is best.

On arrival at the ground, groom out any dirt, feed the animal and water it, then bed it down to rest. After a final comb-out you can use a light grooming oil on the coat to keep it in place and give an added gloss. Hooves can be oiled with pig oil and horns can have a light coat of linseed oil. In some shows pig oil on black patches and chalk on white underparts helps to show up the contrast in pied animals but check to see what the show regulations allow in the way of cosmetics.

In the ring, cattle are halter-led. Bulls can have a chain clipped to the nose-ring and another on a leather head-collar. Halters and head-collars must be as clean and polished as the animal and its handler. The animal should walk on your right-hand side on a short lead held fairly close to its head so that you can keep the head up. (Once it goes down, you could soon be out of control.) Keep your eye on the judge all the time. Make sure you know whether the entries are expected to parade clockwise or anti-clockwise and see that the judge has an unobstructed view of your animal. All animals, even bulls, must stand quietly when requested to do so, with their feet properly placed (see the Training and Handling chapter), and it is essential that they remain quiet while the judge handles them.

Pigs

You will have been taking care of your pig's skin and coat for several weeks beforehand. Give it a final wash the day before the show, then on the morning brush out the sawdust. Black or partially black pigs are often oiled for showing.

Pigs *must* be well trained for the ring: there is no halter to control them. A pig bat is used for anything other than a boar, which needs a boar board. The bat is a flattened stick which is used to guide the pig's direction by tapping it frequently just behind the forelegs on either side. Do not use a rounded stick as it will leave marks on the pig. The real professionals paint their bats to contrast with their pigs.

Chatter away quietly to your pig all the time. Its interest will be sustained and it will look perky and move better. Pigs are very intelligent and can be taught to respond to your voice; if they like you they will happily go where you want. Keep pieces of apple in your pocket – the promise of a titbit does wonders to a pig's deportment. If your pig is walking with its head on one side, you may have been careless enough to get water into its ear when you were washing it.

Boars can be more of a handful: lengthy training and a quiet temperament are important. The boar board can be used to block the animal's view of other boars and thus avoid distractions. It is only a light piece of board: the theory with any pig is that if it cannot see through a barrier it assumes it is solid and does not bother with trying to crash through it; well, most pigs most of the time.

The trick in the pig ring is to keep your animal constantly under the eye of the judge, almost tripping him up, always in view wherever he looks. The other trick is to manoeuvre your pig so that any faults it may have are on its far side, out of view. There is no point in drawing attention to a fault!

Sheep

As with other stock, show sheep need to be selected from the flock long before the show — perhaps a year before the season starts — and then given special treatment. Show rams are generally fed to greater weights, for example, and fleeces of all show sheep must be at their best on the day whether being displayed in full fleece or shorn. Richard Wear's article in *The Ark* series 'Getting Prepared' applies to all breeds of sheep, not only the rare ones.

Although, in many ways, the preparation of sheep is similar to that of other livestock, with an emphasis on correct feeding, grooming, foot care, regular handling and halter training, even more attention needs to be paid to the sheep's fleece than to a bull's coat or a pig's skin. The main shape trimming begins a month or more before the show. Next comes regular combing and carding to scratch out the dirt and tease up the wool so that you can hand-trim all the ends. This exercise should be carried out at least three times, with a final go a couple of days before the show. Occasional dipping (there are special show dips) keeps the fleece clean, fresh and healthy.

The fleece needs to be *shaped*, by careful trimming, to emphasize certain features of the breed such as breadth of back or meaty rumps, and every showman has an individual style. A fleece can be trimmed to create an illusion of perfection, and that is an art. No judge will be fooled by the illusion — probing fingers will soon detect the framework of reality — but, as ever in the ring, first impressions count and, mentally at least, marks are awarded for trying. A blatant con can sometimes win grudging approval for its cheek.

Hill sheep and primitives do not require so much titivating and some breeds are much preferred shown 'rough', in a natural condition, so that the true quality of the animal can be appreciated. That does not mean the exhibitors are any less diligent, nor do they show a half-shed primitive with its fleece coming out in random handfuls all over the ring. They prefer to show a good practical animal that displays the best its breed's genetic potential can produce. It seems a very sane approach to the whole controversial matter of showing — truth and reality versus illusion and glamour. But if shows are to be encouraged as display cases for the qualities of minor breeds, they need to draw a wide public and Hollywood has always had the edge on Ealing. If a prettified example of a breed catches the eye, then it draws attention to the breed and the real qualities under that fluffed-up poodle fleece can be examined and appreciated later.

Goats

Goat classes usually include milkers, goatlings and kids, with milking trials playing an important part in the final judgement, and not forgetting the occasional billy. Fibre goats will in due course have special classes where coat quality is of the essence. Meat has not so far been important in the goat industry in Britain but this could change and one day there may be sections for meat kids.

Preparing goats for exhibition does not require the same labour and dedication as preparing other livestock. They should conform to the British Goat Society breed points where appropriate, and these are sensibly lenient on the minutiae but more stringent on practical conformation, laying down ideals rather than strictures. Goats are presented looking their best, of course, their feet in good trim and well scrubbed, and their coats clean and groomed. Some people trim the coat to some extent but it is really a matter of personal preference. Horns should be scrubbed clean and lightly oiled. Stained white knees can be chalked.

Lead-training is of course essential but most goats are so accustomed to handling that training is no problem. They do need to be taught to stand correctly for the judges (see the Training and Handling chapter). Use a slender collar to emphasize the fineness of the neck.

The essence of a good-looking show goat, whatever the breed, is encapsulated in the general breed points recommended by the British Goat Society.

FARM PARKS

Farm parks are growing in number and popularity as show cases for minor breeds, and they are vital to the future of the breeds. For that reason they must be well run; every care should be taken to ensure that the livestock are in excellent condition and are good examples of their breeds. The layout needs careful planning; the animals should be easy to see but in as natural a setting as possible, each breed very clearly labelled and described with plenty of supporting literature available for those whose interest goes deeper.

There are farm parks and rare breed centres all over the country in a variety of settings. Some are in cities and suburbs, some in the parklands of large estates, some on working farms or in school playing-fields. The good ones are excellent; others leave a lot to be desired and are damaging to the cause of the breeds they display.

The aims are as varied as the settings. Most are commercial but many are idealistic and philanthropic. Most aim to inform. Many are involved directly with education, giving guided tours to parties of school children and providing projects, quizzes etc. Some specialize in providing stimulation and practical hands-on experience for the young or the disabled or the deprived. Others are interested in encouraging tactile fulfilment, providing 'patting corners' where children can mingle with young stock, or adults can stroke and offer titbits to all kinds of animals. Great joy can be given to the blind for example, if special arrangements can be made for them to touch good-natured animals — and it is not only the blind who appreciate such an opportunity. Several farm parks treasure memories of the delight of old ladies who have never before felt the fleece of a living sheep, or schoolboys intrigued by the texture and scratchability of an affable pig.

All the senses find new stimulation. Many town dwellers are surprised at the size of pigs — somehow pork chops and story books do not give any idea that a pig can be so *big*. The different smells are often remarked on too — a nice change from exhaust fumes!

People can spend hours just gazing at the interactions of a mixed group of species and breeds — the bossy Bagot billy facing up to a peacock, or a precocious little Vietnamese boar strutting at his large Tamworth rival in the neighbouring yard. Standing and staring: the best therapy of all.

Some farm parks are thematic. There is the classic Iron Age farm at Butser, near Petersfield in Hampshire, which is a serious research project investigating agricultural methods at the dawn of British farming. The livestock breeds at Butser are as close to the genuine primitives as possible — Soay sheep, Dexter cattle trained to the plough, for example, all of them small hardy animals suited to the theme. Under the capable administration of Peter Reynolds this ancient way of life is made accessible to the public and makes a considerable impression.

There are Saxon farms, Norman farms, Roman farms, medieval farms and Victorian farms scattered throughout Britain, all with the livestock which seems appropriate to the period — all of them the minor breeds.

Joe Henson's Cotswold Farm Park in Gloucestershire includes a large number of breeds. The farm park is within a working commercial farm and the animals are managed by a farmer and stockman rather than a zoo-keeper or museum curator. They are rotated through grazing areas, which give them ample space, but are small enough to ensure that the public has a reasonably close look at the breeds from dry walkways. In common with many similar enterprises, bags of suitable titbits are sold at the turnstile so that people can have the pleasure of animals eager to meet them at the fence.

Ideas for making the public welcome as well as keeping the animals healthy and contented can be gleaned from visiting all sorts of similar enterprises, including zoo parks. Here are some practical thoughts.

Location

The site must be accessible to the public; it needs to be either near a large centre of population or in an area with other tourist attractions to draw the crowds.

Access

Roads to the site must be adequate. Several centres are down country lanes and need to be very clearly signposted from main roads and at every possible diversion on the way. Reminder notices should be placed at intervals: people get worried, even in a lane with no junctions or crossings, if they are not reassured every now and again that they really are on the right road despite the grass growing down the centre of tarmac. A recognizable symbol with a direction arrow can be a discreet, inexpensive trail marker.

Local authorities

It is essential to consult local authorities before setting up an enterprise of this kind. Planning permission may be needed for any building, and certainly for change of use. The highways department will want to know about traffic volume and access on to the road. The public health department will inspect toilet facilities and catering areas. And even the building of an Iron Age hut has in some cases required not only planning permission but also inspection by the building surveyor! It is not all hindrance, however. District and county councils might be prepared to help with grants or to suggest other organizations which could do so, in the interests of bringing tourists (and their money) into the area. Advice can also be sought from organizations like the Council for Small Industries in Rural Areas (CoSIRA), the Country Landowners Association, the Nature Conservancy Council, or a land agent. The RBST has plenty of experience of such enterprises and will be glad to help in any way it can.

Facilities

Quite apart from the actual livestock and its accommodation, you will need at the very least: a car-park, a reception area where entrance fees can be collected, public toilets with wash basins, areas for refreshments and sitting down, and a sales area. Extra facilities might include areas for a children's playground, for picnics, for pet corners, for indoor displays and libraries — with imagination there is plenty more. It often helps the business if you can offer something different.

Layout

Design is crucial. First of all you are dealing with the general public more often than with other livestock owners, so they will probably not be equipped for mud. Either provide dry surfaces, or wellingtons in a wide range of sizes, or trailer rides. (An idea: if you visit the Grand Canyon you can hire a mule to take you down into its awesome depths and back up again. Is there any potential on the farm park for ponies, donkeys, llamas, buffalo carts . . .?)

Car-parks should be surfaced, or at least well enough drained not to deter customers at the first hint of rain — being towed out by tractor is so undignified. Paddocks and yards should be laid out so that people are, without being too aware of it, guided along definite paths in definite directions so that they have a chance to see all the livestock. (Talk to a supermarket manager about this.)

The collection of entrance fees is a painful necessity and it is best to funnel people through one point before they can get anywhere near the display areas, preferably as soon as they leave the car-park. The titbit bags can be sold at the same point. You can use a turnstile if you must, but a friendly face which can smile and answer questions and give advice is far better. Members of staff should be identifiable as such and always pleasant, approachable and informal.

Space can be a problem. Too little gives the feeling of the old type of zoo where the animals paced forlornly in concrete enclosures behind bars. The public like their farm animals to roam freely on grass, but a large space can be overwhelming and needs to be very clearly signposted and mapped. Do make sure that people who find walking difficult or who use wheelchairs can enjoy the animals too: avoid steps, steep slopes, cobbled surfaces and stiles, and make special arrangements so that they can park as close as possible without feeling conspicuous.

You first concern is, of course, for the welfare of your livestock but if you are open to the public it must seem that your first concern is for the welfare of the public. Treat them as guests, not nuisances, whatever you really feel behind your cordial and charming welcome. The general public can be hell, and destructive too, but look upon each of them as individuals. It might help.

Labels
Every breed in every enclosure should be easily identifiable. A guide with photographs and breed details helps and can be an extra source of income if it is well produced, but it is not flexible enough to keep pace with new introductions. The ideal is to have clear labels on each enclosure for each breed in that encloure, set at a height where children can read them but not so low that they are masked by the thick of the throng. Well presented labels give greater credence to what is printed on them; a scruffy handwritten note protected by a polythene bag is no good at all. The labels should give the breed in large letters, with a simple quick-identification illustration (photograph or line drawing) especially where there is more than one breed in the enclosure, and a brief text pointing out particular items of interest. Regional identification enhances the breed: people do like to know where the breed originated. Keep the label text brief but have a good supply of more detailed printed information available in the sales or indoor display areas. The labels used at Croxteth Hall and Country Park in Liverpool are excellent models: they have the breed name large and clear above a picture of the breed, and a series of symbols highlighting text on description, produce, area of origin, special points of interest, and, where appropriate, an RBST symbol drawing attention to rarity status and the reasons why the breed is endangered.

If the labels are made in wipe-off materials, you can add details such as the pet name of a particular animal and the date of its birth. This is particularly appreciated in the pet corner; children like to identify very closely with animals and will respond more to a lamb called Lottie than to an anonymous 'Leicester Longwool wether' or a pompous 'British White heifer calf Cadwallader Caroline IV.'

Public liability
Make sure your insurance policy is adequate for possible damage to or by the public. People have been known to sue for a nibbled finger or a chewed sleeve, and certain children have been known to behave with extreme callousness towards the livestock — for example tossing a squealing piglet from one to another as if it was a beanbag (true story!). Take care over the design of your fencing: it is no good telling Mrs Smith that her little Fred

should have had more sense than to climb into the field in the first place, when he has just been knocked for six by your recently calved West Highland. Horns, incidentally, can be quite a problem. They cause all sorts of gasps of admiration but they can also quite unintentionally bruise the funnybone of an unwary elbow, or worse. *You* know that a scratch on the poll might lead to an enthusiastic and appreciative upward flick of the head, but the public does not, and they will always want to rub, tickle or stroke whatever they can reach. Their safety is very much your responsibility and you must make full allowances for ignorance and sheer stupidity.

Sales

There is probably a greater return to be made in the sales area than through the turnstiles. Many people come just for an outing; the animals may be an incidental feature in a pleasant environment for picnics, teas, strolling or shopping. A refreshment area usually does well; it gives people a chance to sit down and gather themselves together as well as refuel, and it can offer simply tea, coffee and cold drinks, or snacks and cream teas, or, in a really ambitious scheme, a menu of farm produce like cheeses, butter, homemade jam and ice-cream, eggs, home-cured farm-raised bacon and, if you dare, a full-scale meal centred on roast rare breed meat. This can shock. At least one farm-park manager has been accosted by indignant customers because he displayed leaflets advertising the sausages, chops and hams which his Tamworths and Middle Whites were good enough to supply. Some people feel that eating an animal you have just talked to is wrong. But a produce counter can still be a success.

Pictures, cards books, pamphlets and posters all sell well and are easy to stock, as are souvenirs of all kinds. Most of the minor breeds have distinctive good looks which can adorn all sorts of items, especially if there is a touch of handicraft about the goods. Hand-fashioned produce does well in its own right — Jacob woollen goods, horn-topped walking sticks, natural Shetland hand-spun knitting wool for example, or occasional novelties like horn lamps. There is plenty of scope for products connected with the livestock or with its setting. One well-run centre does a roaring trade in bunches and pots of primroses, cowslips and other kinds of flowers seen all over the estate, and those it sells are all raised from seed and grown in the greenhouses, not picked from the wild stock!

The hand-fashioned items might serve as an outlet for local craftsmen, who could even have workshops within the farm park as an added attraction.

If some of the minor breeds never find a place on a straightforward commercial livestock farm, they can certainly act as a focus for other profit-making enterprises, or at least as additional assets to an already thriving business of another kind. Or they can find good homes in urban community farms tucked away in city back lots where they bring a lot of pleasure and interest to children who might otherwise never meet a pig in the living flesh. These urban farms are usually very well managed indeed, and there is a National Federation of City Farms in Bristol which advises on all aspects of setting up and management. The farms are increasingly important in a social context. They bring the reality of livestock right into a town, and they could well cause the whole huge agricultural industry to think very seriously about exactly what its role is in the countryside.

7 Training and Handling

Some species are said to be more 'intelligent' than others, which is usually taken to mean that some are more amenable to training. Quite often, however, the fault lies with the trainer, who fails to understand and then exploit the animal's natural behaviour. All livestock handlers would find their work much easier and more rewarding if they made a point of learning everything they could about behaviour, both through their own experience and vicariously through the observations of others. Several useful books on behaviour are listed in the Bibliography.

Routine is a great aid to training, as any human athlete knows. Food is an essential aid to training for most animals, as every stockman knows. Firm but kind handling is far more successful than shouting and rough discipline.

The aim of this chapter is to give practical guidance on matters of particular relevance to minor breeds. It is not the book's aim to be a general book on the management of livestock and this section is therefore limited to routines like training for showing or display or work, with a few notes on handling some of the breeds which behave rather differently from the ordinary farm beast.

TRAINING TO LEAD

Teaching any creature to accept restriction should start at the youngest possible age, especially with larger species before they are aware how much stronger they are than their handler. Mind you, even a pretty young Jersey heifer can drag you across the field if she gets her head down and her suspicions up. But on the whole, given time and patience, a level-headed child can soon control a young calf and have it walking quietly and willingly most of the time, especially if training takes place every day.

With older cattle, after you have caught the animal tie it firmly to a very strong rail or post with a very strong rope on a suitable halter and let it argue furiously with that arrangement for a day and a night. It will be the structure rather than the handler that will seem to be the opponent. Then practise a gentler touch and spend time every day with the animal, getting to know it, talking to it, and taking it for exercise on the halter. You are in charge, so be a leader and friend rather than a rival. Incidentally, many livestock follow out of curiosity, and in normal handling it is always best to let them traipse after you rather than try and herd them in the direction you want them to go.

With most sheep and goats the initial training is easier, except in some of the primitives and hill breeds of sheep to whom restriction of any kind is an insult and a challenge. Some say that the more intelligent the animal, the *less* likely it is to be obedient, unless it finds an advantage in being so, and some also say that the more primitive the breed, the higher the intelligence because domesticity has softened the reactions and has retarded development into self-sufficient adulthood because of dependence on humans. Whatever the truth may be, Soays and Black Welsh Mountain sheep for example certainly have minds of their own and are adept at escape, whether from a rope or through/over/under a fence. More about that later.

It may be very possible to train a pig to the lead but not on a halter, which would soon slip off. It needs a harness. But show pigs need no rope: they walk freely under the guidance of the pig bat. The problem is that they, too, are eager to follow their handler and in the ring they are supposed to walk ahead.

TRAINING TO STAND

If an animal is to be shown, it must be trained not only to walk smartly in the ring with head up and a general look of alert interest, but also to stand well so that its qualities are displayed to the best advantage. Training to stand is part of training to lead. Every time you pause on a leading exercise, encourage the animal to stand properly. Eventually it will do so automatically. First teach it to stand still without fidgeting (easier said than done) and then edge it half a step forwards or backwards to get the feet in the best position.

Dairy cows should stand with front feet slightly apart but aligned with each other, and one rear foot slightly in front of the other. When the stance is right, the top line will be nice and level in true dairy fashion and the cow, with her head raised brightly, will look elegant rather than solid.

Beef cattle, on the other hand, should stand four-square to emphasize their stockiness.

Sheep also stand four-square, particularly the meaty breeds, and rams need rather more patient training. They do best by following the good example of an experienced show animal.

Goat exhibitors also aim to show off a straight top line, with the forelegs straight down and the hindlegs slightly back and apart.

TRAINING TO THE PUBLIC

Any animal on display to the general public, whether at shows or in farm parks, at open days or at the sales, needs to be trained to accept the unexpected without panicking. Training involves getting the animal used to sudden noises (clapping, cheering, shouting, children, barking dogs), loud and sustained noises (like traffic and crowds), sudden movements (people, dogs, vehicles, flags flapping in the breeze), artificial lighting and spotlights etc., and also being loaded and transported. The latter can be traumatic for many animals, an unpleasant reminder of removal as a calf from a familiar environment for example.

An animal which is shown often enough will eventually accept the hustle and bustle and attention without a qualm, and will even enjoy it, but a first-timer will be easily alarmed among so many strangers and will neither look its best nor behave well in the ring.

TRAINING DRAUGHT ANIMALS

At the Butser Iron Age farm they have been using Dexters as draught animals. The medium or long-legged type of Dexter is similar in shape to the Iron Age *Bos taurus* (from bones which have been excavated) and is in keeping with the context. It takes about six months of training at a gentle pace (no one hurried in the Iron Age!) before the animals are able to work as a team and draw a rough plough. Both sexes have been used and the cows give milk as well as working.

In East Anglia, at the University's Rural Technology Unit, a pair of Hereford × Friesian bullocks and a pair of British White bullocks have been working under yoke, ploughing and harrowing, and having their work efficiency estimated. At Edinburgh's Centre for Tropical Veterinary Medicine, cattle and buffaloes have breen pulling loads wearing either an ox collar or a yoke. Collars were also tested in East Anglia. The main aim of all these tests is to see which harnessing technique is the most efficient for draughtwork in Third World countries.

In Costa Rica, Jersey cows aged two to three years old and in mid-lactation were 'worked' to see if their labour affected their milk production. The 'work' was a daily walk of 10.7 kilometres (6.6 miles) and they also 'raised themselves 320 metres (350 yards) each day'. (The meaning of this is unclear but what a vision it engenders!) It did not seem to make any difference to their yields and researches continue to see if they might be used for draught-work, although they hardly seem to be the right build for it.

In Nairobi the University's Department of Agricultural Engineering found that donkeys were very efficient at pulling carts, ploughs, harrows and weeders, as long as they were properly harnessed, but their pulling power was obviously less than that of heavy oxen.

In Nigeria's Banchi State, cattle are still commonly used as draught animals. They are paired and are not castrated. They are trained at three to five years of age, and the common practice of ridging is an asset in training as it guides them to walk in the previous furrow. Apparently it can take a mere three weeks to acclimatize an untrained pair and have them able and competent to undertake sustained controlled cultivations.

In Florida, USA, a small Hare Krishna community farm at Alachua works four teams of fully-grown oxen — three of Brown Swiss and the fourth of Guernseys. Their training methods depend on the older animals setting an example. They begin training when the oxen are three or four years old and start them off in the middle positions, with experienced animals on the outside of a four-abreast team. They only use castrated steers; cows are kept solely for milk production. Very occasionally an animal is temperamentally unsuitable for work; for example, one ox was 'extremely paranoid of human beings'. Some, not surprisingly, are better workers than others — less idle and more 'intelligent'.

The Florida team works slowly at an acre of ploughing a day for a four-oxen team. They work best in cooler weather, getting irritable and breathless if it is very hot and tending to try and break for the shade given half a chance. In such weather they need to rest for ten minutes each hour though in cooler conditions they probably rest only twice a day. They work to voice commands and reins, with a light-weight nylon horse whip for occasional emphasis.

Those 19th-century Kaffirs who were said to contort their beloved cows' horns into bizarre shapes also used to ride their oxen and use them as beasts of burden. Riding was somewhat uncomfortable without a saddle on the sharply-ridged backs of the cattle (if you have ever tried it yourself you will appreciate the problems) and steering was by means of an eighteen-inch stick through the nostrils with a cord tied to each end. (All the cattle had their nostrils pierced in this way at an early age because the Kaffir knew that the slightest twist of a stick through those holes was an effective if unkind method of control.) Europeans who tried riding Kaffir cattle found it very difficult to do so, not only because of the spine but also because the skin was very loose and riders could not get a grip with their legs. Although most Kaffir animals were horned, polled animals were used for riding 'in order to avoid the danger of the rider falling forward and wounding himself', but sometimes a saddle ox had horns which had been trained to grow downwards out of harm's way.

Horns are sometimes an asset in draught animals and some methods of yoking and drawing make use of them. At Butser they experimented with load/weight distribution and steering devices which took advantage of the horns. They also tried binding the yoke to the horns of a ploughing pair; one person guided the direction of the team by walking alongside with a hand on the horn of the dominant partner as a gentle reminder of who was really in charge. The Nigerian teams used nose ropes, tied behind the long, thick, upswept horns, for control by long reins, with a wooden pole tied across the pair's shoulders just in front of the hump as a yoke. Mrs Brigid Longley of Cranbrook, Kent, has worked nearly pure Sussex oxen on her farm and takes them to shows; she also uses them for film work and the horns add to the team's good looks.

A well trained team, properly harnessed, will work methodically at its own pace with little need for human guidance once the furrow has been set. The voice is usually the best form of control, and firm, kind, patient training is the recipe for success.

HANDLING SHEEP

A word of caution to those who use sheepdogs. There are certain breeds of sheep that simply cannot or should not be worked with dogs. With some the sheep become agitated and will be generally less easy to handle in all situations. With others the dog itself will be ruined as a sheepdog for the rest of its life, however good it was to start with.

Soays, as writer Christopher Curtis describes them, are the supreme 'dog-worriers'. Their behaviour is just not what a dog expects of sheep. Soays do not bunch together into a reasonably homogeneous and biddable unit. Instead, their first instinct is either to stare boldly back at the dog or to scatter every which way — and they can flee as fast as any deer. There is no 'eye' in the world that can hold them. There are countless tales of good dogs driven to despair by anarchical Soays. The psychological damage to the dog is often irreparable: once its natural authority has been so joyfully disregarded it loses all the self-confidence that originally gave it such authority. In the battle of nerves that is characteristic of the predator/prey relationship between dog and sheep, the Soay always, *always* wins.

The same is true of the Soay's other potential predators: people. An army of men is not enough to drive or catch a flock of Soays. The primitive breeds are full of cunning as well as fleet of foot, and there is no point at all in using normal shepherding techniques with them. You have to 'think Soay'. The primitives are independent and free-spirited; they need space and they select their own home ranges, setting up definite routines, establishing where they want to be at different times of year. Those who keep Soays (perhaps 'keep' is the wrong word — it is more a case of accommodating them) should exploit this natural ranging, give them plenty of space, let them manage their own grazing rotations, and exult in their characteristic exuberance.

Fortunately Soays are a healthy, hardy breed needing less attention than many others, but there are times when they must be rounded up. At the Cotswold Farm Park the technique is simple. At the same time every single day of the year the flock passes unrestricted through a race for evening feeding. The race is associated with *good* things (food) so there is no problem in occasionally catching them up in the race. Well, there are *some* problems of course. Most Soays do not like confinement.

There are always exceptions to the rule and it may be possible to take advantage of the technique of using Judas sheep, though the flock might not accept them. Judas sheep are trained: they are encouraged to become tame and familiar with their handlers; they are handled frequently and in the friendliest manner at all times — groomed, scratched, fed titbits and so on — and are eventually made accustomed to the tether. In due course they are encouraged to follow their handler voluntarily (oh, the value of feed pellets rattling in the tin!) and then taught useful tricks like opening gates. Finally, they can learn to lead the unwitting flock through areas it would otherwise refuse to enter. Or that is the theory. With Soays, they may be far too smart to be taken in by such stooges.

In that case the only helpful advice is this. Remember that sheep — all sheep — will, for preference, run up a slope, towards the light, and in straight lines (even Soays, except that each individual chooses a different straight line). They do not like walking into their own shadows, and they do like to think that the way straight ahead is clear for escape. Remember that Soays in particular can jump just about anything and that they can read your mind and know your intentions at quite a few hundred yards! The tamest hand-fed Soay kitchen lamb will be out of sight in a flash if you are even thinking of catching it. And bear in mind that the Soay is the nearest British sheep to the wild *mouflon* and that the subsequent evolution was probably something like Soay — Hebridean and Jacob — Manx — Shetland. They, too, can at times be awkward.

At the other extreme in the dog/sheep relationship are the Portlands: they move so slowly that the dog simply gives up.

HANDLING FERAL GOATS

Those who are interested in harvesting feral goats for cashmere (see Goat chapter) may be wondering how to do so. Dogs can be used for the round-up but, alternatively, bear in mind that goats, even more than sheep or cattle, like to follow. There will usually be at least one or two in the herd who are prepared to trot after you, and if they do so the rest will come along too, especially once they are used to the extra feed they have been having all winter. Thereafter it is simple: head in a yoke, the goat stands there with one person on either side of it combing out its wool. The goats might even enjoy it.

8 Cattle

Four stiff standers,
Four dilly-danders,
Two lookers,
Two crookers,
And a wig-wag.

The wild European aurochs bull stood six foot tall at the shoulder and topped it all with a dramatic out-and-forward, up-and-inward sweep of long horns, their weight supported by a very powerful neck. It was a black animal with a pale muzzle and a white stripe, or finch, along its back and a white curly patch of hair between those magnificent horns. The aurochs cow was smaller, more slenderly built, with smaller horns; she was reddish brown in colour with darker head and legs.

The last living wild aurochs, a cow, died in 1627 in a Polish forest. It was the end of an era for the progenitor of all the domesticated cattle in the world today.

Long horns were a feature of the majority of those cattle, humped and humpless, from time immemorial. But during domestication short-horned types developed, with smaller bodies, different skulls, smaller horns. The new type were physiologically better adapted for the production of milk.

In Britain the first shorthorns appeared during the Bronze Age. By the Iron Age, in common with most of central and northern Europe, the cattle had become much smaller animals, and by the Middle Ages they were smaller still. Yet they were to form the basis of most of our modern dairy and beef breeds.

In this chapter there are sections for each of the breeds which have been selected for inclusion under the book's generic subtitle 'minority' — and let it be said that the choice for inclusion is an entirely subjective and sometimes arbitrary one. Some breeds have been selected because they are of particular interest even though their numbers may be quite respectable or even exceptionally healthy, and no offence should be taken at their inclusion. Some are minor in that they are locally abundant but not seen often outside their own area; some are minor in this country but much more numerous overseas; some are minor because they are recent introductions. Many are classified as 'rare', in which case they are included in the RBST list of rare breeds. The six RBST priority ratings are detailed in Chapter 1, and they are indicated where appropriate.

It should be noted that the RBST census figures, where given, indicate the number of females used for pure breeding. Breed society figures, on the other hand, often represent the number of animals living or registered during a year, and a proportion of the females (and males) may well be used in crossbreeding programmes.

COLOUR

There are many ways of grouping cattle and one classification is by colour. Very broadly the main colours are black, red, dun and white. Mixtures and gradations include mahogany, blue, blue-grey, blue roan, red roan, brindled and smokey. Patterns include pied (like the Friesian), line-backed or finched (with a white dorsal stripe like the original aurochs, the Longhorn and the Gloucester), belted or sheeted (a white band encircling the middle of the body), coloured points (black or red ears, muzzle, feet etc. on a white animal — the opposite extreme of the dark finched cline), and white-faced (like the Hereford).

The coloured pointing is often called the White Park colouration (it is also seen in the British White and in several variants of other breeds) and it is dominant to other colours and patterns. Black is normally dominant to red, which in a red breed is dominant to white.

Breed societies have various views on colour. Some know that the breed characteristics are strong enough to be recognized whatever the colour; others are fussy about the slightest deviation from an agreed standard; others again will have a preferred colour like black and will tuck other colours like red into a sub-register or bar them altogether. Some breeds are refused separate recognition as breeds in their own right because it is said they are merely coloured varieties of a more common breed. Others are mocked for being too easy to create by crossing two breeds (e.g. the Blue Albion type can be the result of a cross of a white or blue roan Shorthorn bull on a Welsh Black cow, and a Luing is a cross of a West Highland and Shorthorn). It all depends, again, on definition of the word 'breed' — a semantic problem as much as a genetic one.

In the 18th century colour seemed to be quite strongly linked with region. For example, in much of Scotland, Wales and Cornwall most cattle were black 'Celtic' types (and there was a pocket of black finchbacks in south-west Wales). Reds were preferred in Sussex, Devon, all along the east coast of England, in the Hereford area and around Glasgow.

THE BREEDS

The purest British minor breeds are probably the White Park and the Kerry. Others have had various infiltrations of blood from other breeds at one time or another, though the fact is not always traceable or admitted by breeders. For example, the Northern Dairy Shorthorn has a trace of Ayrshire, and the Ayrshire itself probably had infusions of Channel Island breeds for milk quality, Longhorn for thriftiness and Dutch for milk yield. The Red Poll has recently been boosted by the Red Dane; the Dexter was tangled up with the Kerry; the belted breeds probably got their belts originally from the Dutch Lakenvelder; the Gloucester took in quite a bit of Shorthorn and Friesian and probably some Welsh Black, White Park, Jersey and heaven only knows what else. The Welsh cattle probably mingled with the White Park; the British White has also been improved here and there with dashes of Guernsey, Shorthorn, White Galloway, White Park and a Swedish Fjallras which may well have been responsible for introducing a degree of infertility into some lines of the breed. Shetland cows crossed so well with beef bulls like the Beef Shorthorn and Aberdeen Angus that at one stage very few pure Shetlands were left at all; the Beef Shorthorn carcase is currently being pumped up with Maine Anjou and the Sussex's with Limousin . . . And so on.

The procedure works both ways, of course. While some of the minor breeds are less than pure, some of them have in return managed to sprinkle their genes among other breeds both in Britain and abroad, so that a genetic pool is more widely available (if only it can be appropriately filtered and recoagulated) than the numbers of purebred animals suggest. Some of the combinations have become recognized and given a name of their own, like the Blue Albion — or at least recognized by some people.

ABERDEEN ANGUS

Glossy black. Polled. Early maturing beef.

Angus meat, lightly marbled and succulent, is the very best. Numbers of pure Aberdeen Angus cattle are quite low in the UK (perhaps five or six thousand) but about 20% of British-bred beef bulls are Angus and they are used as terminal sires on many crossbred suckler cows. In addition there are 24,000 registered Angus breeding cows in New Zealand. More than 15,000 Angus cattle were registered in Canada in 1984 (a quarter of them were red rather than black) but this was a considerable drop from the 1980 registrations of some 20,000. The breed has been exported to more than sixty countries all over the world and it is an important producer of quality beef in, for example, Argentina, Australia, Brazil, South Africa, Uruguay and the United States.

The breed is fairly recent and in the first decade of this century it was described as being a fair milker but valuable for beef and very hardy. The cows were known as Doddies. Since the sixties the type has been altered to meet the demand for leanness and increased size but it has not lost its famously fine bones. It always had quality — only the quantity was lacking.

The black of the breed is dominant and it colour-marks all its progeny.

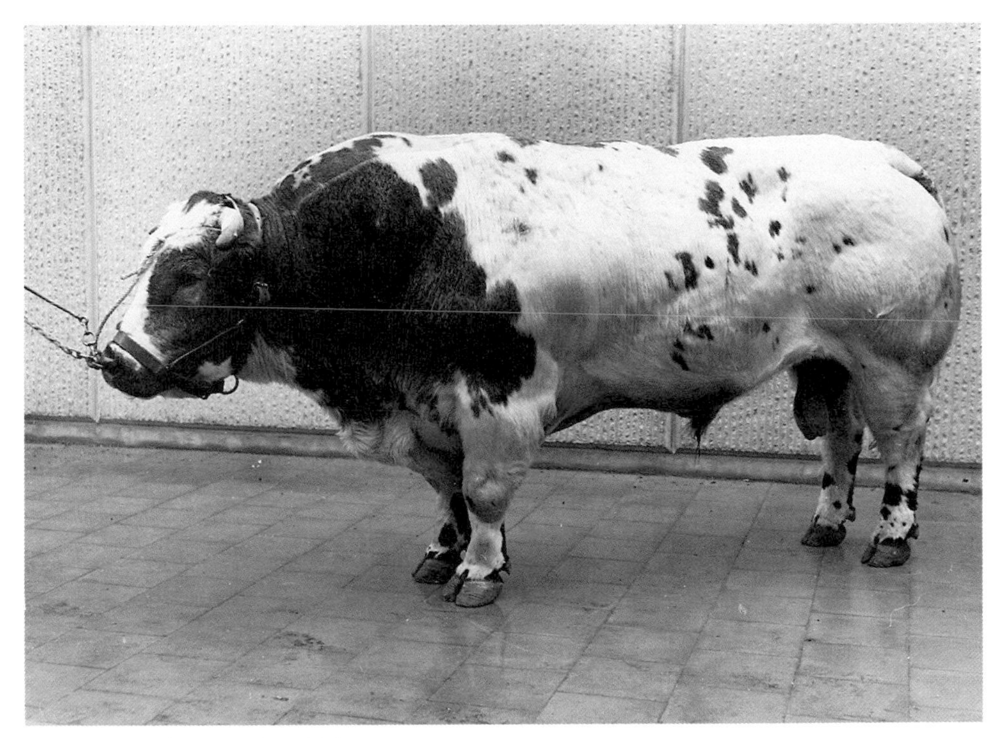

Belgian Blue. (*Farmers Weekly*)

BELGIAN BLUE

White, blue, blue roan or black-and-white. Beef.

This breed is the new fashionable foreigner that excites lots of beef farmers and causes plenty of controversy. It is an extreme example of double-muscling. Also called 'cularde', this is the gross enlargement of individual muscle fibres accompanied by an absence of fat under the skin which therefore fits the muscle like a glove so that the back end of a Belgian Blue looks like the thighs of a body-builder. This condition results in calving problems so that pure Belgian Blue cows frequently have their calves delivered by Caesarean section. Other breeds put to a Belgian Blue bull do not seem to have too many calving difficulties and usually have a shorter gestation.

Double-muscling used to be seen in South Devons and was classified as a deformity — double-muscled animals were automatically culled. However the trait has been selected for in several Continental breeds which have always been larger beasts than the British breeds because they were used as draught animals until more recent times. In the Blonde d'Aquitaine any tendency towards double-muscling seems to go hand in hand with a chromosome translation that results in the infertility of a particular sperm or ovum. In the Charolais one heavily muscled bull widely used in the south-west of England left a legacy of problems in its progeny. It is a dangerous line of breeding.

At present there are probably 200 pedigree bulls, 300 pedigree heifers and 700 grade registered heifers in the UK, plus numerous crossbreds. The breed is the ultimate beef type, easily growing to high weights without putting on excess fat; it had its origins in the Shorthorn which was exported to Belgium in the second half of the last century to improve local dairy-type cattle.

BELTED GALLOWAY: see GALLOWAY

BLUE ALBION: see WELSH

BLUE-GREY: see GALLOWAY

BOLIAN GWYNION: see WELSH

BRITISH WHITE

White with black points. Polled. Originally dual purpose, now tending towards early maturing beef. RBST status: vulnerable.

The 'Siamese' colouring of the British White is also found in other breeds, notably the White Park (which is horned rather than polled). In the British White the muzzle, eyelids, teats and fetlock fronts are coloured — usually black but the recessive red types are not debarred. Sometimes there are black freckles elsewhere on the body. The red recessive colour-pointing is fairly common. The polling factor is not absolute in the breed: scurred calves are sometimes born and may indicate crossbreeding in the past.

For many years the polled and horned White Park cattle were registered in the same Herd Book but in 1948 the polled cattle were split off into a separate register and were called British White cattle. It is now believed that the two are quite separate breeds with very different origins. Their colour genetics are different: White Parks will only throw either typical offspring or all-black calves from a cross, whereas the British White cross, although colour-marked, shows a gradual gradation from the typical, with colour building up successively starting on the front legs and neck, then along the sides leaving a white back (finch-style) and finally looking something like a Gloucester. This final colouring is seen in a British White × Welsh Black.

British White.

Originally based in Lancashire and East Anglia, the breed is now spreading to some other regions and abroad. Comparative numbers of registered cattle alive on 1 January in 1983 and 1986 were as follows (Source: *British White Cattle Society census*):

	1983	1986
Pedigree females	389	507
Pedigree males	63	81
Grading up	214	255

(Note: these are all provisional figures – final numbers were slightly higher.)

At this rate of increase, the British White seems to be all set to shed its rarity tag in a few years. The RBST numerical basis for rare breeds is less that 750 breeding females: the national herd has already increased from 285 female British Whites living in 1980 to 507 at the beginning of 1986, and there are also substantial numbers grading up. However, the 1985/6 RBST census, which is concerned only with females used in *pure*-breeding, records a figure of 302 cows — well within the rarity guidelines.

The British White was originally a dual-purpose animal and quite a good milker, giving as much as a thousand gallons with butterfat not far short of 4%. Today, however, many breeders are aiming for a beef-type animal and the breed as a whole seems to be heading in the direction of beef sucklers. The milk yield is really too much for single suckling but sometimes not enough for two calves, though most of the cows have the temperament to accept fosters.

With a mature weight of about nine hundredweight in the cows it is a medium-sized breed. It is backed by enthusiastic breeders who are exploiting its commercial potential in the beef industry, and the Breed Society is concentrating successfully on creating more breeding lines (both male and female), which is an important aim in all minor breeds in order to get away from potential inbreeding.

In conformation there seem to be basically two types, one with a good rear end, good head, good top line and bottom line, which 'meets you well', and the other a lean type with a good head but not so broad behind — more like the original British White — and which seems to make a good cross with, say, a Friesian or an Aberdeen Angus. In general the beef conformation seems to be improving but probably as much by chance as by design. There is plenty of good muscling in some lines, though in one of those lines there is an unfortunate tendency to show the occasional white hoof, which is highly heritable and is not acceptable to the breed society because it is thought to be a throwback to an earlier Hereford cross.

With its blue-black skin and sun-reflecting white coat, the British White can be useful in hotter climates. The black-skinned teats do not get sunburned, and the black eye tissues seem to increase resistance to eye cancer. The skin tends to be thin but the animal is perfectly hardy and particularly resistant to tuberculosis and ticks. The breed is becoming fairly popular in Australia, and also in the United States where it is confusingly called the White Park.

The old infertility problem seems to be on a lesser scale now. Difficulties were caused by chromosome translation which resulted in the prevention of implantation of the embryo. The Australian herd has specifically been bred to be free of the problem: ranchers cannot afford infertility in a range system where a bull is serving a large number of cows, and the Australians will not import an animal unless its fertility is guaranteed.

Cows calve fairly easily on the whole but the RBST Ease of Parturition study found that the British White had more calving difficulties than other rare breeds. Bulls are active and work well, and share with the cows a quiet temperament that makes them easy to handle. The cattle are good foragers, eating the rough stuff as well as the good. Kept by professionals, good results can be obtained from crossing with Continental beef breeds or from using British White bulls on commercial Friesian dairy herds. In Australia they are put on Galloways. The meat of the purebred and the crossbred progeny is claimed to be low in fat, fine in texture and of a good colour, and it achieves premiums in the United States.

Heifers, however, are not good on the beef market even if crossed to a Charolais. They tend to become too fat and do not grow well, but some breeders would eat heifer meat for choice regardless.

Some heifers of other, smaller breeds may have calving problems if they are too young when put to a British White bull and there seems to be a great variety in the size of calves. The breed is very deep through the brisket and this can make for difficult deliveries in a smaller breed.

Milking ability, which was the main quality of the breed from about 1920 to the 1950s, is still an asset, and one hopes it will not be lost because of concentration on beef. The quality of the milk tends to improve during the lactation; fat levels are low at first but increase, and the milk is much creamier by the end of the lactation. It makes a good soft cheese.

Purebred beef bulls need extra feeding on barley to produce a really good carcase. They grow fast but will not eat enough bulk for fattening until they are more mature. Young bulls (as with most beef breeds) should be kept on their mother as long as possible and should continue to be fed very well after weaning so that they put on flesh and avoid becoming leggy.

A decision needs to be made by British White breeders about calf quality. At present calves are often big (43kgs/95lbs average at four days old) but it may be better to follow the American preference for smaller calves (32kgs/70lbs) with a better potential for quick growth. Some of the bigger calves do not mature until they are three years old. An obvious difference between the British White and the White Park is that the White Park calves start bigger and continue to grow to a great size, no doubt because they were always selected for size in order to look impressive in a parkland setting.

At least one breeder claims to have chosen the breed in the first place purely because of its colour: it stands out a mile against bracken-covered hillsides and is quite impossible to lose!

DEVONS

There are two red breeds native to Devon, neither of them classed as rare: the stocky 'Red Ruby' beef animal of Exmoor and the 'Big Red' of the South Hams known as the South Devon.

Red Ruby Devon

The early maturing Ruby has been in its native area for hundreds of years and has a uniquely dense, mossy winter coat which protects it from the endless moorland rain and the bleak winter cold. It is equally tolerant of heat. It was originally a triple-purpose breed — rich milk for butter and cheese, heavy build for draughtwork, and the ability to finish rapidly for beef. The type has changed over the last eighty years. At the turn of the century it was described as follows:

> 'The colour is a whole red, its depth of richness varying with the individual, and in summer becoming mottled with dark spots. The Devons stand somewhat low; they are neat and compact, and possess admirable symmetry. Although a smaller breed than the Shorthorn or the Hereford, they weigh better than either. The horns of the female are somewhat slender, and often curve neatly upwards. Being fine-limbed, active animals, they are well adapted for grazing the poor pastures of their native hills, and they turn their food to the best account, yielding excellent beef. They have not yet attained much celebrity as milch kine . . . its quantity is small.'

The Ruby is an exceptionally hardy and thrifty breed, as its habitat demands, and the bull throws excellent cross calves on Friesians, Highlands, Ayrshires, Blue-Greys and Hereford × Friesians. It has successfully adapted to the extreme climates of Australia, the Middle East and Canada.

There are now separate sections in the UK Herd Book for Horned Devons and for Polled Devons. The breed society has recently begun a controlled breeding programme to modernize the Ruby Red using Salers bulls, a French breed very similar to the Devon.

South Devon

The South Devon was described early in this century as 'with a somewhat ungainly head, lemon-yellow hair, yellow skin, and large but hardly handsome udder.' Youatt† described it as 'equally profitable for the grazier, the breeder and the butcher; but their flesh is not so delicate as that of the North Devons. They do for the consumption of the navy; but they will not suit the fastidious appetites of the inhabitants of Bath, and the metropolis.'

Today it is a large animal mainly used for beef; it is a heavier, late maturing beast. It has been in the South Hams for at least two or three hundred years and was renowned for its ability to convert grass into meat efficiently and profitably. From the 1920s to the 1950s it was bred more for its Devon-cream milk (almost as rich as that of a Channel Islands cow) than for meat and its beef conformation began to deteriorate, but since then breeders have returned to its beefy qualities. It is now often classified as a beef breed. Some still call it dual-purpose but it only formed 0.2% of the national dairy herd ten years ago and, with its yields in 1983/4 averaging the second lowest of all dairy breeds at 3,362kg (7,412lb) with 4.01% butterfat it is not listed at all in the dairy section now.

The South Devon can boast an unequalled growth rate on grass and at the Royal Smithfield Show in 1985 there were more purebred South Devons entered than any other pure-breed.

DEXTER

Black, red or dun. Horned. Short legs. Smallest British breed. Dual purpose. RBST rating: below numerical guidelines.

The Dexter's is a success story. Partly because of a very active breed society, its numbers have increased substantially in recent years and some three hundred females are registered annually. There is a significant grading-up population. It has found its niche.

Like the Kerry, the Dexter is descended from the old wild Irish mountain cattle. It comes from south-west Ireland and seems to be similar in type to domestic cattle of Iron Age Britain and early Christian Ireland. In the late 18th and early 19th centuries it seems to have been selectively bred for small size by a Mr Dexter on Lord Hawarden's estate in Co. Kerry, and until the end of the last century it was known as the 'Dexter-Kerry'. Even then it was considered valuable for beef and for milk production. It was described as:

'smaller and more compact than the Kerry, shorter in the leg, and intoed

†William Youatt (1776–1847), a veterinary surgeon and prolific writer who produced a series of handbooks on the breeds, management and diseases of farm livestock during the 1830s.

before and behind. While black is the usual colour, red is also recognized, with, in either case, a little white. When of a red colour the appearance of the animal has been aptly compared to that of a grand Shorthorn viewed through the wrong end of a telescope. The Kerry and the Dexter are readily distinguishable. The Kerry has a gay, light, deer-like head and horn, light limbs and thin skin. The Dexter has coarser limbs, a square body, flat back, thick shoulder, short neck, and head and horn set on low.'

Dexter. (*Jane Paynter*)

A Major Barton founded a herd of Dexter-Shorthorns in 1860 in Straffan, Ireland, and they were said to breed true to type and to blend permanently the prominent characteristics of the two breeds.

The smallness of the Dexter is emphasized by the shortness of the cannon bone (between knee and fetlock). They have been kept as park curiosities but in fact they are a very hardy breed with the potential to perform well under professional management and they have the advantage of high stocking rates (they do not even poach clay).

Breeding needs to be carefully planned. In the past too many fanciers have gone for out-of-proportion types standing at about 90cm (36in) with heads more appropriate to a 100cm (40in) adult. A good size to aim for is 100cm (40in) but they can stand as high as 112cm (44in) at the shoulder. A maximum desirable weight for cows is 360kg (800lb) liveweight, the average being about 300kg (660lb), but a mature bull or steer can reach more than 460kg (9cwt) at three years old. For early maturing beef the best weight would be 305–330kg (6–6.5cwt), and on an intensive feeding system a satisfactory killing-out size can be attained at twelve months old. The joints are small, economical and of excellent quality and are ideal for the freezer. An interesting outlet is selling surplus stock to hotels and guest-houses in tourist areas; they can then offer their guests 'homegrown' milk and cheese with beef from the bull calves.

Milk production can be at commercial levels under good management, as has been proved with Jane Paynter's Knotting herd at Yielden, Bedfordshire. This is a large, brucellosis-free, recorded dairy herd and the average herd yield is 2,855kg (6,294lb) at 4.09% butterfat and 3.41% protein. Jane Paynter aims for 305-day lactations and her best cows peak at about five gallons a day. Other recorded figures include a cow in her twelfth lactation yielding 3,125kg (6,889lb) at 4.60% butterfat over 305 days; another gave 3,550kg (7,826lb) at 4.17% in her sixth lactation and beat that with 4,229kg (9,323lb) at 4.04% in her seventh. Averages for the breed are butterfat over 4% (some exceed 5%) and yields of six or seven hundred gallons on grass, hay and an economical supplementary ration. The MMB-recorded herds averaged 477 gallons (2,168 litres) in 1983/4. A really good house-cow could yield seven or eight hundred gallons, giving a steady three or four gallons a day for the first five months of the lactation.

At the beginning of this century the Dexter was taking prizes in London dairy show classes and in the 1907 Smithfield Show beef classes. But in the 1940s it was said that 'milking presents a real problem for they often have pendulous udders so close to the ground that it is difficult to get a bucket under them.'

Breeding problems have been experienced with 'bulldog' calves. The factor which dwarfs the typical Dexter by shortening the bones seems to be controlled by a partially dominant gene. Recent research (*The Ark*, June 1986) suggests that a series of alleles at one locus is responsible for a gradation in phenotypes in a Dexter: a longer-legged type which is in effect virtually a Kerry, an intermediate medium-legged type, and the very short-legged dwarf. A fourth type, which is non-viable, is the 'bulldog' — an abnormally dwarfed calf with a large head which is usually aborted between the fifth and ninth months of the pregnancy.

The same problem can also occur in other breeds, for example the Hereford and Angus, but it is probably of a different kind from a recessive gene.

Bulldogs tend to result from a mating between two short-legged out-of-proportion parents and breeders are well advised to go for big, rangy bulls which can sire some very pretty heifers. A short, dumpy bull gives short, quick-maturing heifers that look like cows by the time they are two-year-olds, but the rangier sire's heifers will not look like cows until their second or third calf and will then continue to be productive until they are at least eight years old.

There was a time when extreme dwarfism was favoured in the show-ring, but fortunately for the breed that trend is no longer so extreme. More than a hundred years ago, in *The Times* of 16 September 1850, there was an advertisement offering a small bull and cow from the African grain coast, three years old and measuring 30in at the shoulder. The advertisement said: 'They have nothing of the buffalo about them, but are most like the small Guernsey breed.' What were they? What happened to them? Who knows? The bulldog defect is still seen in Africa.

It is not advisable to steam up a Dexter cow because if she is too fat at calving she may need a Caesarean. On the other hand, many smallholders (and the Dexter is often a smallholder's cow) underfeed their animals, making the common mistake of assuming that a breed which is able to survive on poor quality grazing will actually thrive on it. Most of the so-called thrifty breeds *can* survive in such conditions but will do very much better on more food. Because of their size, of course, Dexters do eat less than other breeds, and they are also very adaptable to different grazing conditions and climates. They can usefully be tether-grazed.

Dexters are now being exported to Canada to infuse new blood into existing herds over there and enquiries are being received from other overseas sources. The park pet and smallholder's milch cow is now being taken seriously and bred more carefully to avoid show-type extremes and the lethal consequences. The future of the breed is very promising.

GALLOWAY

Black or dun, and variations. Polled. Quality beef suckler.

The Galloway itself is hardly a minor breed: it is one of the most essential ingredients of the British beef industry and fulfils an important role overseas as well. It is one of the great converters of the millions of acres of rough upland and moorland grazing that make up nearly half the United Kingdom's farmland, and it can take whatever the climate throws at it, protected by a double coat of longer outer hairs to shed the rain and a mossy undercoat for insulation.

Probably because of its native environment (and some stockmen's lack of enthusiasm for sharing it too often) the Galloway is sometimes a little quick and perhaps unapproachable unless used to human company. Upland living encourages independence and the protective mothering instinct is very strong in the breed.

The Galloway has been used as a purebred and also with great success for crossing, particularly to a Whitebred Shorthorn bull to produce the famous Blue-Grey suckler cow which is the traditional choice of Scottish beef producers and gives enough milk from the Shorthorn to raise two calves combined with the extreme hardiness of the Galloway. The galloping Galloway is booming and exports to countries like Germany are thriving so well that there are not enough native cattle to meet the demand. The Germans appreciate the taste and quality of Galloway meat in contrast to the blandness of some continental breeds.

Belted Galloway

(See front cover for photograph.) In New Zealand they prefer the Belted Galloway and they have twice as many Belties as plain Galloways, albeit in very small numbers in both cases (250 Beltie breeding females). This gives them cause for concern about restricted bloodlines and the danger of inbreeding. For example, 10.5% of the New Zealand Belties are the result of matings between parent and progeny. The New Zealand breeders have decided in principle against outcrossing to, say, Welsh Black or Angus, and are therefore looking to imports for an infusion of new lines.

The Belties are increasing in popularity in the UK, almost doubling their numbers between 1980 and 1985 to a total of 1,429. By 1986 they were no longer classified as a rare breed here (there were about 800 pure-breeding cows recorded in the 1985/6 RBST census) and there are another thousand or so in the United States and herds in Australia, Canada and West Germany. They have all the attributes of the ordinary Galloway: they make excellent sucklers, they are very hardy and long-lived, they cross well, and they convert rough grazing into good, lean beef. In addition, the Beltie is a better milker than the standard Galloway and this is probably because it was used as a crofter's and smallholder's cow. There used to be herds of milking Belties.

Its other advantage over its plainer relation is the eye-catching white belt (the rest of the coat is black or dun) which means that it is easy to spot out on the moors and hillsides. A herd of Belties seen far away across the wild stretches of Dartmoor is a memorable sight.

The original dual-purpose nature of the breed did at one stage detract from its beef conformation and some still say that you need to put a back end on a Beltie. In fact they are now regarded as a beef breed and are being bred for improved conformation. They have the advantage of intrinsic size — the frame-work for the meat is already there — and although they are ideal suckler cows the intention now is to improve the beefiness of male calves so that they are marketable as purebreds as well as crossbreds. Breeders are determined that this will not be at the expense of essential qualities like hardiness, thriftiness and the ability to continue as a suckler cow for as much as twenty years out on the hill, and the most promising method of improving the Beltie is to breed across to black Galloways.

The Beltie can be black (with a slightly rusty tinge) and white or red (dun) and white. Red is recessive in Galloways, as in other black breeds, and has been regularly culled out by the Galloway breed society in the past but there are now supplementary registers for Red Galloways and for Red Belties. Belties put to a Whitebred Shorthorn bull produce a good Blue-Grey, often belted, and the cows also cross well to Continental bulls like the Charolais, Simmental and Limousin. The cows are big enough to have fewer calving problems than some other breeds.

White Galloway

The White Galloway was given its own section in the Herd Book as recently as 1981 but the oldest herd still in existence was founded as long ago as 1919 (the Creetown herd, near Newton Stewart). It is another variation on the Galloway theme: it has the typical White Park colouration, mainly white with black, dun or red points (ears, eyelids, muzzles and feet) and there may be a touch of White Park in their ancestry. They have the typical stocky, woolly Galloway body and the points seem to emphasize the amusing Galloway shape and endearing face. In performance they are similar to the black or dun Galloway, and White cows put to black bulls nearly always throw white calves.

GLOUCESTER

Mahogany with white finching. Horned. Dairy. RBST rating: critical.

(See back cover for photograph.) The unique colour and the markings of the Gloucester are very like those of the wild aurochs depicted 13,000 years ago in the Lascaux cave paintings in southern France. The rich mahogany coat has a striking white stripe (finching) running along the back, over the tail and rump and all along the underside — a feature also seen in the Longhorn and the Irish Moiled. The long, white, upswept horns are tipped with black.

It was always a dairy breed and its high-butterfat milk was well known for cheese-making; Double Gloucester and Single Gloucester cheeses were renowned in the 18th and 19th centuries. The fat globules in the milk are small, palatable and easily digested (as near as cows' milk can be to goats' milk) and protein levels are high. The Gloucester can be used as a suckler cow, giving quality rather than quantity, and she is a good mother.

The breed is very docile and was originally used for draughtwork as well as for milk and beef. It became very rangy and long-legged and is now a fine boned animal of medium size, a little smaller than an Ayrshire. It has changed over the years, with major infusions of Shorthorn, Friesian, Ayrshire and Red Poll in the fifties and sixties, plus a dash of Jersey for good measure. Numbers fell to only seventy purebred registered cattle in 1975 but now there are thirty small herds and numbers are slowly rising, though it is still on the RBST's critical list. The 1985/6 RBST census recorded 182 breeding females.

Today's breeder prefers to improve from within the breed by carefully planned mating and urgent steps are being taken to avoid random inbreeding. Nor can a breed so recently rescued from the brink of extinction afford to lose its identity in a welter of outcrossing. It is beginning to find a commercial toehold in cheese production, in beef, and as a multiple suckler and it still has potential for improvement of milk yields which could reinstate it as a dairy cow.

The Gloucester quite often conceives twins but rarely gives birth to both of them. One will be aborted in the womb and the remaining calf tends to be infertile.

HIGHLAND

Various colours. Shaggy. Characteristic horns. Beef.

(See back cover for photograph). The West Highland is by no means a rare breed — certainly not in its Scottish homeland, and it has become popular overseas as well, particularly in Canada and the United States.

It is being included here for its differences. It looks unlike any other British breed for a start, and it engenders great enthusiasm among its supporters. It is a breed that appeals to the individualist and it has a terminology all its own: for example, it congregates in folds rather than herds. One Yorkshire farmer regularly rides his Highland bull; he used to ride Ayrshire bulls which, he claims, were much springier in step and much more amenable to learning tricks like jumping through hoops (the Highland's horns put it at a disadvantage for that one) or playing 'dead', and he also used to ride them to hounds.

The Highland is a romantic breed from the wild romantic scenery of the

Scottish Highlands and the Western Isles. It is said to be descended from the black Kyloe cattle which were capable of swimming across the firths. The colours of its very shaggy coat are many: it can be white, creamy, light dun, tawny yellow, tan, dark brown or black with a full range of shades in between. The widespread horns are distinctive.

In the UK about five hundred pedigree animals are registered annually and there are probably about a thousand born each year. The current British population is about fifteen thousand, and worldwide that figure can be doubled.

Although sometimes kept for decoration and pleasure it is basically a practical adaptable breed. It is extremely hardy, with the thick, shaggy, double coat that several breeds and species develop after many generations of living in the wilder, wetter uplands of Britain — long guard hairs to protect the animal from the rain and a short, warm undercoat for insulation from cold and heat. The winter coat can become very matted and tangled, especially if the herd is wintered on straw, and for show animals the coats are thoroughly shampooed, combed out and de-liced before turn-out. Matting varies from one animal to another and some of them become very felted.

They are tough enough to winter out in the worst of weather, and probably prefer to do so (they are not so happy if confined) but it may be more convenient, especially on heavier poachable land, to yard them in winter. Ideally they should be given free range over spacious, open concreted areas with access to airy shelters like pole barns if they wish. Their widespread horns can cause problems under any more intensive arrangement but it is noticeable that, despite the horns, they are often bottom of the pecking order in a herd of mixed breeds. They are quite small animals.

The mothers are highly protective of the newborn young and on no account should they be approached for the first few days, however well they know their handler. In other circumstances frequent handling encourages docility, and regular grooming is generally enjoyed. For the sake of the vet, make a point of regular handling.

Home-mixed rations are the secret to success in the showring and sometimes the southern breeder manages to have the edge on the Scots even at the Royal Highland Show. As with other upland breeds, they can do well enough on poor land and in adverse environments but they can do even better with extra feeding, within reason.

The Highland steer can produce beef of excellent flavour and texture. There is a tendency for less-than-best conformation and stock bulls need to be selected carefully. The breed is naturally slow maturing, ripening slowly like a good cheese, but the breed society is working on breeding pure Highland steers ready for slaughter at two years old, 'hopefully dispelling the myth of five years on peat and heather!' The breed is efficient at converting low-cost feed into quality beef; indeed it is a waste of time feeding a more expensive ration as the response will not justify the extra cost.

Females sometimes lack size, and again breeders are asked to be careful about selection of breeding stock. However, the rejects still make good commercial cows and cross well to any type of Shorthorn.

Luing

The Cadzow family set about creating a new breed from just such a cross. They purchased two thousand island acres off the west coast of Scotland in 1947 and embarked on a planned breeding programme to produce a commercial breeding herd for raising calves reasonably cheaply on grass. They aimed for an ability to stand the exceptionally wet and wild climate of the islands, an ability to produce a calf a year, and an ability to breed its own replacement.

The Cadzows began with the Highland cow for its hardiness, longevity, ability to survive Scottish winters and produce a good side of beef, and its capability for foraging and good mothering. They crossed it to the old type of Beef Shorthorn which contributed good muscle development, early maturity to counteract the Highland's natural slowness, well-marbled beef, and adaptability to various climates. The first cross was a good combination, and a second cross with the Shorthorn was even better.

Thus the Luing breed was born. By diligent breeding the Cadzows fixed the type, tackled the age-old question of 'how to become a breed?', and in 1966 the Luing was officially recognized as a distinct beef breed. Today it is strictly a commercial beast and it has spread as far afield as Essex and Somerset and abroad to Canada, New Zealand and Brazil. The Luing has found its niche, mainly as an economic cow for mating to a terminal beef bull, and it does best in the type of environment for which it was bred. In yards it may sweat a bit, but this can be avoided if the long back hair is clipped.

IRISH MOILED

Red and white, white finch. Polled. Dairy. RBST status: critical.

The Irish Moiled is Britain's rarest breed but its position is slowly improving though it is struggling to reach three figures.

Irish Moiled. (*Croxteth Hall and Country Park*)

Its name refers to its poll, the Irish word *maol* meaning 'little mound'. There have been other interpretations of the word. For example, in 1931 a correspondent wrote to *The Field* to seek help in identifying old engravings of livestock, published about 1790. Among the cattle were 'Lancashire Cattle', apparently Longhorns, and the once famous Suffolk Dun. The writer, Ruth Tennant of Leicestershire, said that she occasionally saw cows like the pictured Suffolk Dun in the eastern counties of England even in the 1930s and found that they were usually called 'moilly'. She wondered whether the word was a corruption of 'mealy', in reference to the dun colour. She did, however, mention in passing that the eastern cows were hornless.

The breed used to be found in a range of colours, not necessarily line-backed, in various parts of Ireland. In 1926 an Irish Moiled Cattle Society was formed to develop the Moilie as a hardy dual-purpose small farmer's animal, with the emphasis on milk yield and thriftiness on poor land, and the decision was made to choose the red line-backed type as the standard for the breed.

At first the breed produced some outstanding animals, still calving at an age of twenty or more and giving large yields of high-butterfat milk. Within two years of opening the new register, 220 animals were in the book, and by 1934 they had increased to a fairly healthy 578. That was the peak year, and then matters began to go downhill.

In 1950 a Finnish Polled bull was imported to help the breed because the Ministry prevented the licensing of bulls unless cows were milk recorded, which very few Moilies were. Unfortunately the breeders still failed to record and the situation deteriorated even further. From 1960 to 1966 only eighteen animals were registered in total, and by the early seventies only a score of purebred females and five bulls were still in existence. By the late seventies this had decreased to thirteen females and six bulls: the situation was critical.

In 1983 four cows and a bull were imported into England. Since then the entire mainland stock (six cows and two bulls) has been moved to the RBST approved centre at Croxteth Hall Country Park in Liverpool, and the numbers are still dangerously low, with inbreeding a serious problem because only three bulls were used between 1966 and 1978 throughout the breed. The 1985/6 RBST census recorded thirty-one breeding females.

A dual-purpose animal, its milk yields are high for the low amount of feeding it needs. Easy-calving and docile, as well as economical to keep, it is usually red or roan with a mealy white face and white finching. There is a long way to go before this pleasant breed is safe.

KERRY

Black. Small and dainty. Horned. Dairy. RBST status: critical.

The Kerry is another Irish breed at very low numbers. During the course of the 1970s its total population — already very small — was almost halved. By 1981 there were officially only 108 registered Kerry cows; there may have been as many again unregistered but that still made it a very rare breed indeed. The 1985/6 RBST census recorded 197 breeding females, which included the population in Eire.

There are now perhaps ten privately owned Kerry herds in Ireland, and the Royal Dublin Society has been given special responsibilities to investigate the status of the breed, with the financial support of the Department of Agriculture. A few cows have found their way to England and Miss Ruth Leslie, for example, has a small herd which has become well-known in the show-ring.

The Kerry cow has the look of a dairy cow and in the first decade of this century the breed was much more widespread and had acquired some

Kerry.

celebrity as a dairy breed. From photographs of the period they were perhaps a little longer in leg and body than some of today's animals, and they were lyrically described as 'active and graceful, long and lithe in body, and light limbed.' It was noted even then that on the richer pastures of England they increased considerably in size and were excellent milkers.

The Kerry still milks well enough — perhaps 3,277kg (7,224lb) with 4% butterfat — and the milk, with its small fat globules, is good for cheese and butter. Her productive life is a long one and many a Kerry is still milking at the age of twenty. The yield seems to build up gradually over early calvings and only really comes good in the third lactation. Calves raised for beef mature slowly but are worth waiting for as the flavour of the meat is excellent.

This agile little Irish cow is probably hardier than most dairy breeds and she can subsist on the roughest and scantiest of grazing if necessary. For her size (perhaps 355–380kg/785–840lb) she is highly productive. It is claimed that three Kerrys can be kept where only two of other breeds can, and if they are allowed to retain their up-turning horns a herd of glossy black Kerry cows is decorative as well as useful. There is occasionally a touch of white on the udder.

Like the Irish Moiled, the Kerry has suffered because so few animals have been registered or milk recorded. If there are no recordings to show how good they are, who will take an interest in them? It is a breed of character and deserves better.

LINCOLN RED

Cherry red, large. Polled. Beef.

This hefty, hardy breed is native to the windswept flat lands of Lincolnshire, an environment which seems to encourage size and hardiness. (The Lincoln Curlycoated pig and the Lincoln Longwool sheep are also big and tough.) It was originally the Lincoln Red Shorthorn but in 1939 the first steps were taken to poll the breed with the use of Aberdeen Angus bulls, and in the mid 1950s the first polled Lincoln Red was accepted for licensing.

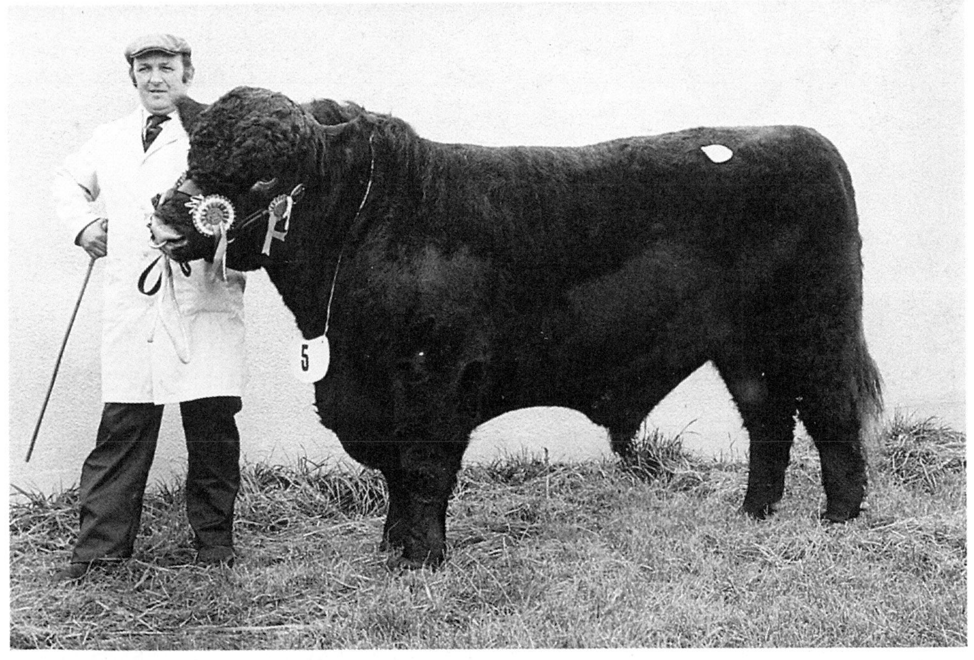

Lincoln Red. (*Lincoln Red Cattle Society*)

At the beginning of the 20th century the Lincoln Red was described as the best pedigree dual-purpose breed — for milk and meat — in the UK, and it was said that its cherry-red colour brought it into high favour in tropical countries for crossing with native breeds. It is still the kind of beef animal which is able to finish on grass in all sorts of climates and it has spread to South America, Canada, the United States, Australia, New Zealand and South Africa, and even beyond the Iron Curtain to Hungary, where you can see 260 Lincoln Red heifers in one field, part of an 800-head herd of pure and grading-up Lincoln Reds.

Its breeders always kept faith with its size; they did not follow the post-war fashion for small, blocky types and today the Lincoln Red is the largest of Britain's traditional beef breeds, able to hold its own against the Continental invasion. It is an early maturing breed with a rapid liveweight gain and it makes an excellent suckler cow or a crossing sire on dairy and beef breeds. Its population in 1985 in this country was 1,918 pedigree cows and heifers and forty-seven bulls in thirty-two herds.

LONGHORN

Light red roan to dark brindle, with white finching. Large. Characteristic horns. Dual-purpose. RBST status: vulnerable.

Longhorn.

The English Longhorn was the dominant breed in Britain in the 18th century. It was a triple-purpose animal, used for draughtwork and also providing beef and plenty of high quality milk. It was selectively improved by Bakewell for its draught-animal size and tallow-making fat, qualities that were much in demand at the time, and it crashed out of favour when fashions changed. The emphasis on size and fat had radically reduced its milk yield and reduced its fertility, and it was ousted by the new improved milk-and-meat Shorthorn. The noble Longhorn was trampled in a stampede worthy of its Texan namesake and almost disappeared in the dust.

Fortunately, some survived, and today, although a rare breed, the future is looking considerably brighter. Longhorns are long in body and small in bone, giving large, lean carcases of slowly maturing but very good meat. Their milk yield is now more than adequate for good suckler cows and they retain the older breeds' qualities of hardiness, longevity, easy calving and good mothering. They can produce high quality meat on a low-cost roughage diet and, always a favourite for gracing parkland, they are now finding their feet again as a useful crossing breed with commercial potential. Berwickshire breeder Peter Close, for example, is getting profitable results from Longhorn × Welsh Black suckler cows put to a Charolais bull as a terminal sire, and also putting a Longhorn bull on Galloway heifers and selling them with calf at foot. For the sake of a horn-shy market, Close is using Lincoln Reds to introduce the polled factor into his Fishwick Longhorns — which will make the purist and the romantic shudder and perhaps shed a tear or two. Certainly it does worry one or two owners of well-known pure Longhorn herds who feel that the breed is quite capable of producing what the market wants without being lost in the mix.

The cows give almost too much milk for suckling, especially if they calve down in May, and sometimes a cow has teats which are too big for comfort. But they are hardy, outwintering happily, with few calving problems either as purebred or crossbred. The milk is high in butterfat, with small fat globules which are good for cheese-making.

Current performance tests give figures of an average 400-day weight of slightly more than 476kg (1,050lb) with 3.5mm backfat. A bull of that age stands about 120cm (47in) at the withers and has a massive look about him, yet you can walk into a family herd and he will accept your presence most peacefully. Quiet handling pays dividends in docility and improved performance: the breed really does seem to respond to kindness.

However, care needs to be taken in some herds when they are first yarded for the winter. A sudden restriction on space can lead to a series of minor battles to restore the pecking order and it is best to yard them gradually in small groups. If necessary the weakest and/or the most aggressive might have to be separated completely. New Longhorn breeders would do well to read Roger Carter's series of articles on Longhorn management in *The Ark* (1981).

They are fine looking animals, with those distinctive huge, curving, sweeping white horns — some drooping, some lop-sided, some beautifully balanced, but all with character. Colours range from a light red roan to a dark red brindle, always with an eye-catching white finching running the length of the back, tail, backside and underside and catching the sunlight so that the animal seems to have a bodily halo. A white patch on each thigh is much admired.

Horns are fine decorations but they have their drawbacks, and the demise of the Longhorn was hastened when cattle began to be transported in railway trucks and ships rather than in droves. But they had a lot going for them even then. At the beginning of this century, when they were still called the 'Longhorn or Dishley breed', they were described as 'big, rather clumsy animals . . . slow in coming to maturity but very hardy. The bullocks feed up to heavy weights and the cows are fair milkers. No lover of cattle can view these quaint creatures without a feeling of satisfaction that the efforts made to resuscitate a breed which has many useful qualities to commend it have been successful, and that the extinction which threatened it in the eighties of the last century is no longer imminent.'

Fine words. In 1907 there were twenty-two Longhorn herds containing about 400 registered cattle, mostly in the Midlands and on the Isle of Man. In 1982 there were 350 registered breeding females and they were distributed throughout Britain and were on the increase. In 1986 there were 412 breeding females. In 1981 a Longhorn won the top beef prize at the Royal Show. The wheel is turning again and the breed's worth is being recognized.

LUING: see HIGHLAND

NORTHERN DAIRY SHORTHORN: see SHORTHORN

RED POLL

Deep red. Polled, with tuft of hair. Dual-purpose.

The Red Poll is the successor to the famous milking Suffolk Dun, long since extinct, and the beefy Norfolk Red. It remains a genuinely dual-purpose breed, with good food conversion rates for both milk and meat. Lots of expensive cake is unnecessary and would be wasted.

In Britain there are recorded dairy herds and double-suckler herds of Red Polls. As a milker, its lactation curve is much steadier than most dairy breeds: an average cow might yield about 4,000kg (8,818lb) in a long, flat production curve, giving up to perhaps 22kg (49lb) a day at first and still giving 10kg (22lb) a day at 305 days. They can go on for much longer than most breeds, too: a Norfolk herd of Red Polls at the turn of the century had cows which milked for up to 469 days.

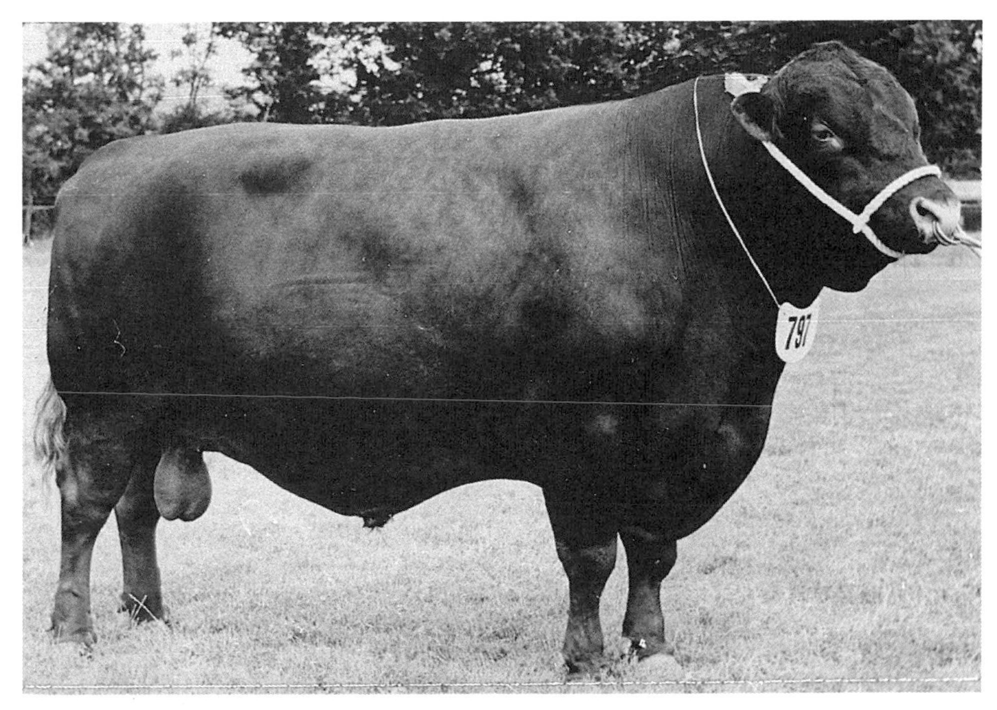

Red Poll. (*RBST*)

Average butterfat for the breed is 3.9%. The fat globules are small and easily assimilated, and the milk is good for cheese-making. The owners of a herd in Dyfed are making a whole-milk Llanboidy cheese from their Red Polls and it is proving to be a very successful enterprise.

Cows often milk well into their teens and can easily raise two calves, fostering readily. But some of the older cows have poor udder conformation, which can give the calves a bit of a problem. In New Zealand there is a notable incidence of twins being born.

The breed is disease resistant and very hardy — typical of East Anglian cattle, who have always had to do battle with winds from the North Sea blowing unchecked across the flat lands. They are used to cold eastern winters and dry summers. The skin is pigmented under the deep red coat and this gives protection in hotter foreign climates; the breed thrives in Brazil, Jamaica and Colombia where it is crossed to make local breeds like the Pitangueiras, Jamaican Red and Velasquez. It is found in all parts of the Americas and Australasia. In Britain it can usefully be crossed with pure beef breeds and the suckled beef calves mature fairly early.

The breed has sound, hard feet and a good constitution; it is claimed to be the longest living dairy breed in the UK. Some people have slight reservations about its temperament; it is usually very quiet but, like the South Devon, it over-reacts if it is upset.

There are more than 1,300 breeding females in this country and the size of the national herd is increasing. Worldwide, the Red Poll's numbers are quite substantial. In February 1986 the Fourth World Red Poll Congress was held in New Zealand and brochures were circulated to more than 2,000 listed Red Poll members all over the world. Since the 1960s the breed has been boosted with Danish Red blood to increase its productivity but this was found to detract from the Red Poll's food conversion rates, longevity and hardiness, and Danish crosses are no longer popular with the breed society.

SHETLAND

Black-and-white. Horned. Dual-purpose. RBST status: critical.

In a book published in 1903 about breeds of British dogs, and in the context of a description of the double coats of Skye terriers and Scotch collies, W.D. Drury said: 'The swine native to the northern parts of Scotland were covered with short wool, and the sheep of the Shetlands and Iceland had, in addition to their wool, an outer covering of hair.'

He does not mention the idea that the perpetual seaborne gales and the short winter days have combined to stunt the growth of all the island animals. Nor does he mention Shetland ponies, nor Shetland cattle, a breed of short-legged, deep-bodied, short-horned little animals with a coat as good as any woolly pig could ever wish to have!

Originally the Shetlands came in a variety of colours including solid black, solid red, red-and-white, dun, and, in some cases, with finching, but now they are nearly always pied black-and-white. They are sometimes mistaken for Friesians but they are smaller, shorter, more compact, traditionally horned, and can thrive in conditions so harsh and on food so meagre that a Friesian would simply give up.

This crofter's cow, commonly tethered by means of a rope looped over its horns, was fairly widespread throughout the islands as recently as 1958, when the Department of Agriculture and Fisheries for Scotland took an

Shetland.

interest in the breed, not for the sake of preservation (the numbers were declining but not crucially) but as part of a livestock improvement scheme and at the same time to supply milk for its farm staff. The Department gradually built up a herd sixty-two strong, including twenty-two breeding cows. It was run as a commercial suckler enterprise on hill land, in-wintering on a loose-house system from December to about May. Health problems were few and the diet very economical.

In 1970 it was realized that new blood was needed within the herd, which until then had been self-contained, and that at the same time the size of the breeding population in the islands was in sharp decline. Unrelated bulls were found, despite the fact that the semen of one of the DAFS bulls had been widely used throughout the islands in an AI scheme. Eventually, because of concern about declining numbers, an approach was made to the RBST, who agreed to help by purchasing heifers and placing them in various enterprises in the UK.

In 1979 there were only sixty-one females and nine males. By 1982 there were still only about a hundred breeding females in the UK. The 1985/6 RBST census recorded about 120 breeding females.

As the DAFS herd grew, it was decided to market fat bullocks, reared after weaning on a cheap ration and on any summer grazing left over after other stock had taken precedence. The first group was ready at about twenty-seven months old. Growth rates were impressive on a diet which was mostly roughage, and returns were satisfactory, but there was some criticism about excess fat — possibly a characteristic of hardy breeds which benefit by being able to store up fat to see them through the bad times.

In due course many of the cows were crossed to Shorthorn or Hereford bulls to improve commercial prospects. Another commercial outlet was the sale of in-calf heifers, often for suckling or as house-cows. There was also co-operation with ABRO's multi-breed comparison schemes, which proved that the Shetland's food intake was most efficient. In addition there was co-operation with the RBST for its semen bank, though AI is notoriously unsuccessful with the breed. This may be the fault of the bull (not the cow) or as a result of lack of freshness in the semen.

Individual farms have also used the Shetland commercially, mostly in multi-suckler herds. Some are aiming to improve milk yields. The cows can produce some milk at low nutrition levels but naturally improve their yields on better feeding, which also increases their body size and helps beef animals to fatten readily and produce high quality meat. But care needs to be taken: in lowland conditions cows can easily put on too much weight, which can affect fertility and ease of calving. The breed seems, in fact, to achieve its best yields and fattening in more difficult conditions. They are ideal as sucklers for harsh environments with limited food supplies.

Appropriately enough, a group of Shetland cattle was presented by the RBST to the Falkland Islands government in 1983. A report nine months later said that they were milking moderately and that their beef potential was impressive. They had some problems in acclimatizing — mostly because of the unfamiliar plant species in the grazing — but their ability to thrive after a sea journey of thousands of miles was noticeable, especially in view of their reputation for being one-person cows. In the old days it was said they had to be accompanied by a piece of cloth (cloutie) belonging to their original owner if they were transferred to someone else.

There are those who think that the crofters must have had a hard time with the so-called crofter's cow; some claim they are so tetchy that you cannot get a bucket under them, let alone obtain a pailful of milk!

SHORTHORN

Red, red-and-white, white, roan. Horned. Beef and milk types.

Eyebrows — and hackles — will undoubtedly be raised at the inclusion of the Shorthorn in a book about minor breeds! It must be one of the most common breeds of all, if crosses, types and Shorthorn-based breeds worldwide are taken into account. But it serves to illustrate a few points and it also includes some minor breeds developed from Shorthorn types or interesting crosses.

The Shorthorn Society is the oldest cattle breed society in the world — quite a claim. The first Herd Book was published in 1822 by George Coates, and right up until 1958 all Shorthorns were registered in the same section of the Herd Book regardless of whether they were dairy or beef types. The story, and the type divergence, began back in the 18th century when there were local cattle known as Teeswaters and Durhams in the north-eastern corner of England. In the late 18th century several notable cattle breeders took an interest in these local animals and began to develop them by selective breeding. Prominent amongst these men were the Colling brothers of Ketton Hall and Barmpton, Booth of Killesby, and Bates of Kirklevington.

It was said that Booth bred the Teeswater for the beef and Bates bred for the pail. The Collings, too, bred a dairy type of Shorthorn from the Durham. At a reasonably early date, therefore, the dual-purpose Shorthorn began to divide into beef types and dairy types.

In 1958 the Beef Shorthorn Society was formed in Scotland, concentrating on what might be termed the Booth strain of Shorthorns. The breed is therefore now basically divided into a beef type and a dairy type, but there are many variations on the theme, and the Shorthorns include the following:

BEEF SHORTHORN
DAIRY SHORTHORN (dual-purpose)
NORTHERN DAIRY SHORTHORN (all from the six Dale counties)
WHITEBRED SHORTHORN (white strain of Dairy Shorthorn, registering 150 females and fifty bulls)
LINCOLN RED (split away from the Shorthorn Herd Book in 1941, Bates/Colling type)
AUSTRALIAN DAIRY SHORTHORN
AUSTRALIAN BEEF SHORTHORN
AUSTRALIAN POLLED SHORTHORN
AUSTRALIAN ILLAWARRA SHORTHORN (beef, very resistant to hot climates)
AUSTRALIAN WEEBOLLABOLLA SHORTHORN (dairy — the Shorthorn equivalent of the Holstein)

There are also lots of breeds based on Shorthorn crosses or including plenty of Shorthorn blood, all over the world. For example:

AYRSHIRE (Shorthorn with Dunlop, plus Channel Islands breeds and West Highland)
BEEF MASTER (USA)
BELGIAN BLUE (Shorthorn and Dutch Friesian with local breeds)
BERLINAS (Italy)
BESTUZHEUS (USSR)
BLENDED RED & WHITE SHORTHORN (Dairy Shorthorn plus Red Holstein/Danish Red/Simmental/Red Friesian)
BLUE ALBION (Whitebred Shorthorn and Welsh Black)
BLUE-GREY (Whitebred Shorthorn and Galloway or Beltie)
BONSMARA (South America)
CHINESE or GRASSLAND RED (China)
GALACIAN BLOND (Spain)
LUING (Shorthorn and West Highland)
MAINE ANJOU (Shorthorn and Mancelle, France)
MEUSE RHINE ISSEL (Holland)
MURRAY GREY (Shorthorn and Aberdeen Angus)
NDAMA (South America)
NORWEGIAN RED (Norway)
PIED RED (Denmark)
SALERS (France)
SANTA GERTRUDIS (Shorthorn and Brahman, USA)
SENEPOL (South America)
SWEDISH RED (Sweden)
TAGIL (USSR)
TAYLOR (India)
UKRAINIAN RED (USSR)

In addition to these breeds, there has been some Shorthorn at some stage in breeds like the Australian Droughtmaster, the Blonde d'Aquitaine, the Charolais, the Finnish Ayrshire and the Texas Longhorn. Some thirty-six breeds have Shorthorn in them somewhere.

So it can be seen that, genewise, the Shorthorn has spread itself far and wide and, directly or indirectly, must number itself in the millions. But it is interesting to see what has happened to registrations of the pure breed in its own land. There has been a dramatic fall in numbers from 25,600 registered pedigree animals in 1950 to a mere 3,500 in 1983. The Shorthorn seems to offer everything to everybody — quality meat and milk, economy, hardiness, longevity, adaptability, placidness and reputation. The trouble with success is that it can lead to dispersion and the original breed is absorbed into a thousand other guises, losing its own identity bit by bit in the process.

If that can happen to the ubiquitous Shorthorn, what hope is there for the rare breeds?

SUSSEX

Dark red. Horned or polled. Beef.

A long established draught-type breed looking much like the Devon, the Sussex produces quick growing beef with low backfat measurements. It does well in hot countries (it has plenty of sweat glands) and can cross well with any breed, including the *Bos indicus* types (Brahman and Afrikander) of South Africa, where the Sussex manages to retain a high level of fertility and general soundness. Indeed recent research has shown that, unusually in a British beef breed, the Sussex has a blood factor which is common in *Bos indicus* and it is thought that this factor enables the Sussex to resist heat stress and live on low quality food.

The breed's main drawback, wherever it is used, is that it does not colour-mark its offspring. Recently the Herd Book has accepted a certain degree of Limousin blood into the breed — the progeny of a second backcross (i.e. 87.5% Sussex, 12.5% Limousin) are given full Herd Book status.

A unique characteristic of the Sussex seems to be its apparent lack of taste. Grazing is quite indiscriminate and the herd leaves a field very evenly trimmed. It seems to scour less easily on lush pasture than some other breeds.

In 1938 there were 235 licensed Sussex bulls. Nearly fifty years later, in 1984/5, some two thousand Sussex AIs were supplied by the Milk Marketing Board, representing 0.1% of all MMB AIs, but the Board had only one Sussex bull at its centre.

Milk yield is not a Sussex boast. The breed was originally noted as a plough ox because it was very muscular, but at some stage it was refined a little with the introduction of Shorthorn blood and it is now a prime beef breed.

WELSH

Black and colours. Horned (also Polled type). Beef.

Welsh Black

The most abundant of the Welsh breeds is the Welsh Black, originally a dual-purpose animal but now primarily raised for beef, though it still gives enough milk to make up the occasional pure Welsh Black dairy herd. It is very much a hill breed — hardy, thrifty, with a strong mothering instinct, a particularly easy calver (even to a Continental bull), with a long and very even lactation which can continue right through to the next calving. It has the ability to keep on breeding even at up to twenty years old and it is a very useful suckler dam.

It faces the same risks as the Shorthorn. Because its qualities are so sought after and are incorporated so often into crosses, the pure Welsh Black may in time become something of a rarity. In the last ten years there has been a cut of almost two-thirds in registrations of pure Welsh Black cows.

There are two types in the Welsh. The northern is bulkier and with shorter legs than the southern variety. The original breed is horned but there is now also a Herd Book section for a Polled Welsh Black.

The coat of the Welsh Black is tailor-made for its environment: in winter it becomes thick and mossy (with a slightly rusty tinge) but in hot climates it remains sleek. Its colour is basically black.

Coloured Welsh

Not all Welsh cattle are black. At first there was quite a range of colours — red, white, blue, dun, mouse, pied, brindled and finch-backed animals were found all over Wales, though black was the most common and became accepted as the standard colour, to the exclusion of all others. Dun is dominant to black and it has therefore easily been eradicated from the national herd, but recessive colours like red, smokey and blue survive and keep reappearing here and there. Blues were sometimes actively sought after because it was thought they were better milkers (probably because of some Shorthorn blood).

The various coloured cattle of Wales were not accepted into the Welsh Black Herd Book but some farmers liked them and kept breeding them anyway, although under the old bull licensing laws they were only supposed to use black Welsh bulls. Some years ago Tim Ash, who now runs Parke Rare Breeds Farm in Devon but who was then at the West Wales Farm Park, took a particular interest in coloured Welsh cattle, inspired by Martin Allinson's collection of White and Belted examples. He scoured the remotest areas of Wales and began to build up a dossier of information and photographs. Eventually a group of like-minded people formed 'The Coloured Cattle of Wales', and in 1981 they created a society called 'The Ancient Cattle of Wales' (*Gwartheg Hynafol Cymru*).

The most popular of the colour varieties are the White Welsh and the *Bolian Gwynion* or Belted Welsh. The Whites were eventually offered a special registration section in the White Park Cattle Society's Herd Book.

White Welsh
The White has the coloured points typical of the White Park but tends to be more freckled over the shoulders. In the past red points were favoured but now most of the Whites are black-eared. During the late 19th century there was a herd of White Park cattle at Faenol (Vaynol) Park, Bangor, which a hundred years later was moved to Shugborough, and no doubt White Park bulls were used on White Welsh cows. Patches on the neck and shoulders of the White Welsh tend to be blue, whereas in the White Park they tend to be black.

White Welsh.

Belted Welsh (Bolian Gwynion)
The Welsh belties are black or red with a white belt. The pattern may have come about originally through crossing with Dutch Lakenvelders (which gave the Galloway breed its Belties) or with Belted Galloways. There are two basic types among the Belted Welsh: the modern type, and the small but solid mountain animal of north Wales with shorter legs than the modern.

Belted Welsh.

Line-backed Welsh

As with other colour-pointed breeds, the line-back (finching) pattern is the other extreme of the same colour cline. If a White is mated to a whole black or whole red animal, and the progeny are mated again to black or red, line-back calves are produced.

Blue Welsh and Blue Albion

The Blue Albion is based on a cross between Whitebred or roan Shorthorns on Welsh Black cows, or sometimes on Friesians. It is controversial: the correspondence pages of *The Ark* frequently debate whether or not the Blue Albion is a breed in its own right as it is quite easy to produce a blue animal by crossing. There used to be a Blue Albion breed society and the breed became very popular in the 1920s. The Ministry of Agriculture accepted the Blue Albion as a breed but unfortunately the society ceased to be active by 1940 and was wound up in 1966. It is thought that herds of Blue Albions continued to exist and in 1985 it was claimed that there were at least three hundred breeding females whose pedigrees could probably be traced back to the 1920s stock, though the cessation of the Herd Book after only twelve volumes so many years earlier would make such pedigree tracing very difficult.

Yet again, this is an example of 'What is a breed?' It has to breed true and it has to be more than just a colour; there must also be some consistency of conformation and performance. Not all colour-pointed white cattle are White Parks.

The Blue Welsh was recorded as a colour in the breed before it was crossed with Shorthorns. In North Wales there seems be a close relationship between the Blue, the White and the Lineback.

A Yorkshire breeder refers to a very strong blue line in a herd of Friesians traced back to the use of one blue cow more than twenty years ago. The blue, to varying degrees, shows up in crosses with other beef breeds used, particularly Limousins, Aberdeen Angus (blue hairs on the face and tail), Blonde d'Aquitaine and Chianina.

Red Welsh

In all black breeds of cattle there is a red recessive gene and among the Welsh the red colour is quite common, second only to black. It is a bright colour, nearer to orange than to the deep ruby of the North Devon. Being recessive, red bred to red always breeds true, but reds are not accepted in the Welsh Black Herd Book.

There is an interesting quote in the *Welsh Black Cattle Society Journal* (April 1985) attributed to the late Miss Pauline Taylor, and it is relevant to any breed. Miss Taylor wrote in 1953:

> 'While realizing the undesirability of the red recessive colour, as well as unorthodox colours and mis-markings that appear now and then in our breed, we suggest that, at this stage, the destruction of really good bulls which get an occasional red calf is premature. There may be a danger of throwing out the baby with the bath water. Other invisible qualities in a bull such as the ability to transmit good udders, high butterfat, health, longevity, regular breeding, quiet temperament etc., are of even greater importance than colour. . . . A pure line of colour is no doubt desirable and scientifically possible, but this can only be achieved at the almost inevitable cost of sacrificing those other characters which made the breed an attractively practical business proposition to the farmer in these days.'

Smokies

'Smokey' or 'mouse' is a colour which has always been found in the Welsh. It is a recessive colour and, like reds, it still occurs here and there despite being selected against for so long.

The Pembroke

The 1909 edition of *Encyclopaedia Britannica* makes frequent references to Pembroke cattle. The Black Pembroke is cited as a very ancient British breed: 'When it tends to albinism its ears and muzzle (and more rarely fetlocks) remain completely black or very dark grey', with the rest of the body whitish and flecked or blotched with pale grey. The horns were light in colour with dark tips, growing out-and-forward, up-and-in. There is also a description of 'cattle very similar to the Chillingham (which was white with red ears) found in Wales in the 10th century'. Individuals of this breed were said to have survived in Pembroke to at least 1850, and were at one time kept pure as farm livestock. Their essential characteristics were those of the Chillingham: black-tipped white horns, black inside the ears and on the muzzle, feet black to the fetlock joint, skin 'unctuous and of deep-toned yellow'. Some calves, however, were entirely black and were 'not distinguished from the common Pembroke cattle of the moutains.' The conclusion was that 'park-cattle are an albino offshoot from the ancient Pembroke black breed which, from their soft and well-oiled skins, are evidently natives of a humid climate, such as the forests where the wild aurochs dwelt', and that they were therefore in a direct line of descent from the aurochs and were not descended from a white sacrificial breed introduced to Britain by the ancient Romans. This claim is repeated elsewhere in the *Encyclopaedia*, where it is stated that 'the fighting bulls of Spain, the black Pembroke cattle of Wales, with their derivatives the White park-cattle of Chillingham in Northumberland, are undoubtedly the direct descendants of the aurochs', whereas 'the white cattle formerly kept at Chartley Park, Staffordshire, exhibit signs of affinity with the Long-horn breed.'

The White Park Cattle Society might like to comment on such statements.

WHITE PARK

White with black points. Large. Horned. Beef. RBST status: critical.

The White Park is special. It evokes admiration for its looks, its ancient lineage, its unique genetic structure, and the romance of ferality — the 'Wild White Cattle'. As well as being eye-catching, it also has qualities which appeal to the commercial farmer. No wonder the RBST chose the head of a White Park bull as its symbol.

Very briefly, the framework so far as it is revealed through the mists of time is as follows. White animals were always special: they had a magic about them and often played a part in religious and ceremonial rites in many cultures. The existence in the British Isles of white cattle with dark (red or black) points has been mentioned in records dating back to the 5th century B.C. By the 13th century, herds of such cattle were enclosed in parks to provide sport for the huntsman as well as to enhance the landscape. These chase herds were largely left to their own devices and their territorial and social behaviour was very much like that of wild cattle.

By the end of the 19th century there were still 'wild' or feral white herds in parks at Chillingham (Northumberland), Cadzow Chase (Lanarkshire), Vaynol (near Bangor) and Chartley (Staffordshire), with a few animals from the latter at Woburn. There were also herds of similarly marked White Welsh (a 'resuscitated breed') and a white polled breed (today recognized separately as the British White). The very old Welsh Dynevor herd was domesticated rather than feral.

White Park.

The majority of the Chillingham herd at that time had red ears rather than black and it was said that the occasional dark calf was born but promptly culled. The Cadzows had black ears and muzzles and flecks of black on head and forequarters. In Pembroke, red-eared Whites were known to exist in the 10th century and they continued to inhabit the region until at least 1850; they were quite numerous well into the 19th century and were taken by drovers to pasturages by the Severn and to local markets. The Pembrokes of this later period were black-pointed.

By the early 1970s there were five herds of domesticated White Parks (Dynevor, Cadzow and Chartley, and new herds with RASE and at Bemborough) and the two feral herds at Chillingham and Vaynol. By the mid 1970s a White Park Herd Book and breed society had been instituted and there is now also a Chillingham Wild Cattle Association. The fourth volume of the White Park Herd Book listed more than a score of herds and the 1985/6 RBST census records 138 breeding females, and there were also thirty-six breeding cows in the Chillingham herd.

The breed standards specify a beef type, with mature cows weighing between 560 and 660kg (11–13cwt). The coat is white with coloured points (usually black, but red is permissible) on muzzle, ears, eyelids, teats and

Feral White Parks at Chillingham. (*RBST*)

feet. Overmarked or wholly black animals cannot be registered. Horn shape is variable and strongly influenced by the dam. It falls broadly into three types:

Chillingham type: Very upright, curling inward at the tip. Lyre-shaped in older cows. (Also in Vaynol.)

Dynevor type: Graceful, growing sideways before curving forwards and upwards. (Also seen in Cadzow.)

Chartley type: Tending to grow downwards rather than upwards.

The bloodlines of White Parks are carefully monitored because some are very inbred (especially the Chillingham) after centuries of segregation in enclosed parks. Different bloodlines can produce different markings, face shapes, conformation etc. AI is used in more than half the herds today and the selection of AI bulls is a wide one.

The breed is beginning to find commercial applications although with such low numbers there is still a long way to go. Nor is there any strong inclination within the breed society to 'go commercial': the breed is maintained because for one thing it is genetically far apart from all other British breeds. The main potential outlet will be in the beef sector, though several herds have been milked, particularly the old Dynevor which also produced draught oxen. With yields in some cases exceeding a thousand gallons at 4% butterfat on the second lactation, the cows make good long-lived sucklers. Crosses give lean meat and there have been promising results in using White Park bulls on Hereford × Friesians and on Charolais × Friesians. The one-ton animal is a possibility as a purebred under proper management. Performance tests indicate very low backfat measurements of 1.5–3.0mm, and bulls strongly colour-mark their cross-bred progeny, including crosses with Angus, Hereford, Shorthorn, Welsh Black, Blue-Grey, Belted Galloway, Luing and Longhorn.

Purebred Chillinghams are slow to reach sexual maturity. The earliest age for calving is three years old and the normal age for a first calver is five years old. In the feral situation the young have to be tough to survive the territorial dominance structure of the herd.

Animals from the 'wild' herds are naturally nervous of humans and need a lot of patient handling. The Vaynols, at the Cotswold Farm Park, for example, have been very cautiously and gently treated by Joe Henson to avoid any stress at all.

Whatever the future holds, the White Park looks good and will always attract attention. It is certainly a favourite in the farm parks and in the show-ring.

9 Pigs

Pigs have always been the backyard barometer of public taste. The pig is manipulated more often and more rapidly to meet its market than any other farm animal on four legs. When it *was* a backyarder — when people were more individual in their needs and tastes — the pig assumed all sorts of guises under all sorts of names. But the backyard pig-keeper was chivvied into the towns and cities, swallowed up and homogenized, and the backyard pig, too, lost its individuality, its regional identification and, some would say, its flavour and quality. Today's pigs are uniformly long, lean and white. Colour prejudice is rampant and fat is melting under the onslaught of dietary purists. Dozens of old breeds are not even a memory now, and of those that are left the great majority are teetering on the edge of existence. Nearly all the remaining British pigs are classified as rare breeds.

Some of the breeds succumbed to extinction very recently. For example, in 1954, in a cross-section of more than fifty farms in Devon, Dorset and Cornwall, it was found that most of the sows, whatever their breed, were already being mated to Large White boars though one or two purebred

A painting (c.1850) of Joseph Lawton's prize Gloucester Old Spot at Little Haywood, Staffordshire, reputedly the largest pig ever bred in the British Isles. (*Sotheby's*)

herds used a Wessex Saddleback or a Large Black. The majority of the sows were Wessex Saddlebacks and Large Blacks, with the National Long White Lop-Eared a close third, and there were also Large Whites, Welsh, Gloucester Old Spots and Dorset Gold Tips. Dorset what? That attractive name belongs to a vanished breed.

A year later, in the same area, Landrace sows were first mentioned in the survey. Twenty-five years on, 35% of the sample herds were using bought-in hybrid sows based on the Landrace and the Large White, and nothing else. Only a small proportion continued to use any of the coloured breeds: the Saddleback was the only one to persist and still find some favour crossed to a Large White or Landrace boar for bacon production.

The speed of the takeover by the Large White and Landrace is breathtaking. What happened to all the old breeds? Did they have nothing to offer? Is it really true that everybody everywhere now has exactly the same tastes as everybody else?

Consider fat, which has been the downfall of most of the old breeds. In the days when people worked the land they needed fat, especially in winter. In Poland, for example, where the winters can be long and harsh, there was a real craving for pig-fat during the war when times were particularly hard and fuel was a luxury. Fat gave energy and insulation. Pigs were specifically bred and fed to be as fat as possible: the lardy pig was the working family's friend. The Pietrain, today's extremely lean favourite, nearly died out in Belgium at that time precisely because of its leanness. During the war fat was *needed*.

Today in Britain fat is rejected. However, it still has some value as cooking lard, as a high-energy food, as an ingredient in traditional sausages and pies which would seem dry and unpalatable without it. Who knows what future dieticians might say about fat? Who knows what will happen when the fossilized fuel supplies are exhausted, and nuclear energy rejected for whatever reason, so that muscle power (human and animal) becomes important again and central heating is replaced by internal heating through eating? Then fat might be not just desirable but essential. Yet it will be too late for the old breeds which could have fulfilled that need.

The passion for intensive pig-farming is feeling the first cool draught of rejection. Intensive systems are expensive to install and maintain, relying heavily on fossil-fuel energy; they are also under fire on a more emotional basis. If the day comes when more farmers want to return to extensive outdoor pig-raising (whether for reasons of economics or morality), will the old hardy breeds still be there to help?

Outdoor pig-keeping is increasing again, little by little, and the requirements of such systems are very different from those of intensive ones. The outdoor sow must be hardy, good on her legs, and with good nesting and mothering instincts and abilities; she must farrow without supervision and she must suckle her litter and protect it from other sows. It is said that the brains have been bred out of the docile indoor whites and they simply have not got the character to cope with life in the great outdoors. All the old breeds, however, had the desirable outdoor qualities, and today the Saddleback alone is still in demand to some extent, not as a purebred but as a boar on a white sow to produce blue gilts that have some of those old qualities. The stock of Saddlebacks for such a task needs to be no more than hundreds, even if the cross is Landrace boars on Saddleback sows which tends to give a lower percentage of useful blues.

The Saddleback, however, continues to have a larger appetite than other breeds and a less greedy blue, like the Pietrain, is a leaner pig. But that cuts both ways: a pig like the Saddleback, with her capacity for storing fat and her good coat, is protected out of doors; she is insulated from the cold and the heat. The muscular, black-spotted Pietrain, Belgian Blue of the pig world, is a neurotic beast, susceptible to sudden death from stress, and its meat is unpleasantly pale. It may be lean, but is it edible? Bring back the Saddleback, the Tamworth, the Gloucester Old Spot, the Large Black, if you want a touch of colour and for the sake of hardiness. They are real pigs, and their meat tastes like real pork and bacon.

The crucial colour bar is in the carcase. Consumers do not like any hint of blueness in the rind. But look at eggs and bread: fashions in both have switched from white to brown. Perhaps one day a touch of blue in the bacon rind will be appreciated because it promises good flavour.

Today the pig industry is dominated by mongrels. In the old days it was also dominated by mongrels, until the breeders got to work on developing types, but the difference is that today's mongrels are hybrids, and you cannot breed true from a hybrid. The old breeders had endless variations to choose from and the modern developer cannot afford to lose any more of the old breeds because they are the source material for the hybrids. The minor breeds are the mothers and fathers of the future.

The original native British pig was coarsely bristled, slab-sided, razor-backed and slow to grow. In medieval times it was economically important and it was probably the only regular source of protein for the majority of the population. Unfortunately it was hard to find cheap sources of food for its maintenance, let alone to put any carcase on it.

From manorial records it has been calculated that the average sow's weaned litter was less than five piglets. The very good pig in a really good year probably yielded about forty-five kilogrammes or a hundred pounds of meat and bone. Most of the pigs illustrated in manuscripts of the time, however, look very small indeed. There was room for improvement.

Very much larger regional types had developed by the mid 18th century. A few years later pigs began to be imported from China, probably to introduce the Chinese pigs' ability to fatten rapidly — a quality still lacking in British pigs at the time. In contrast to the contemporary native breeds, the orientals were small, short and portly, with light bones and fine black or white coats.

The British pig began to change. Colours lightened from the old dark brown, and lop ears (accompanied by docility and maternal qualities) began to develop.

It was not until 1884 that the first pig Herd Books were established — much later than those for horses and cattle. In the meantime there had been all sorts of crossing between the regional types and with imported breeds, and this produced some of the breeds still known today like the Tamworth, Berkshire, Saddleback and Large White. The Large White was a big success and was mated to various 'land races' (improved national types) on the Continent, particularly in Germany. At the same time the Danes had been perfecting their own Landrace baconer.

In the first half of the 20th century the Large White, Danish Landrace and two German breeds infused with Large White became a major influence in many parts of Europe. Even the vast pig population of the USSR (nearly 10% of all the world's pigs) was improved by the Large White and Landraces. The long white pigs had taken over.

Pigs are bred for a purpose. Some are good for bacon, others for pork, others are good mothers. The basic meat ranges, by liveweight, are:

PORKER 40–67kg
CUTTER 68–82kg
BACONER 83–101kg
HEAVY HOG 102–120kg

With the emphasis today on leanness, backfat measurements at any weight are crucial. The thickness of the fat is measured over the eye muscle of the carcase by probes inserted at fixed points level with the head of the last rib; the methods of classification and conformation are detailed in the Appendix.

★ ★ ★ ★ ★

Whatever the breed of pig, there are certain commonsense principles that apply to all pigs but which are sometimes forgotten in a too hasty world.

For example, a sow reaches her full flush of milk at three weeks after farrowing. Traditionally weaning used to be at eight weeks, taking full advantage of the goodness of the milk. Today many farmers wean much earlier in order to squeeze an extra litter out of the sow. In fact sows will come into season every three weeks even during suckling but it will be difficult to detect if the pigs are still on her and sometimes a service in these circumstances will not hold. Weaning at eight weeks gives the sow a week to recover before her next season at nine weeks. Early weaning is also likely to lead to mastitis as the sow is still so full of milk. A further argument against early weaning is that it may reduce the size of the next litter.

It seems that reproductive efficiency is at its lowest in July and August and at its best from February to May. Factors which might explain this are that the sow's oestrus is affected by day-length and that the quality of the boar's sperm can be affected by too much heat. The wild boar in Europe mates in the late autumn and winter months.

When choosing a breeding sow, look for fourteen well-placed teats. If there are more, there may not be enough space for the glands to develop adequately. Piglets choose the front ones for preference, and the dominant piglets soon establish their rights up front. It seems that the front-teat pigs often produce the leanest carcases and the best weights, and also tend to remain dominant later.

Avoid an animal with a nipped-in back end: she could have farrowing problems. Do not be tempted to stock a gilt too young; farrow her down at twelve to thirteen months and pig her at seventeen to eighteen months so that she will have developed and grown enough to have something in reserve while she is pregnant and suckling. Look for depth in a sow: she needs carrying capacity for her litters. But if a boar is too deep he will find it difficult to work. Both boar and sow need sound legs.

The most crucial moment for newborn piglets eager to avoid being crushed is just after the last one is delivered. The sow, who is usually recumbent during delivery, gets up and urinates and then lies down again, probably straight on top of a piglet that is not yet quick enough to move out of the way. Wild boar rarely crush their young: they react instantly to a startled piglet's squeal.

Pigs seem to eat more if there is a degree of competition at the feeding trough. The sight of everyone else tucking in seems to increase the appetite and the determination to get a share of the goodies. But too much competition has the opposite effect.

Outdoor sows will welcome a good wallow in a muddy puddle in hot weather: dig out a special wallow-hole for them.

THE MINOR BREEDS

The British breeds which have so far defiantly survived in the face of overwhelming opposition each have their own merits — and their drawbacks. They are nearly all coloured (good for hardiness but in some cases associated in people's minds with fat and blued meat) and, like the old breeds of cattle, they have found their way to many other parts of the world where their qualities are appreciated. They nearly all share qualities which make them ideal outdoor breeding sows but one of their main drawbacks is that some of them are slow to mature. In intensive systems that means they cost more to rear: they take longer to become marketable and they eat more. However, slow maturity produces quality and flavour in the meat (and the risk of fat!) and the future for the minor breeds lies in free-range systems where quality is more important than speed. It is encouraging that there has been talk of premiums for free-range pig meat — all part of the organic movement — and the minor breeds may yet find a safe niche.

Comments about population figures mentioned at the beginning of Chapter 8 apply equally to pigs.

★ ★ ★ ★ ★

BERKSHIRE

Black; white socks and tailswitch. Prick ears. Early maturing porker. RBST status: critical.

The Berkshire was the Wantage pig. It was originally lop-eared, tawny in colour with splashes of black and it was out of similar stock to the Tamworth. It went through a stage of being very large indeed, with big ears and large bones and an up-turned snout and short legs. There is Neapolitan (and therefore Chinese) blood in its veins.

In the second half of the 19th century Lord Barrington began to improve the Berkshire and bred a pig looking much like today's, much more elegant and compact than the original and shorter in the body. In 1900 it was a heavy-jowled pig with a moderately short head, a deep and compact body, and with wide, low and well developed hind quarters with

Berkshire.

heavy hams. At that time it had become somewhat inbred and was less hardy and prolific than other breeds, but it had the honour of improving the Irish pigs and in the United States it was the favourite lard-hog and bacon pig, particularly in Iowa. It seemed to grow into a larger and finer animal across the Atlantic.

More recent improvements have given the Berkshire a longer body and a lighter shoulder. It now has a worldwide reputation for quality.

It is a black pig, with four white socks and a white-switched tail and there are occasionally white patches on the face. Its hair is quite fine. Its well proportioned body is carried on short, sound legs and sound feet. Fine boned, giving plenty of lean meat and small, quality joints, it is an excellent lightweight porker and matures early, reaching 45kg (100lb) liveweight in eighteen weeks or 54kg (120lb) in twenty-one weeks. Crossed with a Large White or a Tamworth it can be a quick growing bacon pig. Despite being a black pig, the Berkshire's skin is pink and it dresses out completely white; crossed to any of the white breeds the progeny are all white.

It is an economical feeder and is renowned for its stamina. As would be expected in an old black breed, it is hardy and the sow is prolific with ample milk to raise her large litter without losing condition herself. The Berkshire, in fact, ovulates at a higher rate than many breeds and can be used to improve the litter size of the less prolific Tamworth.

When fatter pigs were needed, the Berkshire × Middle White was a popular cross. Both are typical pork pigs.

The Berkshire has fared well overseas, and not only in the United States and Canada. Until the 1970s it was the dominant breed in New Zealand, used primarily as a sow crossed to a Large White boar for light pork production. But the Landrace came along and proved to be more fecund and better carcased. In 1985 only eighty-seven Berkshires were registered in New Zealand and only sixty-eight females were registered in Britain.

BRITISH LOP

White. Lop-eared. Large. Pork and bacon. RBST status: critical.

A big pig from the West Country, the Lop was once known as the Cornish White or the Devon Lop and it has been bred in the south-west of England for so long that it is considered a native breed. It was for many years called the National Long White Lop-eared pig — a mouthful but descriptive of its main features. It has also been described as the 'White Large Black'.

British Lop. (*British Lop Pig Society*)

The Lop is a large pig, one of the biggest breeds in Britain as well as one of the oldest. It is well suited to the hilly cider orchard paddocks of its homeland and for most of its history it has stayed within its own region, especially around Tavistock. Recently, however, its qualities are being appreciated elsewhere and a Scottish farmer now claims to have the biggest herd of Lops in the country with twenty-five sows. His main reason for keeping them is, he claims, 'to make money' — a fine compliment to a rare breed. He crosses the sows with Landrace or Large White boars and finds they do well for pork and bacon.

The Large White × Lop cross used to be fairly common. Landrace blood was introduced into the breed in the late 1950s, when the small number of lines within the breed was realized, and some claim to be able to see traces of that Landrace infusion (or possibly Welsh) in the ear carriage of some Lops today.

Lop ears in any breed seem to encourage docility. The theory is that if an animal cannot see where it is going it will not go anywhere. However, it can also be said that a blinkered boar might be *more* dangerous. Floppy ears are sometimes linked with a tendency for sickle hocks, whereas prick-eared breeds generally have good straight back legs.

The old Lop was a hardy, heavy-framed pig. Today it is pleasingly shaped, just as hardy and never coarse. It is a good economic grazing pig that can happily forage out of doors on pasture and stubble or in woodland, and it is excellent as a porker or cutter with very little backfat, whether it is used as a purebred or a cross. It really is very docile indeed.

In 1984 130 females and thirty-four males were registered in the British Lop Herd Book but in 1986 less than a hundred females were registered. All breeds of pig are notoriously subject to rapid fluctuations in population.

BRITISH SADDLEBACK

Black with white belt. Lop-eared. Dual purpose. RBST status: critical.

There used to be two different types of Saddleback: the Essex, with four white feet, a white tail switch and a big broad white saddle, and the Wessex with two white feet and a black tail. The larger Wessex was the New Forest pig; it was at one time the second most numerous breed in the country and it spread all over the south of England and to Norfolk and the Midlands. It was a really hardy animal and the Wessex sow was an excellent outdoor mother who milked very well indeed. But it was a coloured pig and never did well in carcase competitions for that reason. In the old days pigs were butcher-killed and scalded and coloured pigs were not as much of a liability as they are to abattoirs today.

The Essex was best suited to its own area — Essex, Suffolk, Cambridgeshire, Lincolnshire and Berkshire (it never spread beyond Reading). It was never as popular as the Wessex. By the time the two types were amalgamated to form the British Saddleback in 1967, the Essex contribution to the breed was minor.

British Saddleback. (*RBST*)

The British Saddleback is basically black and its white belt varies from something so narrow across the shoulders that the pig seems almost wholly black, to a big, bold white expanse covering most of its body. It is now perhaps the most numerous of the rare breeds of pig, with nearly a hundred females being registered annually, though in 1986 its numbers noticeably fell and its RBST priority listing was revised to Category 1 (critical) instead of Category 2 (rare). It has found a niche as the coloured dam which passes hardiness and (uniquely) hybrid vigour to crossbred offspring used as porkers, baconers and heavy hogs. It is an outdoor grazing breed, sometimes used to restore fertility on overworked arable land, especially in hot climates overseas. Food conversion rates are very good, which is an important quality when rations can be so costly. With more pig farmers going back to outdoor systems and insisting on blue sows, the Saddleback is in demand. She is lop-eared and docile but she is a protective mother who is very capable of looking after her litter. Crossed with a Large White, she produces a very good blue and white (and sometimes nearly all-white) bacon pig. But the Saddleback boar has been rejected as the potential national 'third breed' for use on commercial Large White × Landrace hybrid gilts because it is deemed to be too fat.

In New Zealand only seven British Saddlebacks were registered in 1982, but none at all since then. They used to be more popular in common with other coloured breeds, because they could withstand the rigours of outdoor rearing and would graze well. The coloureds were particularly popular in the days when every New Zealand dairy farm kept pigs to convert skim-milk and whey into meat but they lost their place when bulk whole-milk collection took over.

CHESTER WHITE

White. Large. Lop-eared. Arched back. Pork or bacon. USA.

The Chester White is an American lard-hog but it has very British origins.

North America has no native pigs and all its breeds are based on imported European stock. At first the early settlers took over whatever pigs they happened to have around back in the old country. Later the improved Berkshire and the Wessex were brought over to cross with local animals and develop new breeds like the Chester, the Duroc, the Hampshire and the Poland China.

The Chester White was developed in Pennsylvania during the 19th century. It sometimes has a curly coat and it is possible that the now extinct Lincolnshire Curlycoat featured in its ancestry. The Curlycoat was a large, jowly pig with a good round back end and beautiful fat — which was once its strength but finally led to its downfall. It was also very hardy and prolific, somewhat coarse in the bone, with its ears falling over its face, and it had an abundance of long curly hair which protected it from the cold easterly winds of Lincolnshire.

Another breed which may have contributed to the Chester White was the Cumberland, in many ways similar to the Curlycoat. It was another very fat pig of considerable size, with a hefty jowl, heavy shoulders and big lop-ears. Cumberland ham was famous and the breed was noted for its

Lincolnshire Curlycoat. (*RBST*)

gentleness and good maternal qualities; it was also prolific and hardy. The breed finally became extinct about twenty years ago.

The Yorkshire is another likely component of the Chester White. It was also one of the foundation breeds for the now ubiquitous Large White.

Today's Chester White has been bred for leaner meat. It is still primarily an outdoor pig, robust and hardy, and the sows are excellent mothers, farrowing and rearing large litters. The boars pass a very good feed conversion rate on to their crossbred progeny. There is only one herd of any size in the UK.

DUROC

Red. Large. USA.

The Duroc is another American pig probably based on British breeds, with generous infusions of African, Spanish and Portuguese red pigs. Originally a lard-hog, it has responded well to the modern taste for leaner meat and has an important place in the American and Canadian national herds.

In 1900 it was known as the Duroc Jersey and was the most popular pig in Nebraska and Iowa, the heart of the American hoglands. It could easily make about 135kg or 300 lb in eight months — a large and prolific pig. It spread to Canada and today it is one of the most numerous pig breeds in the world. Britain has been slow to make use of it and it is still a minor pure breed here.

Canada imported plenty of improved Berkshires, Yorkshires and Tamworths during the 19th century, and the Duroc has the colour of a Tamworth or an old Berkshire. It is more red than sandy.

Canadian Durocs were first imported to Britain in the late 1960s, and from the United States in 1980. Its numbers in the UK are still very low but it is cautiously being considered by some pig companies as a third breed to complement the Large White × Landrace combination. Trials are being carried out to test its potential in this role and to locate the best lines. It has stamina and good growth rates but points against it, in some eyes, are that it is coloured and short and is not a good worker. It seems to have a tendency to produce intramuscular fat rather than subcutaneous fat.

GLOUCESTER OLD SPOT

White with a few dark spots or patches. Lop-eared. Dual pupose. RBST status: rare.

The docile Gloucester Old Spot comes from the same region as the Gloucester cow and it has been raised in the Berkeley Vale for many generations. Unfortunately all its breed society records were destroyed during the last war in an air raid on Bristol.

Being coloured, it is a very hardy outdoor pig. Its thick hair gives it good insulation from the cold but is not popular in the abattoir. (Regular use of oil and sulphur and grooming can reduce coat thickness.) Nor do abattoirs like the fact that dark pigment in the spots comes through the rind. There is therefore a tendency for breeders to select pigs with the minimum of dark patches on them, and the Gloucester Old Spot is nothing like as spotty as it used to be.

Known as the Orchard pig or the traditional cottagers' pig, it does have the ability to forage for itself and can turn fairly rough food into lean meat as long as its weight is watched. It is a large, chunky, meaty breed and eats heartily. If it is not slaughtered by about 70kg or 150 lb at the most, it begins to pile on the fat rapidly. To the inexperienced eye it may not seem to be growing at all at that stage but it should be weighed regularly.

The sow is a very good mother, spending several hours building a nest before she drops her litter, and she looks after the pigs well. She was

Gloucester Old Spot. (*RBST*)

originally bred to give two litters a year, which would then fatten quickly on whey and windfalls. They make good little porkers up to about 60kg (130lb) and are best kept on the sow to wean at 27kg (60lb) at eight weeks old so that they are halfway to full weight before weaning. It is important that the growing young should not be checked: they should stay in familiar quarters at weaning, the sow being moved elsewhere, and it is best not to mix them in with strangers. They also need ample exercise to distribute their weight and avoid becoming overfat. The usual age at slaughter is about five months.

There has been a certain amount of performance testing and several boars have scored very high ratings. Top grade bacon can be made from pure and crossbred stock and the Gloucester Old Spot crosses well with white breeds to produce all-white progeny.

Recently the breed has been exported to the United States for probably the first time since 1914. Gloucester Old Spots are now blooming in Bloomingdale, Illinois, and in this country the 1985/6 RBST census recorded 474 breeding females though this figure might have included some young stock.

HAMPSHIRE

Saddleback. Prick ears. Longish legs. USA.

The Hampshire should really be called the New Hampshire Lard-hog: it is another American pig. Like the Duroc, it has managed to shed most of its fat in recent years and thus maintained its popularity. It has also been called the Thin Rind pig, the Belted Kentucky, the Ring Middle and the Saddleback.

It probably springs from the Wessex Saddleback or the Old English breed which used to be raised in Northumberland and the border counties. The Old English was a belted, hardy and prolific pig with an outstanding carcase in its time, but it was slow to mature and eventually gave way to the quicker maturing breeds.

The stress-free and robust Hampshire has the hardiness of a coloured breed but the carcase dresses out complete white. It is frequently used for crossing and in creating hybrids, though some say the boars are not the best workers.

LARGE BLACK

Black. Lop-eared. Dual-purpose. RBST status: critical

In 1900 the Large Black at last received national recognition in the show-ring. It had been bred in the south of England for generations, being

Large Black. (*RBST*)

carefully improved all the while in Cornwall, Devon, Essex, Kent and Suffolk. The Large Black Pig Society was established in 1899, and during the first two decades of the 20th century the Large Black began to spread rapidly all over the country. By 1922 the society had nearly two thousand members. In 1954 it was one of the major sow breeds in the West Country, but today there are less than fifty breeders and only eighty-three litters were registered in 1984. Two hundred and two breeding females were recorded in the 1985/6 RBST census.

It is a very handsome pig, wholly black with a mealy hue and fine hair. It is as big as the Large White and has large lop-ears — and, true to the rule, it is very quiet and docile, a contented grazer; it can be contained with a single-stranded electric fence. It is hardy, tolerant of hot climates as well as cold, and it is also early maturing and a better bacon pig than the white. It used to have a very good back end but this has perhaps been lost to some extent because of breeding for greater length.

The sow is an excellent mother with plenty of milk for her litter, which she rears to very good weaning weights, and the pigs grow fast and well. She does best in an outdoor system where she can exercise herself and keep in good, hard condition for a long working life.

Unfortunately there is some pigmentation in the skin.

MIDDLE WHITE

White. Small. Prick ears. Snub nose. Porker. RBST status: critical.

(See front cover for photograph.) The Middle White is a character pig, with the sort of face that photographers, caption writers and film-makers cannot resist. Its head is short and its face is very Chinese-pig — there is a generally squashed look about it, but it is far more appealing than the new Chinese Meishans which have just been imported into the UK and which look like Shar-pei dogs.

The Middle White is one of the few breeds which can boast a monument. In the 1930s three Middle Whites were exported to Japan (an excellent market for pigs, incidentally). More than three thousand of their progeny were registered and a memorial was erected to the three founders. Quite recently the Emperor of Japan declared that he would never eat any pork other than that of the Middle White.

The oriental connection goes deeper. You only have to look at the Middle White to know that it has Chinese blood. It is not just that squashed nose but also its love of the comfortable life, a common trait among the Chinese breeds.

In fact the breed has its origins in Yorkshire. The old Yorkshire and the Cumberland were crossed with the improved Leicester, a large light-spotted (or sometimes black) pig with a very broad back and shoulders. The result was the Small White, a very fat little pig but beautifully proportioned and with lots of long, silky, wavy hair. Its 'deficiency of lean meat' however, led to its extinction during this century.

The combination had also produced the Large White, which to begin with sometimes had a few blue spots on the skin with white hairs growing from them. Its ears were fringed with long, fine hair (the quality of ear hair is said to indicate the quality of the pig) and it was very prolific and could grow to enormous liveweights of more than 560kg (11cwt).

The Small and the Large Yorkshire Whites were crossed to create the Middle White — shorter in the head and legs than the Large, fuller of jowl, thicker and more compact in the body, but quite as prolific and with the advantage of earlier maturity as a porker. Even now the Large White on the Middle White (not vice versa) is an ideal cross because it combines the length and lean of the Large with the fine pork texture of the Middle.

Between the wars the Middle White was known as the London Porker. It was slaughtered at porker weights, packed into hampers and sent off to Smithfield Market. More recently a breeder had a contract with Harrods for supplying Middle Whites as suckler pigs, slaughtered at six weeks and roasted whole.

In the 1930s the Middle White outnumbered its Large cousin but eventually the leaner, longer pig won the ratings war handsomely. By 1976 only three Middle White boars were registered and only thirty-four litters had been notified the previous year. The RBST stepped in just in time and ten years later twenty-nine boars and 154 breeding females were registered by about forty breeders. Better — but far from safe.

Now interest in the breed is growing. It is a nice, quiet pig for beginners, easy to manage. It produces real pork, with a delicious flavour and proper crackling. It can be crossed with the Large White to give a good commercial pig and it is a good mother and consistent breeder. Hardy, early maturing and friendly, it does not bother too much with rooting: that short snout is not built for digging under the fence. Admittedly it is still a fat pig but it grows quickly and puts on a better ratio of flesh to bone at an earlier age than others. Finished carcases are in the deadweight range of 36–45kg (80–100lb). After porker weight it tends to be out of its depth and much too fat; it will perhaps make a cutter up to 82kg (180lb) but it will not make a bacon pig. Nor was it ever supposed to be: it is a pork pig and, as pork, it is superb.

OXFORD SANDY AND BLACK

Sandy with black splodges. Semi lop-eared.

Oxford Sandy and Black. (*Nancy Howard*)

There is some controversy about the Oxford Sandy and Black. Some say it became extinct in the early 1970s. Others disagree and display pigs that certainly look like the breed. The counter argument to these breeders is that, like Blue Albion cattle, you can recreate the Sandy and Black type quite easily by crossing almost anything, particularly a mixture of Tamworth and Berkshire with perhaps a dash of Gloucester Old Spot or Large Black.

Originally this very localized breed was a medium-sized red pig with plenty of sandy hair and dark blotches here and there. It was semi lop-eared, quite long in the leg, not much at the back end (no hams worth speaking of) and rather a poor doer. It looked something like the old Gloucesters and Berkshires and may well have had close connections with the Axford, which was bred from red pigs imported from Barbados and which gave the Tamworth its colour.

Donald McLean remembers the pre-war 'plum pudding' pigs as slate-coloured (black and white) with a dash of red and flop ears.

Yet today there are some interesting Oxford Sandy and Black pigs, or types, thriving in Devon, the Falklands and elsewhere. They are sandy with dark splodges and are very hairy. Their feet are pale; their ears are not quite pricked, not quite lop. They are very docile and quiet and a strand or two of wire keeps them where you want them. They never make sudden movements like a spooked Tamworth. They are trustworthy even with people who do not like pigs, and they are very hardy indeed.

Overfeeding must be avoided: they do not need too much protein and they can run to fat if given too much milk and barley meal. Slaughtered at six months they produce a succulent and tasty carcase. The sow is a good mother and if she is crossed to a Gloucester Old Spot, Saddleback or Tamworth, her litter is a lovely mixture of colours and markings — popular in the farm parks and equally in demand as weaners for fattening.

PIETRAIN

White or grey, black spots. Prick ears. Very lean meat. Belgian breed.

The Pietrain looks like one of the old British breeds gone wrong. It is grey or white with black spots like a Gloucester and often has a hint of ginger in the coat. It is a Belgian breed and, like the Belgian Blue bullock, it can have almost obscene muscling at the back and is much sought after for its extreme leanness. It has a higher ratio of lean to bone and bigger 'eye' muscles than other breeds at the same carcase lean content; in common with Limousin cattle and Texel sheep it is leaner than expected from its mature weight and consistently produces crossbred carcases with more than 600g (21oz) of lean per kilogram (616g/kg at 30kg side weight). This is despite the fact that its mature weight is only slightly less than that of a Gloucester, which produces an average of a mere 483g/kg of lean meat and 367g/kg of fat at 60kg (132lb) carcase weight. It is said that the ratio of lean to fat in meat should be at least 5:1 in order to satisfy the average consumer, in which case the Old Spot is a real loser!

The Pietrain was probably derived from a mixture which included the Belgian Landrace, a black breed of some kind, and the Tamworth. It is used almost entirely for three or four way crosses. Unfortunately cross-breeding has resulted in poor meat quality (it is very pale) and in a high susceptibility to any kind of stress. It drops dead at the slightest provocation and this tends to outweigh its good qualities which are docility and a small appetite.

POLAND-CHINA

Black with white parts. Short lop-ears. USA.

This is one of the four American lard-hog breeds which were developed from British imports. However, the Poland-China failed to get rid of its fat fast enough and is now much less common in the United States, where in 1900 it was the most popular breed of pig. It is black, like the Berkshire, but with more white on it, and it has short lop-ears. It is thought to have originated from the Big China, a large white hog with sandy spots which was taken to Ohio early in the 19th century and crossed with the Berkshire and a breed called the Bayfield.

It serves as a gentle lesson to the British rare breeds: lose your fat or lose your future.

TAMWORTH

Golden ginger. Medium. Prick ears. Slow maturing bacon.

RBST status: critical

(See front cover for photograph.) The Staffordshire Tamworth is a challenge of a pig, full of character. It used to be thought closely related to the wild boar or the old English forest pig, but in fact it is descended from the Axford or imported Red Barbadan which gave the Tamworth its distinctive reddish-gold colouring and perhaps also its ability to thrive under a tropical sun. It is also hardy in colder climates and is essentially an outdoor pig that is very happy indeed rooting in paddock and woodland. The long snout is an ideal tool for land reclamation and the pig thoroughly enjoys the freedom to grub about. In fact it can be *too* useful a tool: it comes in handy for digging under fences, and Tamworths are always interested in going somewhere else. There *is* a touch of the wild pig in them! Several people who have kept free-range Tamworths remark on their very natural and self-sufficient behaviour. They know how to build igloos and nests, where to lie up in difficult weather condition, and how to protect their young. In extensive systems they may take longer to reach bacon weight but the meat is all the better and tastier for that, and cheaper to produce. The carcase is lean and dresses white.

In 1985 fewer females were registered for the Tamworth than for other rare breeds and there were 139 breeding females recorded in the 1985/6 RBST census. The Tamworth is popular overseas. It has been an important breed in Canada and the United States, for example. In New Zealand it was often seen on the dairy farms, grazing out of doors and using up the skim and whey, but its numbers there are now very low and the last registrations (ten only) were in 1983. Ironically the similar coloured and more aggressive Duroc is now being imported in New Zealand as a coloured terminal sire on Large White × Landrace hybrid sows.

Every Tam is an individual, even more so than other breeds of pig. They are intelligent, not to say cunning, and if they cannot dig under it they will climb out instead. Some lines have been inbred and produced a rather neurotic strain. Other lines are still too heavy in the shoulder. The boars can indeed be a bit of a handful at times and are greedy enough to put on too much weight unless their feeding is watched. Like the Large Black, the breed probably used to have a better back end, which has been lost a little in breeding for length. It is certainly a longer and slimmer pig than most of the rare breeds; it is an ideal baconer and crosses usefully with a Berkshire.

One problem has been a lack of prolificacy. At the beginning of this century Tamworths were described as prolific (and hardy, active and extensively bred) but they did deteriorate for a time from inbreeding. Selective breeding to the more prolific strains and the use of new boar lines imported from Australia in the 1970s has improved the situation. It also seems that the litter size increases if the sow is kept in hard condition and not overfed.

The Tamworth has the looks to catch the eye, the hardiness to thrive out of doors wherever it is kept, and the potential for producing lean carcases for either bacon or fresh pork. Sows can usefully be crossed to the Large White for bacon or the Landrace for pork and the performance figures for the breed are improving every year in all respects.

With their intelligence and their practical snouts, perhaps there is another role for the Tamworth as a *Schnuffenschwein*, a successor to 'Emily', the porker who can outsniff any dog in the search for contraband drugs.

VIETNAMESE POT-BELLIED

Black. Small prick ears. Squashed face. Large belly.

A few years ago the Vietnamese pig was heralded as the smallholder's pig. That was a mistake. Even its most ardent fans will admit that this extraordinary bulbous little black creature is all gristle and lard, and no good at all for eating. It makes an interesting addition to a farm park; it grazes down the orchard grass; and it makes an unusual pet which can be taught a few tricks and enjoyed for the sake of its company. It is not a practical pig.

The Vietnamese boar is exceedingly precocious and exceedingly randy.

Vietnamese Pot-bellied.

But with his awkward shape — the bulging belly and the very short legs — he can have some difficulty in serving his sow. The sows are very regularly in heat, and very obviously too, but in addition to the boar's problems the sows often have trouble farrowing. They tend to take too long over the whole business, so that they develop uterine inertia and need veterinary assistance. It is not at all unusual for the majority of the piglets to be born dead, and those that do survive (which usually seem to be more boars than gilts) find it difficult to suckle because of their mother's awkward shape. The sow is very milky, if only the pigs can get at her, and she is also a protective mother but, again, her shape defies her good intentions and she cannot help squashing a few piglets here and there. Thus breeding Vietnamese is fraught with problems!

The young are not as hardy as the parents (who do not mind being out in the snow). They should not be given creep feed, which is too concentrated for them. Nor do adults need high-protein feed. Rolled barley and sow nuts are quite enough and they should be allowed ample free-range grazing: they tend to become morose if they are shut in. As a breed they do not generally rootle, with the exception of the occasional individual.

There are one or two other problems. They can get rather scaly skins, but this can be cured with an internal dose of cod-liver oil and an external rub with vegetable oil. Some of them develop 'cabriole' legs — very short, with a dropped fetlock — and this may be hereditary. More seriously, they are prone to death from pneumonia, and autopsies in such cases usually reveal hard white deposits around the heart. This is probably a congenital weakness. Unfortunately they show no symptoms until it is too late to help.

In their favour, especially as pets, is their complete lack of smell, nor do they seem to get lice. Although the little ones grumble and argue with each other most of the time, they and the adults are very affable towards people and are just as happy in the kitchen as in the yard.

That pot belly may seem like a gross deformity (in late pregnancy it can be difficult for the sow to keep it clear of the mud) but it is a feature of many oriental pigs and it does serve a purpose: it offers plenty of storage space for bulky roughage. This asset is explained under CHINESE PIGS on page 150.

THE 'IRON AGE' PIG

(See back cover for photograph.) Several farm parks feature 'Iron Age' pigs, which are actually the result of a cross between one of London Zoo's wild boars and a Tamworth sow. Successive generations from the hybrid have been selected for docility on Joe Henson's Cotswold Farm Park. The adults have good long snouts for competent rooting, harsh coats, and smallish prick ears. The piglets are striped in true wild fashion and they seem to have a different smell about them. (Incidentally, all the many feral pigs of Papua New Guinea, which come in every colour, pattern, shape and size, have striped piglets.)

David and Ann Miller in North Wales are now breeding wild boar quite seriously, putting Wild Boar Pie on the menu of regular dinner parties.

At the Meat Research Institute they decided to study the Iron Age pig to compare it with modern breeds and see if it was true that in the actual Iron Age our pigs were much leaner, and have been fattened by domestication. Over a seven-year period they built up a collection of Henson's approximations to the type of pig thought to have existed in Britain two thousand years ago and managed them under the same system as several other breeds, including the Large White and the Pietrain. Every carcase in that period was dissected and analysed at three different weights (65kg, 90kg and 120kg liveweight). The results very much surprised them.

Far from being incredibly lean, the Iron Age pigs were substantially fatter than either the Large White or the Pietrain. In fact, in all three weight classes they had nearly double the amount of fat. They also had less bone and far less muscle.

At 90kg, male Iron Age pigs had more fat than muscle (40.9%:48.8%) whereas the Large White had proportions of 57% and 26.6% and the lean Pietrain 61.1% and 22.6%. Backfat thicknesses measured at P2 were 8.6mm in the Pietrain, 10.2mm in the Large White, and — wait for it — 33.5mm in the Iron Age pig. It was also the hardest, whitest fat the researchers had ever seen, which was a point in its favour.

This all goes to show what diet can do. Wild boar in the wild may well be lean, foraging about for a low energy diet and using up a lot of energy in doing so, but, transplanted to the softer life of the pampered modern pig, they, too, might become fat. Very fat.

THE CHINESE PIGS

Several types of Chinese pig were imported into Britain in the late 18th century and had a radical effect on some of our native breeds. They brought in squashed ('dished') faces, heavy jowls, black coats, earlier fattening, shorter rounder bodies, shorter legs and short prick ears, and they stamped their mark on the native British pig by setting a trend for the smaller, fatter beast. In particular they shaped the Berkshire, the Small White, the Middle White and the Small Black. And they have not finished with Britain yet. The first of a new wave of Chinese pigs has reached our shores, bringing with them the highest porcine birth rate in the world and expected to revolutionize pork and bacon production in Britain — again, two hundred years after they first did so.

The new breed is the Meishan, and very strange it looks. Its ears are very long and pendulous (rather like a hound's), its face is wrinkled and worried with a big, broad snout, its belly hangs a long way down between short little legs, and the back line seems to run parallel to the curving shape of the stomach. It is said to have litters of twenty or even thirty piglets (average eighteen born, sixteen weaned) which may be due to a higher ovulation rate or, more negatively, a lower rate of embryo losses.

The Chinese pigs are claimed to 'live on rather a little and yet produce and suckle a lot of piglets.' They seem to have other qualities too, in several of the breeds:

★ Very early sexual maturity (60–100 days at first heat)
★ Plenty of teats (16–18)
★ Longer heat periods, and slightly shorter oestrus cycles
★ Docility

Chinese Meishan. (*Farmers Weekly*)

On the other hand, they are also slow growing, with a small mature size and a fat carcase with a low killing-out percentage.

Their gross bellies are ideal for the typical Chinese needs. They can make the best of large amounts of roughage, for which western pigs are simply not designed. The oriental pig chomps its way through quantities of forage and by-products and turns it all into rather fatty meat. Until recently China did not have enough grain for pig-feeding and the pot belly was essential. Not only can the pigs store bulky fibre but they also have the ability to convert it, which western pigs do not.

Prolificacy is the major asset of the new imports from the point of view of the pig breeding companies. Whether or not the capacity for roughage will become valuable in Britain is a thought for the future, but the tendency to fat must be watched.

The pet Vietnamese Pot-bellied might yet find a commercial niche.

10 Sheep

The mountain sheep are sweeter,
But the valley sheep are fatter;
We therefore deemed it meeter
To carry off the latter.

(Thomas Love Peacock, 1785–1866:
The Misfortunes of Elphin,
ch. II: The War — Song of Dinas Vawr)

There are more than thirty-five million sheep and lambs in the UK and there are far more breeds of them in this country than there are of cattle or any other farm animal — sheep for all environments, all uses and all tastes. Long may this variety continue! And it is based on the diversity of Britain's climate and geography. Sheep were strongly identified with the regions that gave them their particular qualities in the first place.

Wool was for several centuries the major product from sheep and the source of much of Britain's wealth. The type of wool reflected the regional environment. Fleece character is affected by the type of grazing, the soil minerals, climate and altitude, and there is a case to be made for keeping breeds in their own region. If they are run in alien environments, their qualities may change, quite possibly for the worse.

Very broadly, colder climates contract the skin's pores and encourage the growth of finer wool which can matt for extra protection against frost, snow and storm. In warmer regions the pores are more open, and the fleece is less weather-resistant. On good pasture the sheep's body bulk and its fleece length both increase, and on poorer grazing the sheep is more lean and its wool is short and fine. In the more extreme climates of the islands and far northern regions a double coat protects the sheep from the weather, with an outer coat shedding the rain and soft inner wool acting as insulation.

The many combinations of climate and grazing in Britain therefore gave a background for many different sheep. Consumer demands also encouraged the development of different qualities. For example, until about the 16th century ewes were customarily milked, making milk yield an important factor. Today ewe-milking is once again being practised commercially and certain breeds are specialists for the job.

STRATIFICATION

Wool governed breed development for a long period but today most of the income from sheep comes from meat — from lamb rather than mutton. The whole British sheep industry is geared to lamb production, and wool is almost a by-product. In the modern stratification system each general type of sheep has a specific role. At the top of the pyramid (and at the top of the hill!) are the hill breeds which provide the industry with draft ewes — sheep with the typically well developed maternal instincts and hardiness of all hill livestock. The hill ewes are not prolific, however: they tend to drop single lambs and average only 100% lambing. They are therefore brought down from the wild heights to the comparatively better environment of the uplands and are crossed to longwool rams to provide halfbred ewes with better prolificacy (140%) and hybrid vigour. The halfbreds come down to the lowland areas for crossing with Down rams to produce lambs for fattening on good pastures.

If the pure hill breeds were to disappear or weaken, the whole structure could collapse: there would be no basic stock for this succession of crossing.

FIGURE A
THE STRATIFICATION SYSTEM FOR BRITISH SHEEP

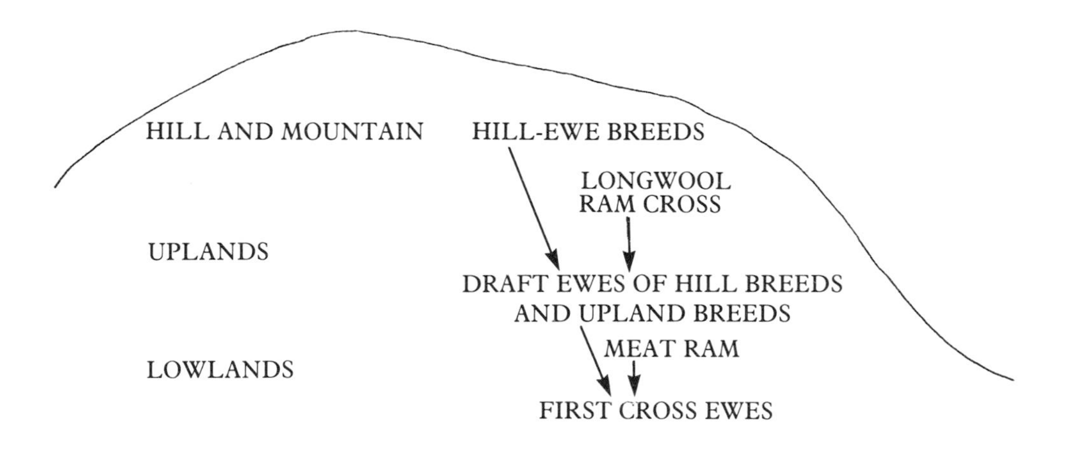

Ovulation rates are governed by environment as much as by breed and the same sheep will have a higher rate in lowland conditions than up on the hills or at more northern latitudes. Lambing seasons also reflect environment: lowland flocks usually lamb January to March but in the most temperate areas lambs can be born as early as November or the beginning of December. Different breeds, too, have different dates for the onset of oestrus activity, which is also affected by feeding, day-length and general management. There is one sheep, the Dorset Horn, which can breed at almost any time of year.

The hill-ewe

Hill flocks fulfil several roles:

- ★ They utilize extensive areas of hill grazing with little or no supplementary feeding.
- ★ From this they produce:
  Store lambs from ewes for three to five crops (castrated male lambs, and ewe lambs excess to replacement requirements).
  Draft ewes — ewes which have already had three to five crops.
  Wool — a more important source of income for the hill flock than for upland and lowland flocks.

The hill-ewe breeder seeks to improve or maintain the qualities of lambing regularity, survival fitness of ewes and lambs, mothering instincts and the ability to keep the lambs growing well, and good fleece weight and quality. For replacement stock, hill breeders should always select from ewes which consistently produce the top weight of lambs.

Several of the minor breeds are hill and mountain sheep but very few are used commercially in the stratification system.

The upland-ewe

Upland flocks produce:

- ★ Significant numbers of breeding females for sale to lowland flocks, either as purebred ewe lambs, 2-tooth ewes or draft ewes, or as first-cross halfbreds.
- ★ Castrated male lambs sold as stores.

The upland-ewe breeder is interested in the same qualities as the hill-ewe breeder, though with less emphasis on wool, and also looks for prolificacy. A high twinning rate is needed to ensure high outputs and to produce a crossbred ewe which will be prolific in lowland conditions. In upland conditions, however, increases in twinning rates add to the risk of lambs dying at birth and the upland breeder therefore selects for well-milking ewes which can drop strong lambs. The lactation needs to be not only high in yield but also continuous over a long period so that lambs are well grown at weaning and make good wethers for finishing elsewhere.

Several minor breeds are upland sheep with good mothering abilities and some are quite prolific.

Longwool rams

The longwools are used to sire crossbred ewe lambs from the hill and upland breeds. The ram contributes increased size, prolificacy and milk yield in those ewe lambs. The breeder looks for high ram fertility, the ability to cover a large number of ewes, high prolificacy transmitted to the progeny, and a good constitution to increase hybrid vigour in the ewe lambs.

There are several longwools among the minor breeds, but one of the reasons that they are minor breeds is that not many rams are needed for the job.

Downland meat rams

Down breed rams are used to put meat into lambs for slaughter. They are put mainly to crossbred ewes from longwool rams but also to all classes of commercial ewes. They dominate the quality and type of carcase of British lambs and the breeder looks for high fertility (to achieve high conception rates in the ewes), good growth rate potential to be passed on to the lambs, and — increasingly important today — a potential for lean carcases.

There are minor breeds which could well be used to some extent in this context, for example the Oxford Down and the Southdown. The Oxford has been studied in comparative trials by the Animal Breeding Research Organization (ABRO); it was one of the larger breeds considered (which meant a very slight increase in lambing problems). The breed was deemed to be suitable, along with the Suffolk, for most systems requiring rapid growth to 40kg (88lb) liveweight, though a Dorset Down was better for early achievement of low liveweights. Oxford and Suffolk cross lambs were heaviest at all ages, and therefore the youngest at slaughter — and this was in comparison to breeds like the Texel, Oldenburg and Ile-de-France. In another test, Southdowns produced lambs with the best conformation while Oxford Downs and Wensleydales produced the heaviest lambs at fat class 3. The Texel, however, was 'way ahead in respect of lean percentage' — a very important point today and one which sheep breeders neglect at their peril. The Wensleydale, incidentally, produced crosses with a lower growth of fat than several of the Down breeds, but in early flocks their crosses had lower rates of lean tissue gain than most other crosses.

PROLIFICACY

As explained in the Breeding chapter, some traits are more highly heritable than others and are therefore worth pursuing in a breeding programme. It is worth the while of those who keep minor breeds to follow Lawrence

Alderson's example and set up group breeding schemes, co-operating with other breeders to improve and sell the sheep. This gives each participant access to more rams and also a wider sample of performance tests on which to base a breeding programme. There is a useful booklet on the subject published by the Meat & Livestock Commission (see Bibliography).

Prolificacy is influenced not only genetically (depending on breed and line) but also by environment, nutrition, season and age. The number of eggs produced at each ovulation usually peaks with the second or third oestrus in the season, so if tupping is timed to coincide with this peak there should be a higher lambing percentage (lambs born). Natural prolificacy tends to increase in a ewe for the first four years and then remains constant for perhaps another four (if her teeth hold out!), so you get more lambs from a more mature ewe.

The body condition of the ewe has an effect on ovulation and on successful lambing. Ewe lambs need to be at an appropriate body weight: for best results they should be at least 60% of their mature weight.

CONDITION SCORING

Condition is assessed by pressing the fingers along the top and sides of the spine around the loin area, just behind the last rib and above the kidneys. You need to assess the sharpness (or roundness) of the vertebrae (the bony bits sticking upwards), the prominence and degree of cover of the bits on each side of the backbone, the extent of muscular and fatty tissues under these sideways projections (how easy is it to pass your fingers under the bones?) and the fullness and fat cover on the eye muscle (press between the upwards and the sideways bits of backbone).

That is all very well for your own purposes, like assessing a ewe's condition for breeding, but if you want to tell someone else about her condition — say a potential purchaser — you need a more precise description than 'quite good'. There is therefore a scale of condition scores ranging from 0 (so emaciated that the animal is dying) to 5 (very fat indeed and no way can you feel any part of the spine anywhere) and this is detailed in the Appendix.

MEAT

The market for lamb carcases is mainly in the weight range of 15–22kg (33–49lb) in Britain, with the heavier carcases usually making lower prices. In Europe they prefer 15–19kg (33–42lb), in the Middle East 12–15kg (26–33lb) and in the Mediterranean countries only 11–13kg

(24–29lb). Nearly all markets require lambs at fat classes 2 and 3L; some sectors of the domestic market will accept class 3H, but class 4 lambs will be rejected by retailers and class 5 have not got a hope. Conformation plays a part too, especially visually, and the ideal lamb to aim for is 15–20kg (33–44lb) carcase weight in MLC fat class 2 or 3L with good to average conformation.

Apart from carcase weight, fatness and conformation, the fourth factor taken into account in sheep carcase classification is the category for variable premium purposes. The whole scheme is outlined in the Appendix.

Talking of fat — a subject which keeps coming up — New Zealand has an answer for the overfat lamb. They have found a way of processing surplus fat (or tallow) from lamb carcases into methyl ester of tallow, which is a very efficient fuel with a higher combustibility than conventional diesel oil. They have estimated that an average lamb could provide up to 2kg (4.4lb) of tallow, which would be converted into 2.95 litres of the new fuel for blending in with ordinary diesel used in engines. New Zealand, which has seventy million sheep and only three million people, could produce enough lamb fuel to meet up to 10% of the country's diesel requirements. The stuff is also very efficient, and has a higher combustibility than ordinary diesel oil.

So do not despair if your breed is one of those which is a little too fatty for today's tastes. It may become very valuable when the oil wells dry up.

Some of the minor breeds are beginning to do well on the meat market, thanks largely to the efforts of a few imaginative and determined individuals. For example, the Black Welsh Mountain breed has managed to take itself out of the rare section by identifying a market and getting out there to sell. Breeders looked closely at the sheep, worked out that it had three growth periods (quickly initially, then muscling out, then putting on fat) and selected the prime moment for slaughter at maximum meat but before the fat began to accumulate. They went further than simply selling lambs: they hung the meat, blast-froze it and then packaged the popular small joints in film-wrapping and in smart boxes which caught the eye of the consumer and let them know what they were eating — that is, 'brand identification'. They also found an outlet for older ewes which are converted into smoked meats, salamis and pâté. A specialist butcher in London found that customers very much appreciated Soay lamb but the problem was the iregularity of supply of fresh meat. Several restaurants have specialized in rare breed lamb: the joints of the primitives, for example, are small and convenient and the meat does have a different flavour (a bit stronger, so it needs to be cooked gently) and it is quite often much leaner than commercial breeds.

It all goes back to the old question of marketing: find a market for your product, create a regular supply and go out and sell it for all you are worth, and professionally.

WOOL

The main technicalities about wool have already been discussed. Many of the minor breeds of sheep have an interesting range of fleece colours, notably among the primitives and among breeds which have not been subjected to the degree of improvement suffered by some of the lowland sheep. For several centuries there has been a prejudice in favour of white wool, because it can take dyes, and most of the major breeds have been selectively bred for white fleeces.

The coloured sheep of Britain include:

Black Welsh Mountain
Castlemilk Moorit
Coloured longwool breeds
Hebridean
Herdwick
Jacob
Manx Loghtan
North Ronaldsay
Shetland
Soay
Torddu, Torwen and Baalwen

If you decide to breed selectively for colour, make sure that you do not at the same time overlook other qualities. It may be tempting to use a ram because of his colour potential, forgiving any other faults he may have, but you will be perpetuating the faults as well as the colour. Quite apart from general hardiness, prolificacy and so on, you also want quality and quantity of fleece.

MILK

Sheep dairying is a growth industry in Britain but, as it is a new one (albeit resuscitated), its products require energetic marketing. The British are no longer used to sheep's milk, though in medieval times substantial ewe flocks were kept. For example, in 1322 six thousand ewes were milked on the Canterbury Cathedral estates.

The essentials in a good dairy sheep are milk yield (high totals, regular production and long lactation), milk quality, good parlour temperament, and a sound *accessible* udder. In the latter respect, long-legged sheep have the advantage and woolly-udder ewes are avoided. Short tails and clipping aid hygiene and access to the udder, and the naturally bare (though long) tail of the Friesland is a useful asset.

The main breeds currently used in commercial British sheep-milking flocks are probably the British (or East) Friesland and the British Milksheep. Prolific breeds like the Lleyn and the Llanwenog are potentially interesting and there are also several Continental breeds which are traditional dairy animals. New hybrids are getting a look-in too: the Colburn family, who created the Colbred (which is 25% Friesland) have been trying out their breed in the parlour, for example. The ewes suckle lambs to about six weeks and are then machine milked for fourteen or fifteen weeks, twice a day at first and then once a day. Yields in the Colbreds vary widely between individuals, from perhaps seventy to a hundred gallons (320–450 litres) per ewe in the parlour-milking stage of the lactation. Most of the Colbred milk is used for yoghurt and some for cheese-making.

British Milksheep.

Sheep cheeses cover a wide range of types. They can be soft, fresh (harder than a cream cheese), pickled (feta), hard or very hard, and they tend to taste stronger as they age. The milk, and thus the cheese, contains little carotene and is noticeably white. The original Wensleydale, incidentally, was made from sheep's milk.

Sheep's milk is slightly sweeter and has a much higher butterfat content than cows' milk — typically 6–7% (the ewes of Roquefort do even better at 8% but to make Roquefort cheese you also need the caves for curing it in). The fat is naturally homogenized and easily digested. The milk also has more protein, vitamins and minerals than either cows' or goats' milk and the curd retains a high proportion of protein, fat, calcium and vitamin A, though lactose and vitamin B tend to drain off with the whey.

Like goats, sheep are mainly seasonal milk producers which might lead to marketing problems but, unlike cows' milk, sheep's milk can be frozen — a distinct advantage. Some breeds, including the Dorset Horn and the Friesland, can breed out of season to give better continuity of fresh supplies.

Hand-milking sheep is a little more difficult than hand-milking cows or goats: the teats are shorter, for a start. In the old days ewes were milked from behind (goodness knows what went into the pail besides the milk to flavour the cheese!) or the milker stood astride the sheep facing its rear. It would be easier to adapt a goat-milking arrangement, with the ewe standing on a platform. In the 1940s a Breconshire farmer used a ladder to yoke his milk-sheep in the parlour.

Commercial dairy flocks are milked by machine and special units for ewes are manufactured by the major milk-machinery companies, who have experience of large Mediterranean milking flocks.

It is quite simple to adapt portable milking machines for sheep, and a small sheep-milking enterprise is an excellent first step on the farming ladder. For a start, capital investment is much lower than for dairy cows: you could buy quite a few ewes for the price of one cow, and other overheads, such as buildings and equipment, are proportionately cheaper. You can begin on a small scale with a handful of ewes (not necessarily dairy breeds) and expand the flock when expertise and opportunity permit. Most ewes will soon become accustomed to the parlour (especially the greedy ones) if they are handled quietly like first-time heifers and they have the advantage of being small enough to be handled into position if necessary — not so easy with a cow!

As with other enterprises, success in a small sheep-milking unit depends on finding and exploiting a market for the product and supplying it consistently, whether it is fresh or frozen milk or curd to retail outlets or to processors, or your own yoghurts, flavoured cheeses and other specialities.

Trials run by the Agricultural Development Advisory Service (ADAS) in the south-west, based on milk-breed ewes suckling lambs to five weeks and then yielding 350kg (770lb) milk to the machines, indicate the possibility of very healthy gross margins per ewe as long as there remains a good market for dairy ewe lambs and a well developed market for the milk products. In Cornwall an enterprising British Milksheep farmer has located his markets so successfully that he buys a substantial volume of sheep's milk from other producers to fulfil his customers' requirements.

THE BREEDS

Each breed is described in the following pages and average BWMB figures for staple length, fleece weight and Bradford Count numbers are shown within square brackets. Remember that the Board's assessment of breed fleeces quite often fails to correspond with those of breeders and breed societies.

As with cattle, RBST census figures (where shown) reflect the number of females used for pure-breeding but figures from other sources usually include all registered females, whether used in pure-breeding or in cross-breeding.

★ ★ ★ ★ ★

BLACK WELSH MOUNTAIN

Black fleece. Black face and legs. Rams horned.

This is *the* black sheep — black all over with a blue skin and quite unmistakable. The rams have bold horns in an open curve. The breed developed by selection of black lambs from Welsh Mountain flocks and they now breed true, the black colour gene being dominant.

They are very hardy and self-reliant, and are claimed to be resistant to fly attack and to have generally sound feet (a feature of many mountain and primitive breeds). The sheep are good scavengers and are useful for land reclamation as well as being decorative. On lowland grazing, of course, they grow bigger and develop more of a fleece.

The ewes make excellent mothers, rarely having any lambing problems at all and giving plenty of milk. They are reasonably prolific, often producing twins, and tend to lamb in February and March. The lambs are fast on to their feet, quick to suckle, vigorous and resilient, and they grow fast, finishing on average at 14–18kg (31–40lb) carcase weight. The meat is sweet, well flavoured and close-grained with a good colour and a good ratio of meat to bone. In medieval times Black Welsh mutton was renowned for its richness, but the lambs tend to become fat if left too long.

The fleece is black (with a reddish tinge in winter), thick, firm and short. It is used undyed for durable, light, warm clothes and combines with quality white wools for checked tweeds. [8–10cm, 1.25–1.5kg, 48s–56s.] Cured sheepskins are used as rugs. The black wool was known as *cochduu* (reddish brown) in the Middle Ages and was as famous as the mutton.

The Black Welsh is a sheep of character, very active, full of curiosity, a good leaper and excellent at escaping: rams in particular spend plenty of time on the other side of the fence. Once classified as a rare breed, the Black Welsh is now widespread and thriving and has the support of some enthusiastic and professional breeders who recognize its qualities and make sure that the world knows about their breed.

Black Welsh Mountain.

BORERAY

Cream or grey fleece. Rams and ewes horned. RBST status: feral.

The Boreray is a small feral sheep found mainly on the island of its name,

Boreray. (*RBST*)

in the St Kilda group, where the flock probably numbers more than four hundred breeding females. Its fleece is mainly grey or creamy and is shed naturally in July. The face and legs are mostly grey and white or black and white; the legs are quite long and the tail short. An adult ewe stands about 55cm (22in) at the withers and weighs around 28kg (62lb). Both sexes are horned, the ram having typically extravagant spirals. There is something about the shape and stance of the ram that is instantly recognizable: he looks as if he is about to spring into the air on all fours like a lamb.

The breed originated from a mixture of Scottish Blackface and a Hebridean variety of the Scottish Dunface during the late 19th century.

BRITISH FRIESLAND

White fleece. White face, pink lips and nostrils. Polled. Dairy sheep.

The Friesland is a large-framed dairy sheep with a narrow head, fine-boned limbs and a characteristic long, bald tail. The face is white and the long ears are held horizontally. It is native to Dutch East Friesland and has recently become quite widely established in Britain in commercial dairy flocks for the production of cheeses and yoghurts.

It is a prolific and precocious breed and ewe lambs can be mated in their first year. Having always been a dairy animal, it is docile and quiet to handle but somewhat greedy. The milk yield is substantial: properly managed, the ewe can maintain a very even yield until the autumn and can give as much as 400–450 litres (88–100 gallons) a lactation, though the average is somewhat lower.

The ewe has a large, roomy pelvis and lambs easily, with an average lambing rate of 230% (Frieslands cannot be registered unless they have at least twins). However, ewes which are pushed too hard for productivity may be rather short-lived. The breed is generally less hardy than other sheep: it is used to a degree of cosseting as a dairy animal and its feet tend to be on the soft side. Mastitis can also be a problem.

The ram is useful for crossing to improve prolificacy in crossbred ewes and for fat lamb production. Rams are eager to work and, like the ewes, precocious. The ewes make useful crossbred dams from various hill and lowland breeds. The meat is lean, whether purebred or crossbred, and (like dairy cattle) the fat is deposited internally rather than in the carcase. However, purebred carcase lambs are often difficult to finish; indeed some people despair of them and find that they get a far better return from milking their ewes right through the lactation.

The fleece is clean and white, with no kemp. [10-15cm, 4-6kg, 52s–54s.]

BRITISH MILKSHEEP

White fleece. Clean white face and legs. Polled. High milk yield and prolificacy.

This medium to large sheep was specifically bred by Lawrence Alderson for prolificacy plus high milk yields to raise the extra lambs. It was influenced mainly by the East Friesland, the Blue-faced Leicester and the Dorset Horn/Polled Dorset, with minor contributions from the Prolific and the Lleyn. Although a new breed, it is by no means rare: about three thousand ewes are mated to British Milksheep rams. Apart from the breed's innate qualities, its success is also due to a uniquely comprehensive recording system — every animal's performance is recorded, collated and centrally analysed. This practice not only supplies interested farmers with solid facts about the breed but also identifies superior breeding stock.

The sheep are noted for a quiet temperament but they are also robust, active and long-lived. The ewes are precocious and breed readily in their first year, and the ram has good libido. Ewes have roomy pelvises; they lamb easily and quadruplets are quite common.

The udder is well shaped and parlour yields average 100 gallons (450 litres) over a 210-day lactation — adequate for raising triplets with a growth rate of 0.33kg (0.72lb) per lamb per day.

The breed is mainly used as a dairy animal or as a sire for high-performance crossbred daughters. In particular the ram is a useful sire on hill breeds (for productive halfbred ewes), low-performance longwools (for more productive ewes adapted to the native area), Dorset Horns or Polled Dorsets (for high productivity and out-of-season lambing) and lowland flocks (for homebred replacements and increased productivity). The average lambing rate for purebred ewes is 298%, and 195–245% reared for crossbred ewes.

Carcases are lean and can be taken to heavy weights without becoming overfat. For example, British Milksheep ewes put to Suffolk and Down rams can produce 86.6% of lambs in the top grades (classes 2 and 3L). The lambs are good for large, boneless joints.

The heavy fleece of demilustre wool has a long staple [10–15cm, 2–3kg, 50s–54s]. The breed society suggests that the BWMB fleece-weight figures are much too low and that a more realistic average is 5–6kg.

CASTLEMILK MOORIT

Moorit fleece. Ram and ewe horned. RBST status: critical.

The Castlemilk is a long-legged, short-tailed sheep with a moorit or light tan fleece and white underparts. Rams and ewes are horned.

The breed was developed by the late Sir Jock Buchanan-Jardine to grace the park of Castlemilk, Dumfriesshire, and came from a combination of Shetland, Soay and Manx Loghtan, with perhaps a touch of other breeds as well. The dwindling flock was dispersed in 1970, when Joe Henson spotted an advertisement in *Farmers Weekly* for some 'moorit Shetlands'. On examination, they were not remotely like Shetlands: they were the colour of blonde Soays with a very distinct *mouflon* pattern and flashing white rumps. The ewes had fine up-and-outward curving horns and the rams (about the size of a large Manx) had heavy outward spiralling horns. Henson bought six ewes and a ram; four other ewes were bought by Lindsay Wallace (now chairman of the breed society) but the rest of the small herd was slaughtered. However, the breed is now dispersed in several flocks in the UK.

It is a decorative breed. Its short, tight, kemp-free fleece is chocolate-brown underneath and pale fawn on top, and is much appreciated by

Castlemilk Moorits.

hand-spinners. It was originally used to make the Buchanan-Jardines' family tweed.

The sheep are hardy and self-reliant, and they react well to quiet handling. The ewes are good protective mothers, producing singles, twins and, occasionally, triplets and giving plenty of milk. The wethers make tender, fat-free meat which tastes more like venison than mutton.

The breed was accepted in the RBST lists in 1983 and given a Priority 1 rating. The 1985/6 census recorded ninety-five breeding females.

COTSWOLD

White. Longwool. Polled. Forelock. Heavy lamb. RBST status: rare.

The Cotswold is the classic heavy-clip longwool type of sheep that made medieval England prosperous. Big, handsome and graceful, it has a white face with a typical shaggy forelock hanging over its forehead. The nostrils and upper lip are dark. Good, strong, wideset legs support a heavy, broad-backed and capacious body.

Since the 18th century, Leicester blood has been used to boost the size

Cotswold. (*RBST*)

of the Cotswold and increase its ability to convert forage into flesh and to grow quickly.

It is a hardy and consistent breed with high growth rates and, despite its size, it can tolerate high stocking densities and can be confined to its field with quite low stone walls. But it is big and heavy for turning at shearing time and its handler needs to be strong.

The ewes are good, milky mothers, normally docile but very protective against predators. They can give too much milk for a single lamb and may need hand-milking. Lambing rates are 150% to 175% and the ewe crosses well with a Down ram for rapid growth rates, good conformation and lean carcases; lambs are marketed at anything from 16 to 23kg (35–51lb) dressed carcase weight. The Cotswold has potential future use for heavy lamb production; overheads on the breed are low and lambs could be kept on for an extra three months without adding to rearing costs. The present demand is for smaller carcases but the heavy lamb could be used for boned and rolled meats and it is ideal for large, lean lambs grading at 18kg (40lb) or more. It was never appreciated as a mutton sheep except at a very early age.

The fleece weighs up to 7.5kg (16.5lb) on the ewe and 9kg (19.8lb) on the ram, averaging 5 or 6kg. [15–25cm, 4–7kg, 38s–48s.] The wool should be kept away from the eyes.

Numbers are now increasing after a low point since the war, and the 1985/6 RBST census recorded 461 breeding ewes.

THE DEVON BREEDS

There are several breeds which are common in the south-west of England but rarely seen elsewhere. One or two of them are so low in numbers that they may soon acquire rare-breed status. For example, the 1985/6 RBST census recorded only 852 pure-beeding Dartmoor ewes — a huge drop from 2,350 in 1975.

Dartmoor. (*Farmers Weekly*)

Dartmoor

A very hardy longwool which can tough it out through the harshest moorland winter. It is well woolled all over, including legs and face. What you can see of the face is white with black or grey mottling and it is sometimes called the Grey-Faced Dartmoor. Its long, curly, lustrous fleece is used for carpets and woollen cloths or shorn as lambswool. [15–20cm, 6.5–8kg, 36s–40s.] It is a solid looking sheep; the rams are very occasionally horned and the ewes are heavy milkers and good for crossing to meat sires for early fat lambs with lean and juicy meat. Lambing rates are about 140% and the carcase deadweights are 20–22kg (44–48lb) at twelve to fourteen weeks and 27–29kg (60–64lb) at eight to nine months old. The breed can thrive almost anywhere.

There is also a White Face Dartmoor, with nearly 900 females registered annually, and it is usually found on meagre pasture up to 2,000 feet above sea-level. It used to be a horned breed but horns are not so common now. Its white face and legs are clean, in contrast to the woolly look of the Grey-Faced, and it has black nostrils and lips which give it a smudgy look. It is broadly built and its white fleece has a fairly strong crimp. [15–20cm, 5.5–7kg, 36s–40s.] A record fleece weighed 21kg (46lb).

Devon Closewool
Originally a Devon Longwool × Exmoor Horn, the Closewool has a dense, protective fleece which often contains some kemp. Its white face and legs are covered with very short wool and it has a generally stout appearance. It is a hardy grassland sheep, able to live on grass all year round. There are no horns.

Devon and Cornwall Longwool
The Longwool looks very similar to the Dartmoor and is an amalgamation of the big South Devon (or South Dum) with the northern Devon Longwool. Both had quite a bit of Leicester Longwool in them. It has a heavy, lustrous fleece which often looks reddish, but that is only superficial colouring from the red soil of Devon! It is a very docile breed, and an easy grazer. Crossed to a Down ram it produces early fat lamb, or with a Dorset Horn the crossbreds can lamb out of season. Purebred lambs are finished on fodder crops to meet the late winter market. Its breed society has seventy-five members, and there are more than six thousand feeding ewes.

Exmoor Horn
This hill breed is almost as old as the moor itself. It is a strong, chubby looking sheep which does well on moorland grazing and produces fine quality wool. Unlike most hill sheep, it is quite easy to contain and handle, and it is also more prolific than other breeds.

DORSET DOWN

White fleece. Greyish brown face and legs with wool. Polled. Early maturing lamb.

The Dorset Down is a well travelled breed which can be found in some numbers in New Zealand especially with the increasing demand for lean meat. It is also in Australia, Argentina and many other countries.

It is really a local variety of the Hampshire Down but a separate breed society was formed in 1904 when the type had been established for about eighty years after being developed from crosses of Southdown rams on Berkshire, Hampshire or Wiltshire ewes. By 1985 there were over six thousand sheep registered in ninety flocks.

The face, ears and legs are a greyish brown and grow short wool. It is never horned. The ewe seems to be willing to take the ram in most months of the year (something in the water in Dorset!) and the lambs produce good traditional carcases. Singles are up to 18kg (40lb) dressed carcase weight at ten to twelve weeks, and twins reach the same weights at twelve to fourteen weeks. Essentially a mutton type of sheep, the Dorset Down matures very early and the lamb carcase is lean. Average carcases are 17–19kg (37–42lb) in classes 2 and 3L.

In New Zealand the ram is an ideal sire for the production of prime export lamb. Rams show great virility and can cover a greater than average number of ewes in a season (quite happy to cover twenty ewes in twenty-four hours) and they remain active for a number of years.

The fleece is springy and of good quality. [5–8cm, 2.75–3kg, 56s–58s.] It is used for hosiery and fine knitting wools and is often blended with other wools to add elasticity to a material.

DORSET HORN AND POLLED DORSET

White fleece. White face and legs, woolled. Pink nostrils. Horned or polled in both sexes.

(See front cover for photograph.) By no means a minor breed, the Dorset Horn is included here for its unique ability to breed at any time of year. It has white woolled legs and face, and pink nostrils and lips.

Both sexes in the original breed have heavy, spiralled horns. The breed goes back a long way in the history of Dorchester and its fecundity was noted even in the 17th century. The polled factor was introduced through Ryeland and Corriedale crosses, and both the Horned and the Polled Dorsets have done very well indeed in New Zealand and Australia, though the Horned is fast decreasing as the Polled gains favour. Between them the Dorsets produce 75% of all Australia's prime lamb.

Both types are used to breed an extended oestrus into crossbred ewes and to achieve more frequent lambings in a flock (e.g. three crops in two years). Although in theory breeding all year round, the ewes seem least likely to accept the ram during March and April in the UK. Some ewes require assistance at lambing, particularly first-lamb hoggets.

It should be noted that the Dorset is a lowland breed and it is not suited to limited grazing on hill farms.

HEBRIDEAN

Black or dark brown fleece. Black face and legs, clean. Small. Multi-horned in both sexes. RBST status: above numerical guidelines.

Hebridean.

This is one of the multi-horned British breeds — both sexes can have up to six horns. It is a small, yellow-eyed sheep with black, clean face and legs, and its fleece is dark brown or black, often streaked with silver as it ages. It used to be quite common throughout Scotland and the islands until the Blackface came along. Now it can be found decorating parkland and smallholdings in several parts of the UK. The 1985/6 census recorded 653 breeding ewes.

There has been a flock of 'St Kilda sheep' (as the breed was once known) at Weston Park, on the borders of Shropshire and Staffordshire, for more than a century and the estate's gamekeepers used to wear suits made of cloth woven from the flock's undyed wool. Over the years at Weston brown-fleeced animals were culled, and so was the occasional individual with the odd white spot on the head or chest. It is a well-bred flock; problems like the split eyelids sometimes found in multi-horned breeds have been carefully bred to a minimum, and two-horned tups are introduced now and then to keep the flock's horns strong and firm as well as to minimize the possibility of split eyelids (which are more frequently seen in four-horned animals).

Dorset Horn tups have been used on Weston's poorer ewes for lambs gradable straight off grass. Lambing problems are very rare and it seems that no ewe or tup has ever died of illness on the estate. They live and breed to a ripe old age and make an excellent job of clearing coarse growth in the park, choosing it in preference to finer grasses, to the benefit of more choosy modern breeds. There is a role for the Hebridean as a pasture improver.

In common with other primitive breeds the Hebridean can make commercial sense if the ewe is crossed to a meat breed. They lamb very easily on most crosses, including the Suffolk, but the Cheviot might be a bit big-headed for them. Longwool rams have also been used successfully. The crossbred lambs will be reasonably large and will finish, and the various possibilities for using primitive-breed ewes in crossing programmes are currently being investigated, tested and recorded. So far the hypothetical gross margins look encouraging: for a start veterinary and forage costs are likely to be lower than for standard halfbreds like the Mule.

Greek restaurants like the light, lean lamb of the purebred multihorn sheep.

Hebridean fleeces are popular with hand-spinners, and this market is being tapped by the Hebridean Workshop. A mature animal yields about 1.5kg (3lb) wool. [5–15cm, 1.5–2.25kg, 48s–50s.]

It is a nice little sheep (a fullgrown ewe weighs about 40kg or 85lb), always appreciated in the farm parks and beginning to find a place in the commercial world as well.

HERDWICK

Fleece various shades of grey. White or grey face and legs with short hair. Arched nose. Ram horned.

Herdwicks.

There is something distinctly Scandinavian about the stocky, shaggy Herdwick — a sheep that could be mistaken for an Old English sheepdog from the rear. It has just that colouring, texture of coat and general stance. At the front end, however, there is a very pale grey 'rimy' (frosted) face with something of a roman nose, a bold eye, and in the rams a thick, leonine mane and a good pair of creamy horns curling around the ears. It is a breed apart, a breed untouched by time and fashion and with no obvious affinity with any other sheep in Britain.

It is very much a sheep of rugged country, blending with the colour of rocks and dry-stone walls, at home up on the Cumbrian fells. They say that God made the Herdwick specially for the Lakeland Fells, and it is the only sheep that could possibly survive in the sort of weather the Lake District can provide. In such conditions it can raise its single lamb, but given better circumstances on good land it can produce twins or even triplets. There may be as many as a hundred thousand Herdwicks scattered around the UK — hardly a minor breed, then, but an interesting and unique one.

The wool of the lamb is a very dark brown, almost black. As the animal matures the fleece becomes a lighter brown and gradually grows more fawny and grey. The adult is usually a grey sheep and turns almost white with age. The fleece is strong and kempy, admirably resilient to the very wet fell climate and protective against blizzard and snowdrift. Because of its coarseness and inability to take dye it is used largely for carpets, and Beatrix Potter (who bred Herdwicks at Troutbeck Park near Windermere) once forlornly forecast that the breed would soon disappear because someone had invented linoleum. She was very wrong and recently ways have been found of spinning Herdwick wool suitable for tweed and naturally-coloured chunky Lakeland sweaters. The average fleece weight of the ewe is 2kg (4.5lb) and the ram can carry as much as 5kg (11lb). [15–20cm, 1.5–2kg, coarse quality.] Fleeces should be rolled fleece out. A Herdwick ram on a Wensleydale could make an interesting fleece.

The colour genetics of the Herdwick have been studied by Dr Marca Burns, BSc, and prove to be quite complicated (see *The Ark*, September 1985).

It is a tough breed, the hardiest in the country, and it lives to a ripe old age. A Matterdale ewe had thirty-three lambs (all lived) before she died at the age of eighteen.

The Herdwick is not eaten as lamb. It is slaughtered as a two-year-old wether, at an average of 20–22kg (44–48lb) dressed carcase (up to 36kg/80lb on good land), and produces a mutton with real flavour, good enough to take its place at the Coronation feast of Her Majesty Queen Elizabeth II. But a Herdwick crossed with a Longwool ram can produce a useful quick-growing lamb for breeding or feeding. It does best to a Leicester. With a Wensleydale the lamb is longer backed but slower to mature, and crosses to Down breeds are not always successful.

There is a drawback to this admirable sheep: it has a powerful homing instinct. Traditionally, and given the chance, it remains within a few hundred yards of its birthplace for the rest of its life. You do not sell a flock of Herdwicks to another farm: you sell the farm and the Herdwicks stay put.

JACOB

Creamy white fleece with dark patches. Multi-horned in both sexes.

The Jacob is unmistakable, with its creamy white fleece splattered with very dark brown patches, and its headful of horns — sometimes two, sometimes four, in both sexes. It is also a big success. A few years ago it was an unusual breed but it has been improved by selection and is now widespread and popular, its numbers increasing all the time, largely thanks to the efforts of a handful of people who recognized that it had more to offer than mere park prettiness.

The variation of natural colours in the wool is attractive to the home-spinners and with good marketing ready-made Jacob products sell well and widely. The Wool Marketing Board has two special grades for Jacob fleeces. [8–17cm, 2–2.5kg, 44s–56s.]

Wool is not the only crop from a Jacob. Commercial farmers are putting Jacob rams over ewe hoggs for a 'catch crop' before they enter the regular breeding flock. Using a Jacob rather a Suffolk avoids possible lambing problems in the young ewes, because the lambs will be slightly smaller and have narrower heads for easier births. They also have a much stronger will to live than some other crosses, and they fatten well and grade easily. Jacob cross lambs are always born black except in a Dorset Horn cross, which will retain the typical Jacob spots.

The ewes are prolific, with enough milk to raise more than twins. The lamb is slow to mature but lean and tender and has a distinctive sweet flavour. The ideal deadweight is 15–17kg (32–37lb); above that there is a tendency to become fat.

A word of warning to those who are considering running a few Jacobs in

Jacob.

the orchard to keep the grass down: they do enjoy browsing as well as grazing and they might ringbark your apple trees. And a word of advice about horns: if they begin to grow awkwardly, they can be wrapped in boiled swede or turnip and gently eased away from the face.

The Jacob is not quite the sheep it used to be. It went through a phase of show-ring mania, when looks were more important than intrinsic merit, and over the years of improvement it has grown and become heavier than it was. Its wool quality has changed, and it does not lamb quite as easily as it did. It is a changing breed — improving in some ways, no doubt, but different. And succeeding.

LEICESTER AND LINCOLN LONGWOOLS

Long lustrous white fleece. White legs and face. Polled. RBST status: Leicester, critical; Lincoln, vulnerable

Lincoln Longwools. (*Lincoln Longwool Breed Society*)

Leicester Longwools are unmistakable, except that they look very like Lincoln Longwools — long corded coats like a Komondor sheepdog, forelock fringe over the eyes, a white face and white legs. The main difference between the two breeds is that the Leicester has clean legs, whereas the Lincoln's are woolled. The Lincoln is the bigger of the two, with a bolder head, and holds the record for weight and staple of fleece (over 20kg/144lb on one ram and a staple of 81cm/32in on a yearling ewe in full fleece).

All the longwools are fairly similar in appearance — the Cotswold, the Devon, the Kent and the Wensleydale as well as the Leicester and the Lincoln. They are all big breeds; they all produce lean meat and heavy wool clips; they are nearly all very hardy. Their ancestries are tangled together here and there — the original Lincoln was one of the oldest native breeds but it was the old Leicester which Robert Bakewell decided to improve and turn into the Dishley Leicester, which was then crossed with the Cotswold, the old Lincoln, the old Bampton Devon, the South Devon, the Scottish Border (creating the Border Leicester), and the old Mug or Teeswater (to begin the Wensleydale). It also found its way into the Ile-de-France and the Lleyn.

The Leicester and the Lincoln both had a large influence on 19th-century New Zealand sheep. Lincoln rams on Merino ewes produced crossbreds which were then backcrossed to make 'three-quarter breds' and later were used for breeding halfbreds and for evolving the Corriedale — with the help of the Leicester which at one stage was the second most numerous breed in that country. After a decline, both breeds are now gaining in strength again, especially as crossing sires for fat lambs and for crossing with Romneys to produce breeding ewes as suitable mothers for prime New Zealand lamb. In 1985 there were eleven new Lincoln flocks, bring the total up to thirty-seven flocks, and one new Leicester flock (total thirty-four) in which there were 2,496 and 2,916 breeding ewes respectively.

The Lincoln has also found friends in South America, Romania, Czechoslovakia, Russia and China, and the latter is still a very good customer.

In 1984 there were only 549 breeding Leicester females in this country and only three flocks had as many as fifty ewes. By 1986 the ewes were reduced to 403. In 1986 there were thirty-five flocks of Lincolns in the UK, including 747 ewes.

Wool was so much the *raison d'être* of the longwools that other qualities possibly deteriorated. The immense fleeces needed large frames to carry them, and prolificacy began to suffer. But a longwool ram on a good maternal breed produces meaty lambs and there may be a case for creating a 'New Longwool' with just such a combination. The fleece will probably suffer, but the breeds might do better in the long run. On the other hand, maybe wool production will be valuable again in the future.

The wool of the Leicester, for example, has recently found a market in Japan, where it is combined with other ingredients to produce a mohair blend. Quality Lincoln wool and skins find a small market. Silver longwools are also finding markets; the fleece colour is typically dark grey on the head, shoulders and back, gradually shading to pale silver on the flanks and rump. These silver greys have a metallic sheen and are found in purebred sheep. As the gene for the colour is recessive, two silvers will always make a silver. 'Black' longwools can arise from a cross with a Jacob or Black Welsh Mountain but the colour is really a uniform dark brown.

The Black Welsh Mountain cross to a Lincoln ram also produces crossbreds with prolificacy, ease of lambing, good carcases — and the Black Welsh's total disregard for boundary fences. A Shropshire breeder used the cross to produce triplets weighing 13kg (28.5lb) and all three were safely reared by the Black Welsh mother.

At present, though, the main commercial use for Leicesters is in producing heavyweight lambs fattened on root crops to eight to eleven months, while the Lincoln sires heavyweight lambs too but not always successfully —lean carcases but too much bone and too much weight in the forequarters, and disappointing growth rates.

The longwools, particularly the Leicester and the Wensleydale, seem to have low tolerance to rainfall: they can take dry cold climates but are very susceptible to prolonged wet and and cold weather.

A Leicester ram and ewe were Interbreed Champions at the Royal Show in July, 1986.

LLANWENOG

White fleece. Black face with tuft of wool on forehead. Clean black legs. Polled.

The docile Llanwenog is a black-faced sheep from West Wales. It has a characteristic little tuft of white wool on its forehead but otherwise it has the look of a finer-boned Shropshire about it — which is because the Llanwenog is based on a fairly varied type of local black-faced hill sheep crossed with Shropshires towards the end of the 19th century. The Shropshire gave the native flocks clean faces, improved prolificacy and earlier maturing lambs.

Today's Llanwenog wins prizes for lambing rates well above 200%. A ewe in the Tiverton area recently crowned her career by producing quads on her twelfth lambing: she has had thirty-eight lambs in eleven years.

Now classified as a semi-lowland breed (they are hardy enough to thrive at up to a thousand feet above sea-level), they can be heavily stocked and are good foragers. They cross well, particularly to Down rams which can produce lamb carcases of 16–18kg (35–40lb) dressed carcase weight at twelve to sixteen weeks old.

The fleece is of high quality, with a soft handle. [6–10cm, 2–2.5kg, 56s–58s.]

LLEYN

White fleece. Clean white legs and face. Black nose.

This white-faced medium-sized lowland breed from North Wales dwindled to very low numbers after the war and by the mid sixties there were barely a dozen of them left. Since then it has made a vigorous and impressive comeback: locally it is numerous and well established again, and it is spreading to England and Scotland. The success is due partly to the great efforts of a few far-sighted breeders and partly to the intrinsic merits of the sheep.

Lleyn.(*RBST*)

The Lleyn is very prolific, very milky and precocious, and all these qualities have been encouraged and increased by careful breeding in recent years. It is also a hardy, healthy breed, easy to look after and handle, and rarely giving any problems at lambing. Twins are normal, triplets common, and quads or quins are not unknown. The new lambs are well woolled and are quick on their feet; the ewe has ample milk for them and they produce good lean carcases. They can be slaughtered at 14–20kg (31–44lb) without being too fat.

The fleece is of good quality. [8–12cm, 2–3kg, 50s–54s.] It is an attractive looking sheep, its warm white colouring set off by black nostrils and bright eyes. In the old days the ewes were often milked for cheese-making and with the recent growth of interest in sheep milking some people are looking to the Lleyn.

The Lleyn's continuing success is a credit to its active and sensible breed society. There is a Group Breeding Scheme, New Zealand-style, which will make the breed even better without losing its breed type. The society began in 1970 with only thirteen members and by 1985 the number of registered flocks had risen to 231 — most of them in Wales but more than seventy in England. The Wool Marketing Board includes the Lleyn as one of the country's 'Main Breeds': how is that for an accolade to a breed which was almost down to single figures twenty years ago?

MANX LOGHTAN

Brown fleece, face and legs. Multi-horned, both sexes. RBST status: rare.

Colour apart, the small multi-horned Manx Loghtan might be confused with the Hebridean. However, the Manx is not so dark — it is much browner. Its clean, goaty face and legs can be any shade from fawn to dark brown. Its name comes from the Manx words *lugh*, meaning 'mouse', and *dhoan*, meaning 'brown'. The fleece is moorit, that reddish or chocolate-brown seen also in some Shetlands and the Castlemilk, and it is popular for hand-spinning, knitting wools and tweeds. [7–10cm, 1.5–2kg, 48s–50s.]

Most of the Loghtans have four horns, though some have two and a few have six. Like other multi-horn breeds, it can develop split eyelids, but whereas the other breeds are very susceptible to New Forest eye disease the feral Loghtans on Man do not suffer from that unpleasant infection.

Along with the Hebridean and the Shetland, the Loghtan is a potential maternal breed for commercial use. Most of the primitive sheep have good pelvic ratios for easy lambing and can take a cross with meatier ram breeds as long as the latter are not excessively broad in head and shoulders. The Loghtan averages about 150% lambing rates on good land and its

Manx Loghtan. (*N.F. Stone*)

crossbred progeny show excellent hybrid vigour. Purebred lambs produce a lean carcase of well flavoured meat.

The little brown sheep is a good mother, hardy and thrifty, agile and intelligent. The breed's feet are very sound and footrot is not a problem (a claim made for several primitive and mountain breeds but not always substantiated). However this situation could deteriorate after a few generations of soft living on better land, conditions in which they grow to a considerably greater size (about 40kg or 90lbs for a mature ewe) than they do on the poorer hill land on the islands (average 9kg/20lb deadweight in the 19th century). They are also virtually immune to fly, and their tails can be left at their natural hock length.

Four horns have generally been favoured in the past and can be very eye-catching but perhaps two horns are more practical and selection can be made accordingly.

The 1985/6 RBST census recorded 440 breeding females.

NEW NORFOLK HORN

White fleece. Clean black face and legs. Spiral horns, both sexes. RBST status: critical.

There was an ancient and well-known heath breed called the Norfolk Horn. At the end of the 18th century it was crossed with Southdown rams to produce the Suffolk, and it is ironic that the Suffolk has become ubiquitous while the old Norfolk Horn became almost extinct. It has now been revived again, using three pure rams and breeding back on Suffolk ewes since 1969 so that by 1985 some of the flock was 90% pure. In 1986 the breed received RBST recognition and ninety-four females were registered.

This 'new' Norfolk Horn is of medium size, long in the body and leg. Its clean face and legs are black, and both sexes have open spiral horns curling

Norfolk Horn. (*RBST*)

around the ears. The fleece is white, yielding a medium wool [7–10cm, 1.5–2kg, 54s–56s] but the new born lambs have mottled coats.

The old horned Norfolk's numbers were already low at the turn of this century but it used to be famous for producing the country's best saddle cut of mutton, with an abundance of lean red meat in proportion to the fat and a taste more like good venison than mutton. In earlier times it was one of the most numerous sheep in Britain and highly regarded for its short, fine fleece. The rams had very large spiralled horns — much like those of the Wiltshire — but the ewes' horns were more like those of Dorset ewes. They were rather narrow over the heart, and much slower feeders than the Suffolk, but they could thrive on heaths so barren that most other breeds would have starved on them. They thought nothing of a hundred-mile trek to Smithfield market in a week.

Numbers of the new Norfolk are still far too low for comfort. Its behaviour is like that of hill sheep and it is sometimes classified as a hill breed, though its fleece is short and tight against the cold winds of East Anglia, rather than water-shedding for the rains of the uplands. The ewes are good mothers and, in due course, there will probably be potential for crossing in commercial lamb production as a useful maternal breed, but at present there are simply not enough Norfolks to spare for such experiments.

NORTH RONALDSAY

Various colours. Small. Short tail. Rams always horned, ewes usually horned. Well adapted to eating seaweed. RBST status: rare.

This small, dainty island breed is unusual for its ability to forage on a diet of seaweed for much of the year. Other mammals also eat seaweed — including various other island and coastal sheep, deer, musk oxen and human beings — but not to the same extent as the North Ronaldsay.

Its colour varies right through the spectrum of Iron Age fleeces and the lambs are often spotted. There are combinations or whole colours of mostly grey and white, but also black and moorit, and the fleece is another popular one for home-spinners and hand-knitters. The average yield for island-bred sheep is about 1kg (2.5lb). The grey and black wools are a little coarse but the white and moorit are as fine as Shetland and can be as high quality as 56s. Staple length is 4–8cm.

The rams are always horned — two fine, wide-sweeping spirals — and so are most of the ewes. The tail is naturally short and there is a little wool on the legs and face.

The breed is a primitive one. In the sequence of development it falls

North Ronaldsay.

somewhere between the Soay and the Shetland. It is native to the Orkneys and was once known as the Orkney but is now mainly confined to the northern island of North Ronaldsay where there are probably about 600 breeding females. There is a much smaller population (about two dozen rams and less than two hundred ewes) on the island of Linga Holm, which is managed by the RBST, and a few on other islands as far south as the Channel Islands, with a handful of small flocks scattered all over the mainland from Scotland to Sussex. Excluding those on Linga Holm and North Ronaldsay, 103 breeding ewes were recorded in the 1985/6 RBST census and these represented animals in the Combined Flock Book.

The island sheep live a more or less feral existence, grazing the seaweeds for preference for much of the year. On North Ronaldsay they are separated from cultivated land by high stone walls except at lambing when they come in for perhaps three months on pasture. On Linga Holm there is an annual round-up for culling, veterinary attention and general management.

Seaweed is an abundant source of potential nutrition in many parts of the world and the breed's adaptation to grazing it may well have value in the future for special situations. However, the physiological changes brought about by generations of such a diet can cause problems in a different environment. In adapting to seaweed, certain dental abnormalities have developed and there are several metabolic adjustments. The breed's rumen microflora have been affected because there is no cellulose in seaweeds and they also contain different elements in different proportions to those found in pasture or heath grazing. For example, a noticeable feature of the North Ronaldsay is its thriftiness with regard to copper: it is an element which is apparently difficult to extract from seaweed and the sheep have become very efficient at doing so. On normal grazing they cannot regulate that efficiency and can quickly and suddenly succumb to fatal copper poisoning. It is essential to avoid copper in the soil, in fertilizers, in bought-in hay, concentrates and mineral licks — which is easier said than done. But in areas of copper deficiency the breed might well be usefully crossed with local sheep to produce a new breed able to make the most of such land.

The seaweed diet is also said to give an interesting flavour to the very small lean joints produced by the island sheep. In 1985 a gourmet club offered North Ronaldsay pies and vacuum-packed hindquarters as prizes, and the London Hilton has expressed an interest in putting a new taste on its British Harvest menu. Smoked meat is another possibility.

It is prolific — twins and triplets are not unknown — but it *is* a small sheep and the meat yield is not high. On the islands the rams have shown a tendency for monorchism and at one stage this was almost selected for by breeders because of a belief that monorchid meat tasted better!

OXFORD DOWN

White fleece. Dark face and legs. Woolly cheeks and forelock. Large. Polled. RBST status: below numerical guidelines.

The Oxford is the one they call the Big One — the largest of the downland breeds. Its square-set legs and bold face are dark; it has woolly cheeks and a forelock, and a heavy, close-textured fleece. It inherited its forelock from the Cotswold Longwool, which was crossed with Hampshire and Southdown ewes to create the Oxford in the 1830s.

The rams soon became popular as crossing sires for lamb and mutton production but after the last war their size began to count against the breed and numbers fell. In the early 1980s there were only about seven hundred breeding females in the UK and they have recently increased to more than a thousand. The breed had also spread to many other parts of the world,

Oxford Down. (*Oxford Down Breed Society*)

particularly the United States, and its overseas numbers make up for the relative scarcity at home.

Its main role is still as a crossing ram: the lambs can be slaughtered early at light weights or kept on to heavier weights without piling on unwanted fat. The growth rate is particularly high. ADAS is looking with interest at the Oxford Down for heavier, leaner carcases which are ideal for boned and rolled lamb etc. Strength, size, vigour and disease resistance seem to be the main qualities passed on to its progeny by an Oxford sire. The fleece is useful too. [10–15cm, 3–4kg, 50s–54s.]

PORTLAND

White or grey fleece. Clean tan coloured face and legs. Both sexes horned, ram with heavy spirals. RBST status: critical.

One of the rarest sheep breeds with only 341 breeding ewes, the Portland has so many interesting qualities that it deserves to be better known. It is a small, attractive sheep with characteristically tan-tinted legs and face. The ram has large, heavily spiralled horns, and the ewes are also horned.

Portland.

The lambs are born with foxy-red wool which gradually matures to grey or white with a few coarse red fibres around the breech area. The rest of the adult fleece is close and fine-woolled, and some hand-spinners say that it almost matches the quality of a Merino.

It is perhaps a controversial breed: those who like it love it, while others fail to appreciate its virtues. It has traditionally been claimed that Portland mutton is the sweetest and most tender of meats, but mutton is a rarity these days and the lamb is perhaps not quite so special. More important in commercial terms is the lack of prolificacy: because of an inherited low ovulation rate the Portland is a one-lamb ewe, though it can to some extent lamb out of season. This lack of lambs increases the breed's chances of remaining rare, which in turn increases the prices paid for it, and at two or three hundred pounds a ewe any meat from the Portland is going to be expensive. Its only outlet in that case is to the wealthy gourmet.

It also means that the breed will tend to remain rare because of the old vicious circle: rarity equals lack of statistical sample, equals lack of information, equals lack of interest, equals rarity. But the ewes seem to give plenty of milk and could probably raise at least a pair of lambs, so a cross to a more prolific breed might be worth considering, though with so few breeding ewes available at this stage the results would be statistically meaningless.

One advantage of single lambing is that the mother takes very good care of her offspring: she can give it her undivided attention without worrying about some twin under the bushes, and she will be that much more zealous in protecting it from predators. The purebred lambs mature early and can make small, lean carcases which remain lean, unlike some breeds which start getting fat if kept a week too long.

They are easy sheep to keep and seem to do better at tight stocking rates. They do not really appreciate hay (though given competition from a couple of house cows they seem to find it rather more tempting!) and can keep their condition on very little indeed. They are easy to handle and the rams are tame enough to be halter-trained without difficulty. In fact their nature is so easy-going that dogs give up trying to work them: the flock is so slow and unconcerned that the dog gets bored.

The fleece is thick enough to deter fly strike: maggots find it difficult to penetrate to the skin. [6–9cm, 2–3kg, 50s–56s.]

The folklore history of the Portland is sometimes more colourful than the likely reality. It is one of many breeds (of sheep and dogs in particular) said to have swum ashore after a shipwreck. It is an old breed in Dorset and probably descends from an ancient mixture of Soay types with the white-faced breeds which may have been introduced by the Romans. Not that the Portland itself claims a two-thousand year history, but the tan-faced type resulting from that ancient mixture, with heavy horns and a sprinkling of hairs in its fine wool, does go back a very long way and was once widespread in Britain.

The Portland seems to be related to the Dorset Horn, which may have been a cross between the Portland and imported Merino types. The infusion may be reciprocal, which would account for the Portland's occasional ability to lamb out of season, and if today's hand-spinners are right then the Merino also passed some of its qualities into the Portland. Other near relatives are the Exmoor Horn and the Welsh Mountain sheep.

RYELAND

White fleece. White legs and face heavily woolled. Close forelock. Polled.

The dumpy, heavily woolled Ryeland presents a classic back view in the show-ring: a sturdy, chunky, *rumpy* rump. Show animals are trimmed to emphasize this shape and also the broadness of the back. It is a white-faced breed with plenty of wool covering everything except the muzzle and the

Ryeland. (*RBST*)

ears. The legs are also well woolled and stand very four-square, increasing the image of dependable solidity and robustness.

The original Ryelands were small upland sheep bred on the rye-bearing lands of Herefordshire by the monks of Leominster. They were improved by crossing to downland rams for size and fleece weight, plus a dash of Leicester and Southdown. The modern Ryeland is certainly larger than the original, and mature ewes average 60–63kg (132–139lb). It has lost the exceptional fineness of its ancestral fleece but an acceptably fine, clean, dense wool is produced. [8–10cm, 2.25–3kg, 56s–58s.] Before improvement, Ryeland wool was the raw material for most of western England's broadcloth.

Some have claimed that the Cotswold is a Ryeland crossed to a heavier breed but Cotswold breeders would probably claim their own breed's greater antiquity. Others suggest that the Ryeland had Merino blood but that could be a supposition based merely on a superficial resemblance in the character of the wool. However, the sheep does *look* a bit like a Merino.

Early in the 20th century the Shropshire began to oust the Ryeland in Britain but as a noted fat-lamb producer the Ryeland was imported in large numbers by New Zealand, where it is now declining since the swing away from overfat carcases. Only 531 ewes were mated in New Zealand in 1984 and only ten flocks registered in 1985 — a drop from eighteen flocks in 1981 and from nearly a thousand ewes in 1977 in twenty-six flocks. It was also exported to Australia, where it played an important role in the development of the Polled Dorset, and to Argentina and many other countries. In Britain, the 1985/6 RBST census recorded 1,577 breeding females.

It is still appreciated as a dual-purpose sheep, especially as a sire on crossbred and halfbred flocks. The ram's great prepotency firmly impresses the Ryeland characteristics on the progeny and quickly creates uniformity in a flock. It is a very hardy breed and has a remarkable resistance to footrot.

SHETLAND

Various colours and patterns. Small. Rams horned. RBST status: above numerical guidelines.

Shetland.

The Shetland, one of Britain's smallest breeds of sheep, is famous for its quality fleece — the finest in the country. It is certainly not a minor breed in its native islands, where it is ubiquitous and always has been. It is also increasing in numbers on the mainland and a Shetland Sheep Breeders Group was recently set up in Berwickshire to maintain the breed characteristics defined by the Shetland Flock Book Society so that there is no divergence of type between mainland and island flocks. Excluding substantial numbers registered by the Shetland Flock Book Society, more than seven hundred female Shetlands are registered annually.

On the islands, the tendency has been to breed out or keep separate any colour variations, with preference being given to white as it can take dyes. The mainland breeders seem to be keen to retain those variations and the soft natural colour range includes white, cream, grey, black and moorit — in that order of genetic dominance. Moorit is recessive, and two moorits always produce true-breeding moorits. Some fleeces are whole, and others broken-coloured.

The successful aims of the SFBS have always been to retain the traditional quality of the wool, to maintain hardy, healthy, robust stock, and to increase the breed's yield of meat. The sheep, about the size of a Welsh Mountain and quite similar in appearance, has a characteristic 10cm (4in) fluke-shaped tail (broad at the base, tapering to a fine point which is almost bare) and attractive bright eyes. Face colour can vary according to the colour of the fleece. Most of the ewes are polled but the rams have well proportioned horns spiralling clear of the face.

It is, of course, a very hardy breed, sharing further qualities of other primitive and hill breeds such as longevity, maternal ability and milkiness. In better conditions than those of its exposed homelands its productivity can improve dramatically and it adapts very well to various environments.

Its fine, soft wool is the quality for which it is best known but it can also produce prime hillbred wether mutton or prime lamb carcases, pure or crossbred. The purebred lamb is small and light and makes good fat-free baby lamb. A common cross is Cheviot/Shetland first-cross ewes to Cheviot or Suffolk rams.

In common with other primitive island breeds, the Shetland has a natural moult in the spring — something which has been bred out of most domesticated sheep. The traditional practice in the islands was to hand-pluck or 'roo' the fleece rather than shear it and this left the sheep with a coat which could still shed rainwater as the fibre ends were not cut. It is possible that modern shearing could coarsen the fleece. [5–12cm, 1–1.5kg, 50s–60s.]

The coloured varieties have attracted some evocative names. A *mirkface* has brown spots on the face, for example. The *catmogit* has a white fleece with black on the rump and underparts and a 'badger' face pattern, very like the Torddu variety of the Welsh Mountain sheep; and the Shetland version of the reverse-patterned Torwen is called *burrit*. *Flekket* describes white patches in a coloured fleece and *blaegit* is a fleece with the tips of the fibres naturally a lighter colouring. *Shaela* is dark reddish brown with a grey tinge. There are many more.

There is still a delightful touch of spirit in the Shetland, another characteristic which is common to the primitives. It is not easy to work with dogs.

So much has been written about the Shetland in books, articles and the correspondence pages of *The Ark* that those who are interested in the breed will find plenty of information to help them, far more so than with most minor breeds.

SHROPSHIRE DOWN

White fleece. Soft black face with woolled cheeks and legs. Polled. RBST status: below numerical guidelines.

A hornless breed with a soft black face woolled on the cheeks and forehead, the Shropshire is shaped like an overgrown Southdown. It is a bulky, medium-sized sheep and it has more of its surface covered with wool than other down breeds.

As the name implies, its homeland was some way from the other down sheep. It owes its origins to local sheep of the Welsh Marches, all of which are now extinct. The old breeds were the fine-woolled types of Cannock Chase, the nimble, hardy Longmynds, and the Morfe Common horned sheep with superb wool and resistance to footrot and scab — all now extinct breeds. They were crossed with Southdowns, which gave the new breed a darker face and suppressed the horns of the Morfe, and the Leicester to improve fattening ability and docility. The Shropshire's breed society, set up in 1882, was the first for any sheep.

Like other down breeds, the Shropshire has done well abroad, particularly in the United States, and in Australia and New Zealand where it was crossed to Merino-type ewes to produce quality lambs. It was exported in large numbers until the foot-and-mouth outbreak of 1922 which almost destroyed the export market. In this country its numbers declined to rare-breed levels, and in New Zealand, where it had found its place in the export lamb trade and the wool market, its numbers have also dropped (only ninety ewes were registered in 1986, in two flocks) probably because

Shropshire Down. (*RBST*)

of the common problem of too much fat in the lamb carcases. Earlier in this century it was boasted that 'no other Down produces a better back to handle for condition — the frame is so thickly covered with flesh and fat.'

The fleece is particularly dense and heavy [10-15cm, 2–3kg, 54s–56s] and much of it is exported to Europe. It is still a useful sire on, for example, a Cheviot ewe for prime early maturing lamb.

The breed's original demise was largely at the whim of fashion. The American export market had proved very lucrative and it demanded a very heavily woolled head. Breeders complied, but when the export market crashed in the 1920s the home market did not appreciate the woolly look or the big carcase of the Shropshire. The breeders complied again (oh, the dangers of bending your breed to fickle markets!), producing a more open-faced and functional sheep with less wool. But once numbers are low, there is less opportunity for breeders to select good commercial animals and the downward trend tends to continue. By 1974 the situation was crucial and the RBST gave the breed all the help it could. By the mid eighties numbers were increasing quite fast — more than 1,200 ewes and over a hundred rams were registered — and the breed was once again finding a commercial role. It might even be as lucky as the Oxford Down, which resolutely stayed as it always had been — big and fast-growing — and suddenly found that the market had changed to suit its type. The Shropshire is still a good sire for quick-growing lambs.

SOAY

Chocolate or fawn fleece. Clean face and legs same colour. Long legs. Small. Both sexes usually horned. RBST status: above numerical guidelines.

(See back cover for photograph.) The Soay is unmistakable, although some mistake it for a small deer, which is forgivable: it does have the look of a gazelle and it can move and leap like one too.

The most typical pattern is similar to that of many wild species of mammal: dark on top, with paler underside from the rump to the lower jaw and around the eyes. In the Soay the usual colouring is chocolate brown with pale fawn, and the top colour and this so-called *mouflon* pattern are dominant. Some animals are lighter brown or tan with pale fawn, and some are whole-coloured chocolate or fawn. The whole-coloured fawn animals seem to be the least viable.

There is also a 'spotting' factor. Some individuals have white patches on the face or feet, and some are piebald. At Butser this trait has been selectively bred for and a greater percentage of white fleece is being seen in each succeeding generation. In a flock kept by Dr Michael Ryder at the Animal Breeding Research Organization in which no males were castrated or culled, a great variety of colours was obtained.

There are two types of fleece in the Soay — hairy and woolly. The hairy fleece, with fine kemps, has a staple length of 5–6cm and a mean fibre diameter of 35 microns (depending on the time of year) whereas the woolly type has a diameter of 24 microns. In general, Soay wool is fine and soft though often interspersed with coarser hairs. [5–15cm, 1.5–2.25kg, 44s–50s.] The woolly part of the fleece is shed naturally and fleece weight depends on how much of it you can pluck or gather up in May before it has all blown away in the breeze. The darker sheep tend to have longer coats than the lighter ones, and the rams usually have hairy rather than woolly-type fleeces.

The adult rams weigh about 35–40kg or 80–90lb and ewes about 25kg (55lb). Both are of slender, dainty build and both usually have horns. In the ram these are heavy and in a single whorl, and in the ewe they are more slender, sweeping up, back and outwards like raised eyebrows. Some ewes are hornless or scurred.

All this variety of fleece type, colouring and horns makes the Soay of great interest to the breeder. As Britain's most primitive sheep, and the nearest thing to a wild *mouflon*, the Soay gives scope for seeing just how sheep began to develop and be altered to suit human requirements. It *is* a domestic breed and is probably the native type first domesticated in Britain: its wool and horns are very similar to those of Bronze Age sheep. For all its long association with humans, however, it retains a great sense of independence. Emparked for its good looks for centuries, it remains almost impossible to contain. It can jump or climb most barriers if it feels restricted, and has been seen to take a flying leap at a barbed-wire fence with strands only inches apart and twist itself in midflight to slide through sideways. Stone walls simply invite climbing. Sheep netting is only effective if it is taut and high. Soays need and appreciate the space to range and choose their own pastures and lying up areas as the seasons dictate. They are astute enough to know when their diet is lacking, and they then go out and find what they need, regardless of fences.

As well as being highly intelligent, crafty and self-sufficient, it is of course a very hardy breed. It rarely gets footrot or fly trouble and it can live to a good age, though by twelve or fourteen it might be losing its teeth. It is not clear whether flies are put off by the wool or by the flesh: a high Soay carcase smells more like game than mutton!

Typically of the primitive breeds, the ewe's pelvic dimensions make for very easy lambing and she has no problems if crossed to, say, a Suffolk or Texel ram. It is a very efficient breed in terms of productivity too. Comparing a Soay to a Scotch halfbred, for example, the Soay gives a higher yield in proportion to its bodyweight. In good conditions a ewe can produce enough milk for twins (or more) and if they are left on the dam until the autumn they grow very fast indeed. The meat is dark, fine-grained and exceptionally tender.

If a meat ram is put on a Soay ewe she can produce a crop of lambs and a good milk yield on very little food from poor quality land that could not support any other breed. In fact Soays are often used for land reclamation and perform an important role in this respect. They are used for grazing in nature reserves, or on china clay spoil tips, for example, where their light treading is as useful as their ability to survive on the most meagre scrub.

Apart from defying shepherding and fencing, the Soay is a trouble-free breed that looks after itself and that has the potential for several interesting commercial roles. But there is a risk that if they are more intensively kept, or mixed in with other breeds, they become more susceptible to disease and need regular drenching and worming. In common with other primitives they are anyway fairly susceptible to New Forest eye disease: like Jersey cows they have slightly protruding eyes which are more easily accidentally damaged and thus open to the fungus. Hayseeds falling from above head height can trigger the problem and hay should always be fed at low levels only. Foggy conditions also seem to encourage eye disease.

Soays *can* be kept tame — a regular titbit does wonders — but they are far too smart to become victims of cupboard love and the tamest kitchen-reared lamb will be off like a shot if anyone is even thinking of catching it. A ram can be a handful, and an underworked ram alone in a paddock needs something to thump every now and again, like a tyre hanging from a branch. In a flock allowed to breed freely, battles between rival rams can sometimes be very serious especially if the balance of power is disturbed by the removal, death or introduction of animals. Interesting comparisons can be made between the behaviour and social structures of Soay flocks and a herd of Chillingham white cattle.

Four hundred and fifty-three breeding Soay ewes were recorded in the 1985/6 RBST census but these excluded the numerous feral populations.

SOUTHDOWN

White fleece. Mouse-coloured face and legs with wool. Polled.

This is the classic downland sheep, long a native of the chalk hills of Sussex (it was once called the Sussex Down sheep) and a great influence

Southdown lambs. (*Jane Paynter*)

not only on the ecology of the downs but also on the sheep industry here and overseas.

The Southdown is a small, solid sheep with a mouse-coloured face well-woolled on the forehead, cheeks and ears. Its short, wideset legs are also woolled, and the white fleece produces one of the finest wools in Britain. [4–6cm, 1.5–2.25kg, 56s–60s.] It was carefully developed from local short-woolled Sussex sheep by John Ellman of Glynde, near Lewes, in the 18th century, and from then on it was used to improve the shortwool breeds very much in the way that the Dishley Leicester improved the longwools. There is Southdown blood in nearly all the down breeds.

Two strains of Southdown had developed by the turn of this century, a heavier 'underhill' type kept on flat lands in East Anglia and the Weald, and the original 'upperdown' sheep.

It seems insulting to include such a famous sheep among the minor breeds but, like many other down breeds, the Southdown's popularity has declined. However, it is still used as a good meat sire for fat lamb production. The meat has always been rated as the best and it is still widely acclaimed — smallholders who keep a variety of breeds always prefer the meat of their Southdowns to anything else. It is a small sheep, of course, which means that the lambs mature early and the carcases are small. They are perhaps a little too fat for today's tastes, and with a small carcase there is less scope for producing lean meat so that they do get fat if kept too long.

Because of the breed's size, the ewe's pelvis is small and there can occasionally be lambing problems, especially if she is too fat. Southdowns are more prolific than most down breeds and under good management using teaser rams they can achieve lambing rates of 150%. They are very docile sheep — they do not bother to escape even if the field gates are left open — and they are a healthy breed with very sound feet. Like all downs, however, they do roll a bit and sometimes end up stranded on their backs.

Being small, they do not eat much and can be stocked tightly to avoid getting too fat, as long as they are flushed for tupping. Carcases dress out at perhaps 14–16kg (30-35lb) and the lambs do best if they are not castrated and are sold on the hoof — then they will get heavier and leaner, and will grade. They produce quality meat and it should be marketed as such.

TEESWATER

White lustrous longwool fleece. Face off-white to grey-blue, often with dark muzzle, marked ears. Typical longwool topknot but clean face. Polled.

This bold but affable longwool has been so effective as a sire for crossing with hill ewes to produce the well-known Masham that the number of purebred Teeswaters is quite low. Such is the price of success!

Indigenous to Teesdale, it is a medium-sized longwool with an elegant, alert look and a friendly, enquiring nature. The face colour varies from off-white to grey with a tinge of blue; the muzzle is often dark or black, and the expressive dark ears are distinctively marked on the inside. A topknot of fine, pearly wool dangles over the face, and the fleece is heavy, fine and lustrous.

The Teeswater ram is traditionally crossed with Dalesbred, Swaledale or Rough Fell ewes (all pretty black-faced horned hill breeds) to produce large numbers of Mashams. More recently the Teeswater has also been used on Blackface, Welsh Mountain and Speckleface ewes to produce Scottish and Welsh Mashams. Masham wethers are a popular lamb crop and the ewes are often crossed with down rams for commercial fat-lamb production. The Teeswater gives them its own fine, long-stapled fleece [15–30cm, 3.5–7kg, 40s–48s], prolificacy (250% average in purebred flocks), milkiness and longevity. Rams are carefully bred and progeny tested, and the standards are strict.

TORDDU, TORWEN AND BAALWEN

There are some interesting colour variations in the Welsh Mountain types of sheep, and as separate breeds they have long histories.

Torddu

(See back cover for photograph.) The Torddu ('black belly') or Welsh Mountain Badger-faced sheep (*Defaid Idloes*) has characteristic dark facial stripes in a 'badger' pattern on a ground colour of off-white, grey or tan, occasionally with a white star. A black band runs continuously from the underside of the jaw along the belly and well up under the tail. The legs are predominantly black with a light tan stripe, and the upper fleece can be pure white, grey, light brown or tan, with the lighter colours being preferred. Red kemp is not desirable, and the fleece should be soft, firm and close. [7–10cm, 1.5–2kg, 46s–56s.] The tail is full length, with black underside. Rams have dark horns in the typical Welsh Mountain spiral, and ewes are polled. A thousand breeding Torddu ewes were recorded in the 1985/6 RBST census.

Torwen

The Torwen ('white belly') is a photographic negative of the Torddu and occurs less frequently. Basically, where the Torddu is dark the Torwen is off-white, and vice versa. It has noticeable light stars near the eyes and a light-coloured moustache. The overall effect is of a dark coloured sheep (dark brown, grey, or sometimes parti-coloured) with a light underside, very much in the classic Soay style. The light colouring is very obvious from the rear between the hindlegs and tail, and from the front as a blaze under the chin and over the breast. The rams have black horns.

Both the Torddu and the Torwen have typical Welsh Mountain qualities of fleece, hardiness and good maternal abilities, and they also seem to have a higher percentage of twins than the standard breed. There are perhaps a thousand of them in this country and a handful have been exported to the Falklands.

All Welsh wool, incidentally, seems to have a special quality of reaching its maximum shrinkage at an early stage when washed, and it is therefore especially useful for flannels.

Baalwen

The Baalwen colouring has similarities to the Torwen but the light parts are even more eye-catching. Most of the sheep is black and it has a bold white central strip on the face and a flashing white ruff under the chin. The feet and tail are also white. It is rather wilder by nature than the others. A similar pattern was found by Henry John Elwes when he crossed a Wiltshire with a Soay ewe and put the resulting ewe lamb to a Jacob ram.

WENSLEYDALE

White lustrous longwool fleece. Blueness in skin. Face blue-grey with ample forelock. Polled. RBST status: rare.

This very big longwool has a distinctive blueness in the skin of its head and ears, and sometimes on the legs and elsewhere. It is one of the largest British breeds — rams weigh more than 136kg (300lb) — and it has even more of a forelock than other longwools. The modern Teeswater and the Blue-faced Leicester have Wensleydale in their backgrounds.

The Wensleydale originated in North Yorkshire early in the 19th century but its ancestry possibly goes further back to an older local longwool sheep. The founding father of the breed was a ram born in 1839 called Blue Cap — aptly named for his very dark blue head. His skin was almost black, and his wool was fine, white, bright and lustrous. He was bred from a Leicester ram out of a Mug (Teeswater) ewe. He weighed more than 200kg (440lb) as a two-shear and was a very wild and active animal.

Numbers fell to a very low ebb in the 1970s, possibly because, like the

Wensleydale.

Teeswater, not many rams are needed to produce plenty of Mashams. Since then, however, the situation has improved (there are about 450 breeding females) but there is some concern that many of the new breeders who now form the majority of flockmasters are smallholders. The average flock is only five or six animals and the largest has only fifty ewes. Many of the smallholders breed Wensleydales as a hobby rather than on a commercial scale and the breed's future would be better assured if it was backed by commercial farmers who recognized its value as a sire for halfbred ewes. It is not really a beginner's sheep: although it has an appealing temperament it needs careful and experienced management, and it is also a very big animal to turn over and needs a deeper dip than many breeds.

The overseas market is beginning to look more promising, with enquiries from Canada, New Zealand, Australia and Sweden, and ADAS in this country believes that the breed (along with the Oxford Down and the Teeswater) could become more important because of their potential for lean and heavy carcases.

Today's Wensleydale ewe is prolific (average 200%). She can produce enough milk for three lambs, and the breed used to be hand-milked. It lives to a reasonably good age. The lambs grow fast and can produce lean, fine-grained carcases at high weights if the right rams are used. The lambs remain lean and are autumn finished at great weights, ideal for the supermarket trade, although their conformation may not be the best.

The Wensleydale has been maintained largely to provide rams for crossbreeding to hill ewes, in the same way that the similar Teeswater is used for Mashams, and it transmits its high growth rate to the progeny.

The fleece is claimed to produce the finest and most valuable lustre longwool in the world [20–30cm, 3.5–7kg, 44s–48s]: it can be used as a mohair substitute and can fetch as much as £150/kilo. Yearling ewe fleeces can weigh up to 9kg (20lb) and in crossbred Suffolk offspring can reach 11kg (24lb). Quality can be affected by environment, as in all wool breeds, and lustre in particular.

A unique 'central checking' factor keeps the Wensleydale fleece completely free of kemp and this property is passed on to all first-generation crossbreed progeny. If the Wensleydale is crossed with a hairy-fleeced primitive breed, the kemp and coarseness will be masked.

The blue pigment in the skin enables the Wensleydale to tolerate tropical climates, a quality it shares with British White cattle and coloured pigs. The export potential is significant.

Being a big animal, the Wensleydale takes quite a lot of feeding and needs plenty of grass to grow really well. It is not as hardy as some breeds and some say that it cannot take wet, cold weather. The fleece is so thick, it is parted down the length of the back and rainwater can penetrate to the base of the fleece at that point, however waterproof the rest of it may be.

It is essentially a lowland breed and does well if it is yarded. The lambs need quite a lot of nursing for the first fortnight or so: they are born with not much wool on them, and are rather leggy which means they have difficulty in finding their feet and suckling. It is best to lamb indoors until the weather improves, and indeed to house in the winter. Bedding needs careful consideration to avoid spoiling the fleece, and peat might be worth investigating.

Hand-spinners are particularly interested in the Wensleydale not only for its lustrous longwool but also because black and grey lambs are born quite frequently. In the past they were automatically culled but now some breeders are selecting for the coloured fleeces instead.

WHITEFACED WOODLANDS or PENISTONE

Clean white or light grey face and legs. Large horns both sexes. RBST status: vulnerable.

This distinctive, strong-boned, horned sheep is one of the largest of the

Whitefaced Woodlands.

hill breeds. It has clean white legs and a clean white or light grey face (no topknot) with pink or bluish nostrils. The unusual tail is long and muscular. Both sexes have large horns, which in the ram are heavy and spiralled. The medium-length wool looks silky but can be harsh and wiry. [10–15cm, 2–3kg, 50s–54s.]

The Whitefaced Woodlands was at first called the Penistone, named after a small Pennines market town more than seven hundred feet above sea-level, between Huddersfield and Sheffield. There had always been a short-woolled, horned type of local sheep, some of which were white-faced and others mottled. There was possibly a different type in the Derbyshire valley called Woodlands, towards Derwent, and this is where the more usual name for the present breed has its origins.

The Penistone was highly regarded by local farmers but it began to decline gradually in the early 19th century, and more sharply after World War One. The main reasons for its decline were probably its mediocre wool and, ironically, its very good meat. Large numbers of the breed were sold as fat sheep during the First World War, when meat prices rocketed, and this drastic reduction in their numbers was further accelerated by the depression of the 1930s. Fortunately for the breed a few families were dedicated to its survival and their efforts were helped by the intervention of the Royal Agricultural Society of England and the Zoological Society of London who, in 1968, classified the Whitefaced Woodlands as a rare breed worth conserving and established a small flock at the National Agricultural Centre, Stoneleigh (a dozen ewes and a tup) as a gene bank for the future. The Norfolk Horn, Manx Loghtan and Lincolnshire Longwool received similar attention, and the Cotswold and Portland found a haven at Reading University.

But there were still quite a lot of workaday Penistones earning their keep in the Pennines, and the arguments about whether Whitefaced Woodlands and Penistone were one and the same began and will no doubt continue. Those arguments really only concern the purist and the show-ring.

The breed, whatever it is called, has certain qualities. It is large, very hardy, prolific (up to 180%) and milky, and its wool now compares quite favourably with other hill breeds. It is undoubtedly a hill breed — its feet may suffer on lowland farms and it may not be immediately immune to local bugs when first taken from its native area. But it has a highly efficient rate of food conversion and is a pleasant breed to keep. There may be inbreeding in some lines, which needs to be watched and which can result in diminution of size, split scrotums and semi-dwarf lambs which are very small and not acceptable; they have short faces but are otherwise in proportion. There is room for improvement, particularly to add a bit of backside and to reduce kemp in the fleece. There is plenty of raw material among the still numerous unregistered Pennine flocks.

If the colour of the face is deemed to be important (some say the pink-nostrilled, white-faced sheep are more hardy), a white face is readily gained by breeding to a Dorset Horn. There does seem to be a tendency for blue-faced ewes to be more stocky and square at the back end.

There can be lambing problems, as with any horned breed. The breed is basically fecund and ovulation can be increased if the rundown ewes are carefully flushed just before tupping so that they are on a rising plane of nutrition. They are long lived, with some ewes still producing superb lambs at eleven or twelve years of age. A few breeders have experienced lamb rejection in some seasons but the orphans thrive on goats' milk, which is handy in that it (and its colostrum) can be kept in the deep-freeze for such emergencies.

The 1985/6 RBST census revealed that about 160 Whitefaced Woodlands ewes were registered annually, but these did not include the unregistered sheep in the Southern Pennines.

WILTSHIRE HORN
No fleece. White. Horned.

Wiltshire Horn.

The Wiltshire Horn is quite unmistakable: it has hardly any wool, never needs shearing or dagging (it casts such fleece as it has in the early spring), is anathema to flies and ticks, rarely needs dipping except for scab, and is sometimes mistaken for a goat. It is white all over, strongly built and long in the leg. The ram has bold, spiralled horns, a little less heavy than an Exmoor's, and the ewes are also horned but less prominently.

There are about two thousand Wiltshires in this country (1,400 pure-breeding females) with perhaps another thousand overseas. It is probably derived from the Old Wiltshire Horn (now extinct) which, ironically, was famous for its wool — the finest in Britain. The Old Wiltshire was also famous for its stamina: it could walk for long distances in the days when it was folded over the Wiltshire downs. In effect it was used as a portable dung-cart, carrying its manure to a different arable area every night after a day of ranging, and improving the cornland not only by dunging but also by treading it.

The modern Wiltshire Horn has a different role as a highly fertile sire for early maturing prime lamb. Pure ewes lamb very easily and are good mothers. The lambs 'mean to live': they are born with a hair-like coat which protects them from the cold and are quickly up on their feet. They grow fast (sometimes more than a pound or half a kilogram a day) and fatten well, even on second-rate pasture. With no wool to grow, everything goes into the production of meat.

The breed has considerable potential for low-cost farming. It has also been used to introduce the fleeceless trait into other breeds. In 1985, for example, after twenty years of trying, Anglesey farmer Iolo Owen produced his new Easycare sheep based on the Wiltshire Horn and the Welsh Mountain. With wool today representing only a small percentage of the income from sheep in general, it makes some sense to shed it and the extra shepherding associated with it.

MERINO

The Merino is a very rare breed in Britain, despite the occasional efforts to establish it here over the last two hundred years or so. In Australasia, where wool is a prime product from sheep, the Merino reigns supreme, but in Britain it does not seem to be practicable to put all your money in wool.

However, the Merino produces the finest sheep wool in the world, and the UK imports something like £70m-worth of fine wool every year. Yet there are only a very few flocks of Merino sheep here, and such as there are tend to be experimental rather than commercially productive.

Why? There are several reasons for British prejudice against the very woolly Merino, and some of them are based more on presumption than tested fact. The Merino is thought to be not at all prolific and incapable of producing carcases of acceptable conformation. These excuses are based on the breed's performance in Australian conditions where its lambing rates are admittedly only about 70% and its carcases of poor quality. But, like our own primitive or mountain breeds, if the environment is improved so is the sheep. Selective breeding in the USSR has increased Merino lambing percentages to 135% on average, and in Germany they have developed the German Mutton Merino which has a bodyweight of 40kg (88lb) at six months and a mature ewe weight of 70–80kg (154-176lb). So the Merino does have potential for improvement in the right environment and also in countries where meat is more important than wool. There has been no incentive to improve these qualities in Australia, where wool is the name of the game

Wool is another problem over here. Firstly as already mentioned, British sheep farmers look on wool as forming only a small percentage of

Merino. (*Farmers Weekly*)

their income from sheep (perhaps 10% for lowland and upland farmers and 18% for hill flocks) and they have little incentive to improve wool quality. In addition there is a prejudiced belief that the introduction of fine-wool genes into the British flock would cause other valuable traits to deteriorate. Yet the Southdown, which grows one of the finest-fibred wools in Britain, is also one of the best meat breeds in the country! It is also believed that our wet climate will weaken the Merino fleece and make it less valuable but the Animal Breeding Research Organization, who imported Merinos in 1955, have found no deterioration in fleece quality in the British climate.

Merinos are slow maturing but the lamb carcases are lean — very definitely a point in the breed's favour. But it is for its intrinsically superior wool that the breed should really be investigated: it is better to take advantage of a breed's unique qualities than to try and change the breed and make it like any other British sheep. Fibre production is a growth area in British farming enterprises and the Merino can be shown to produce the kind of gross margins which in fact make it more profitable than traditional sheep-keeping enterprises on many systems. It could be a lowland sheep for the future.

11 Goats

There is an enormous potential for goat farming in Britain but the estimated population of goats in the country at the end of 1985 was probably about a hundred thousand. This compares with 35 million sheep, 13 million cattle, 8 million pigs and 120 million poultry.

Why? Why is the goat still basically a backyard animal?

A nationwide survey of goats was carried out in August 1985 by the Islay and Jura Goat Society and it highlighted the following facts:

- ★ There are nearly eight thousand goat keepers in Britain and about seventy-five thousand goats.
- ★ Average herd size is 9.46 goats.
- ★ 16.5% of goat keepers — the biggest group — have only two goats.
- ★ Only 0.6% of goat keepers have herds of one hundred head or more. The largest herd is 498 goats. Another two hundred herds have 40–100 head.
- ★ British goats produce 6.5 million gallons (30 million litres) of milk a year at an average rate of 4.73 pints (2.69 litres) per day per goat in August.
- ★ Only 22% of goat keepers keep goats commercially and only 3.4% are full-time goat farmers.
- ★ 88% of goat keepers milk by hand.
- ★ Less than 20% regularly have their milk tested.
- ★ More than 30% of the goats in Britain are not registered with the British Goat Society.
- ★ 60% of the goats are on holdings of 1 to 50 acres, and 0.06% are on canals and narrowboats (which is not so odd: plenty of goats made their way into Britain originally on board ship as suppliers of fresh milk and meat on long voyages).

So the backyarder dominates the goat world. Yet the Farm Animal Welfare Council is planning a welfare code for goats, the National Institute for Research into Dairying (NIRD), as it used to be called, has been studying goat production for several years, and Dalgety believes it is worth their while to launch Spillers goat feeds — they estimate the goat population to be twice that of the IJGS survey results and to have doubled since 1975.

Do they know something about the future? Why hasn't the goat been farmed on any scale in Britain so far, and is a change imminent?

In 1956 the incomparable David Mackenzie looked closely at those very questions in his classic and thoroughly researched book *Goat Husbandry*.

He made a very strong case indeed for goat keeping to be taken up by commercial, level-headed farmers and breeders, but his rallying call has largely been ignored. As he says:

> 'The fact is that the study of the goat has commanded rather less scientific attention than the study of mice and guinea-pigs. The practice of goat-keeping in Britain, though successful in establishing world milk production records and a vigorous export trade, is so highly variable, individual and empirical that it is almost indescribable ... The writer on goats is liable to be treated with the respect accorded to all things pertaining to the goat in Britain ... A goat, however 'modern' and 'dairy bred', is a goat, a member of the species familiarized in nursery picture books and biblical illustrations, target of laughter and abuse for countless centuries ...'

Or, as Alan Mowlem wrote recently to *Farmers Weekly:*

> 'Goats ... are regarded by some as nothing more than pets which are the province of diehard breed enthusiasts, but they also have a useful and unique place in production.'

As a biologist who has studied the productivity and husbandry of commercial goats for quite a few years at the NIRD, Mowlem is fully aware of the goat's rightful place in a farming context and he has recently set up an imaginative and thoroughly practical Goat Advisory Bureau which, it is hoped, will radically alter the image of the goat in this country. It is noticeable that, at last, farming magazines are reporting more regularly on developments in the commercial goat industry.

Nearly seventy years ago an enlightened few made attempts to encourage people to take goats more seriously. The third interim report of the Committee on the Production and Distribution of Milk contained a chapter by Major G.R. Leighton and Mr James Mackintosh on the keeping of goats and the claims of the goat for special encouragement. After exhaustive surveys they concluded that 'in order to increase the supply and consumption of milk in country districts, especially by cottagers, every encouragement and assistance should be given to the keeping of goats of good milking breeds'. They proposed the setting up of two central stud farms, one in England and one in Scotland, to improve types and to increase numbers, with the aid of government grants.

Others are also looking more seriously at goat farming. At the Royal Highland Show in 1986 the newly formed Scottish Cashmere Producers Association announced plans to establish herds of several thousand goats to produce valuable cashmere fibre in Scotland, with the full support of the Hill Farming Research Organization (HFRO), and enquiries are coming in from other parts of the country as well. HFRO has also recognized the potential development of a substantial market for goat meat sales to Asian communities in Britain, and the value of feral goats for land improvement.

The British Angora Goat Society has begun an ambitious grading-up scheme to make the farming of mohair fibre into a real industry in Britain. Goat dairying is beginning to boom, coming out of the backyard and into the parlour. A Goat Producers Association has been formed. The backyarders and enthusiasts will continue to do their excellent and valuable work in the close observation and breeding of goats but it needs the promise of commercial returns to put the goat in its rightful place in British agriculture. Goats are not just attractive, friendly pets or the health crank's answer to everything. They can be very useful livestock indeed.

With numbers as they have been, goats themselves could be called a minor species of farm livestock, let alone the various minor breeds within that species which can be found in Britain. They deserve a book, or several, to themselves (and the needs of serious goat farmers will no doubt soon be met in this respect). This chapter seeks only to stimulate interest by outlining possible outlets and looking at the lesser known breeds and types or those which look as if they might become the farmstock of the future. For the record, the following breeds are already found in Britain:

Anglo Nubian (dairy)
Angora (fibre — mohair)
Bagot (decorative)
British Alpine (dairy)
British Saanen (dairy)
British Toggenburg (dairy)
Feral (potential for fibre, meat, land improvement)
Golden Guernsey (dairy)
Old English (dairy)
Saanen (dairy)
Toggenburg (dairy)
West African Pygmy (pets, potential for fibre)

DAIRY GOATS

Goats' milk is good for you. Now, there is a dead duck of a marketing slogan, but it is true. Goats' milk usually contains more butterfat than cows' milk and it is in smaller globules which are easier to digest. The milk is a blessing to the many people who, whether they realize it or not, are allergic to cows' milk.

The highest yielding commercial goat herd in Britain runs 160 pedigree British Saanens milked in a twelve/twenty-four parlour in a range of converted farm buildings with no land. Its manager was originally a cowman and he began five years ago by applying dairy-cow principles to the goats. Since then he has learned better and has set up his own advisory service. The herd averages about 200 gallons (900 litres) per goat over a 305-day lactation, with some individuals averaging 440 gallons (2,000 litres). Housing, rations and generally sound husbandry have all helped to achieve these results and one of the most important factors of all has been the avoidance of stress and an understanding of goat behaviour.

Recording is essential. The herd is milk-recorded every ten days so that each goat can be rationed individually, in the manner of all good dairy farms. Winter lighting encourages out of season kidding for year-round milk production, which is important for a regular supply to the fresh-milk market. Kids are taken off the nanny at birth, bottle-fed with colostrum and then put on milk substitute until weaning at six to eight weeks. Male kids are sold at four days old to a farm which rears them on for meat.

The parlour routine is similar to that for cows — udders are wiped and the foremilk drawn before the clusters go on, and a teat spray is applied after milking.

Marketing of the product is the key to successful goat farming and it is less straightforward than the actual production. After cooling (the milk is not pasteurized, nor does it need to be) some of the yield is sealed in one-pint bags and sold through shops or at the farm gate. The rest goes in churns to a Somerset cheese-maker.

In Holland, new dairy goat herds are being established all the time and some goat farmers are forming co-operatives to help with marketing. (In Britain the new Goat Producers Association can give advice.) The largest Dutch herds milk four or five hundred goats and are planning to set up more herds of that size, though the majority of the producers are on a much smaller scale and the goats are run as a sideline on cattle farms. Most Dutch goat produce is exported and they know how to package it and where to sell it. Cheeses are exported worldwide, particularly to the United

States and Middle East. Kid meat (and live kids for slaughter) goes to the Middle East. Curd finds an outlet in Belgium and France. On top of that the goat farms, large and small, are exploited as tourist attractions and make the most of selling cheeses to fee-paying members of the public who come to watch the herd being milked. The sale of breeding stock is an important additional source of income.

British goat farmers should take heed of the fact that the Dutch themselves do not drink goats' milk or eat kid meat and yet the Dutch dairy goat industry is thriving. Good marketing and a professional approach are the keys to success. As Alan Mowlem points out: 'Much of the milk sold by hobbyists is not fit for human consumption and it does the industry no good at all.'

Another goat consultancy, based at Launceston in Cornwall, stresses the importance of recording and of sensible costings to calculate the real margins which are being achieved in a goat enterprise. Again the dairy cow can be used as a guideline: dairy farmers are well aware of the importance of assessing margins reliably and looking at them on a whole-farm basis and a herd basis, as well as on an individual basis for culling and breeding programmes. Such calculations highlight efficient and inefficient aspects of an enterprise.

Produce from goat dairies in Britain can be marketed as fresh untreated milk (and every goat keeper can sell the beneficial properties of goats' milk), frozen milk, cheese, yoghurt and ice-cream. At present there are very few restrictions on such sales, though the situation might change if the industry grows. The outlets are there, waiting to be exploited. Someone in Leicestershire has already registered a range of about thirty imaginative goat products including, for example, an eczema ointment manufactured from cream skimmed off goats' milk sold to slimmers.

In the 11th century there were she-goat herds of fifty or sixty head in Dorset and Somerset for the production of goatsmilk cheese. In Scotland they used to make 'crowdy butter' from goats' milk right up to the 19th century. Use your imagination!

GOAT MEAT

Goat meat is lean. It is a potential competitor with lamb, especially if sheep breeders fail to reduce the fat content of their product and if the public can be educated in the ways of cooking goat meat. A new name is needed for the product. 'Goat' automatically evokes toughness and billy-stink; 'kid' is better but is still meeting consumer resistance. A Sunday joint of roast kid? Think about it.

The meat of the goat naturally varies according to its age and diet. Old goat served as kebabs in a Greek mountain village can be inedibly tough (as tough as old goat, in fact) even if its taste is more interesting because of the wild herbs the goat has browsed. On the other hand, the kid which is suckling a good pasture-fed goat can be killed before weaning, at three or four weeks of age, and its meat is as white and tender as chicken or veal — and often as tasteless, with a glutinous texture which wartime restaurant diners will associate with guinea-pig masquerading as chicken.

Kid meat is classified as meat from an animal up to nine months old. At three to four months the meat is like spring lamb and can be roasted as a leg studded with garlic or herbs and kept moist with bacon, butter or olive oil. At six to nine months it needs to be marinaded but it is at its prime, with the tenderness of lamb and a flavour akin to wild vension.

Wethers or sterile goatlings up to eighteen months old make mutton, or 'goat venison' — very lean but rather dry because of its leanness. The meat needs marinading or larding and is best cooked venison-style in liquid — casseroled in wine, for example. Castration at birth, incidentally, can almost double the rate at which the kid converts milk into meat.

Billy meat or old goat meat might find a place in a curried dish. Some people cure goat hams and it may be worth experimenting with smoked or salted meat and sausages.

Although goat has never been a recognized meat in Britain, it is very popular in Asia, the Middle East and along the Mediterranean coasts, and there is an increasing demand for it among ethnic communities in this country. The market is a reliable one and deserves a reliable source of supply; the occasional billy kid off a backyard nanny is no good at all.

Angora goats are said to produce the best meat of all, and feral goats for cashmere will certainly be able to contribute meat as an additional cash crop to the fibre.

Local restaurants could be encouraged to put goat on the menu (under some fancy name) and the London Hilton is frequently asked to provide whole roast kid for their Middle Eastern guests.

FIBRE

The goat fibre market is possibly the most exciting outlet for goat farmers. The bandwagon is already rolling with trumpets and drums in full voice.

It has been tried before. George IV was given some Kashmir goats and for a while there was a minor British industry producing fine cashmere shawls. There is still a Windsor herd of white goats and in 1984 Her Majesty the Queen entrusted six of them to His Grace the Duke of Wellington, president of the RBST.

In 1873 Angora goats were seen in London but they were only passing through *en route* to the Cape, where the production of mohair was to become quite important. In 1981 a score of Angora goats came into Britain from New Zealand and formed the nucleus of a Devon herd at Ash Farm, Iddesleigh. They thrive; numbers are being increased steadily with the help of a grading-up scheme and the British Angora Goat Society is ready for the future.

In 1986, after several years of research, the Scottish Cashmere Producers Association (SCPA) was formed. Note the name: it is *not* an association of Kashmir-goat breeders. The intention is to produce cashmere on a commercial scale by encouraging the growth of suitable fibres in large herds of feral goats. Most goats grow fibres which are fine enough to be classified in the cashmere grade but usually the quantities are far too small to be harvested. SCPA, with the aid and advice of the Hill Farming Research Organization (HFRO) at Edinburgh and with the support of cashmere buyers like Dawson International, intend to act as a catalyst to improve the quality and quantity of fibre in Scottish goats (there are probably already tens of thousands of feral goats in the country) and then to make sure that the product is properly marketed. To this end they are setting up breeding co-operatives and providing advice and assistance to new breeders. They are also co-ordinating the importation of stock, semen and embryos so that the national herd can be expanded and improved, and they will eventually provide a central marketing organization which will co-ordinate the collection, grading and processing of cashmere fibre and the secondary cash crop, goat meat. SCPA believes that both products — cashmere and meat — could eventually be developed as substantial industries.

The semen is being imported from New Zealand, where there are huge numbers of feral goats which were once regarded as vermin but which are now producing cashmere fibre. Note that they are not Kashmir goats: they are improved ferals which have been bred to produce a greater proportion of fine cashmere-type fibres. Kashmir? Cashmere? Confused? Let us start again.

There are three valuable types of fine fibres which can be obtained from goats: cashmere, cashgora and mohair. Cashmere is the second softest fibre in the natural world (vicuña takes top place). The fibre dimensions in each case are:

Cashmere:	less than 19 microns	(average 15 microns)
Cashgora:	19 to 23 microns	(average 20 microns)
Mohair:	23 to 40 microns maximum	(average 25 microns)

The Kashmir, Cashmere or Pashmina ('woollen') goat is a breed which is native to that beautiful area of mountains and lakes in the Himalayas from which it takes its name. It lives at high altitudes (10,000 to 16,000 feet above sea-level) in a dry, cold climate. Such conditions have given it a very fine, soft and silky underwool, excellent insulation beneath its coarse, hairy outercoat. This downy underwool, or *pushm,* begins to grow in the autumn and is shed naturally the following spring. It can be collected, carefully combed to separate it from the coarser hairs. The down is very fine indeed and is called cashmere (with a small 'c'). One goat normally yields only 100–200 grams (3–7oz) of cashmere. Several other types of goat grow such a down but those of Kashmir, Mongolia and Tibet seem to produce the best.

If the Kashmir breed of goat is farmed in Britain, with the wetter, warmer climate and lower altitudes, the quality of its coat seems to deteriorate and the fibres become too coarse to be graded as cashmere. However, fine fibres can be encouraged in feral and domestic goats. They are already present in most goats but only in very, very small quantities. By careful breeding and management it should be possible to increase the percentage of fine cashmere fibres to an amount worth harvesting.

This, then, is the aim of SCPA and HFRO, and it is a scheme which has had good results from the feral goats of Australasia. There are many cashmere-producing areas, quite apart from Kashmir itself: for example China, Iran, Afghanistan, Australia and (recently) New Zealand. There is thought to be a score of breeds of goat producing cashmere-type fibres in an area stretching across Turkey, Iran, India and Russia, and it is believed that the feral goats of Britain might well have the best potential for producing cashmere on a commercial basis.

Dawson International, one of the largest buyers and processors of cashmere fibre in the world, processes thousands of tons of the downy fibre for the high-class knitwear industry and for woven materials and there is a ready market for this expensive luxury product. In 1985 Dawsons were paying about £50 a kilo for top grade fine white down (after removal of hair) — that is the equivalent of £1.42 an ounce. The company is keen to encourage cashmere production in Britain, particularly in Scotland which at present imports the bulk of the £21m-worth of cashmere fibre that comes into the UK every year. That is a lot of imported fibre.

If feral goats can be reared for cashmere the returns should be excellent, especially as inputs will be low. The goats can be left on the hills (incidentally doing a good job by improving pasture for sheep) and gathered occasionally for routine husbandry. They do not suffer from fly strike, by the way, so management is easier than for sheep. They should have free access to some kind of shelter — woodland, bushes, gullies, or a man-made structure — and they can usually be adequately contained with flexinet, with the addition of a strand of electric wire along the top. If they are accustomed to extra winter feeding each day, they will be quite easy to round up when the time comes for harvesting the crop. They prefer to follow rather than be driven and as long as one or two dominant animals make the initial moves in the right direction the rest will come along as required.

The coat can be shorn or combed. Shearing is not advised in this country, however; it involves considerably more sorting of the fibres after harvesting and it also leaves the goats without protection against the weather at a time of year when it can still be quite cold. Combing is preferable: it is more selective and it leaves the goats well coated with hair. HFRO's method is to yoke each goat so that one person on either side of it can comb out the down. As the HFRO goats have been grazing in enclosed fields (because the original point of the exercise was to see if they could be used to improve sheep pastures — cash crops like fibre and meat were secondary considerations) shepherding is not much of a problem. Dogs can be used but leading really is easier than herding. Goats are very curious animals. The only drawback to enclosure is that the goats are more likely to need worming, and they cannot necessarily be treated with the same anthelmintics as sheep.

If ferals are crossed to Angora goats, the first generation offspring have an increased yield of fine down in the 12–14 micron range but great care needs to be taken with the breeding to ensure that the fibre remains fine enough to be classified as cashmere. There is the intermediate fibre, cashgora, for which of course the prices are lower than for good cashmere. It is thought the best results will come from using the imported semen from New Zealand.

Dairy goats can also be crossed to an Angora buck for improved fibre production but they have not been bred for hardiness and therefore have less potential undercoat. In such a cross the in-kid goat needs to be correctly fed because the fibre-producing follicles develop in the unborn kid at about 120 days into the pregnancy. The dairy goat is much more useful in its present context, as a producer of milk. It is with the feral goat up on the hills that the more exciting developments in cashmere production will take place because it will serve several purposes at once: such an enterprise is as much an adventure in ecology and land management as a commercial venture into fibre and meat production, and the combination looks a good one.

Mohair is quite different to cashmere. It is of a very much longer staple, so much so that it forms the bulk of the fleece while the coarser hairs effectively become an undercoat closer to the skin. It is not as fine as cashmere and it can be produced in some quantity by the Angora goat.

Now for a look at some of the more unusual breeds of goat.

★ ★ ★ ★ ★

ANGORA

The Angora is a beautiful looking and sweet natured goat with a fleece that immediately attracts attention — soft, long, wavy and white (by selection) and covering it from the top of its horned head right down to knee level so that only the muzzle and lower legs are visible, with a bright pair of eyes peering out under a fine fringe. Its smallish ears hang on either side of its face but they do not droop; they have a sprightly look to them which is enhanced by the way the horns lift before they sweep backwards and outwards in the females and young animals. The males (bucks) have a fine spread of elegant horns, very long, undulating and twisting. The Iddesleigh bucks' horns seem to have a backwards then sideways and horizontal spread, whereas engravings of Angoras in 1879 show a backward sweep and a description written in the first decade of the 20th century says that the male's horns are 'directed vertically and in shape spiral, like those of a ram'. Whichever, they are dramatic.

The Angora is often mistaken for a sheep and it adds to the illusion with a rather sheepish 'baa', but its upright tail declares that this is truly a goat.

The breed is native to the Ankaran province in Turkey, where the goats have always been greatly prized and jealously guarded. Export was forbidden, under punishment of death, and it was not until the 19th century that the goats found their way to the Cape. They can now be found in the United States, Argentina, Lesotho, Australia and New Zealand, and have recently come to Britain in very small numbers. In 1982 there were four bucks and eighteen breeding females (does) in the UK; by early 1986 they had increased to thirty-eight and forty-nine breeding males and

Angora.

females, with new batches being imported and a considerable number of animals in the grading-up scheme.

The coat of the Angora has two components. The coarser hairs are short, lying close to the skin, and the majority of the fleece is of those long, luxuriant ringlets of wool which make that valuable crop, mohair. Fibre diameter increases as the goat grows older, especially in bucks and wethers. Kid mohair is the finest, with yearlings next. With the doe, the fibre diameter becomes similar to other mature does once she has been mated for the first time (usually at eighteen months). At shearing the various ages and sexes should be shorn in separate groups to simplify fleece sorting: start with the kids, then the yearlings, and then the adults, keeping mature wethers in different age groups and keeping buck fleeces quite apart from the rest.

The goats can be shorn twice a year — the mohair grows rapidly and yields at each shearing can be expected to average up to one kilogram (2.2lb) in kids, up to 1.7kg (3.7lb) in yearlings, from 1.5kg (3.3lb) to 2kg (4.4lb) in does, 1.7kg (3.7lb) to 2.5kg (5.5lb) in bucks, and as much as 2kg (4.4lb) in wethers (which is good news for wethers — in any other breed of goat they would have been meat long ago!). Staple length should be no more than about 15cm at shearing because longer fibres tend to break during combing and processing. Shearing pieces may heat up quickly as there is little lubrication from the fleece.

Care should be taken to avoid shearing-stress in pregnant does. To avoid abortion it is best to shear immediately before tupping and then just before kidding, when it is too late for abortion.

Breeding must be selective for the best mohair. White is much preferred. Long kemp can be a major impediment during processing and goats with too much kemp should be culled. At the same time other qualities in the animal need to be maintained and improved, particularly prolificacy. The Angora is rather an indifferent mother, and not much of a milker, but the kids, though small when born, can grow fast and mature early. The meat is superb — better than any other goat and as good as lamb — but with numbers so low in this country and stock so expensive, Angora meat is a luxury.

A grading-up programme is underway to increase numbers as quickly as possible and make prices more realistic. Three thousand pounds or so for a goat in 1986 is excessive! But they are asking up to $125,000(NZ) for a billy in new Zealand. The grading-up programme involves careful breeding and selection and it is important to consult the British Angora Goat Society, which is determined to maintain the quality of the breed and its product. An embryo transplant technique, as developed originally in New Zealand, is also under consideration.

During grading-up an intermediate cashgora fibre can be harvested.

Despite initial problems with footrot in New Zealand in the very early days, the Angora mohair industry there is now booming, with high fertility, high weaning percentages and high yields of mohair. New Zealand produced 6 million kilograms (12,000cwt) of mohair in 1984. The goats are ranched like sheep but are stocked more tightly, at seventeen to the hectare (seven to the acre).

In Britain the Iddesleigh herd are grazed in large paddocks and have access to large, light and airy polythene or polypropylene sheep hangars with Tensor windbreak cladding on the sides. Hayracks are specially designed to keep hay seeds from getting into the fleeces, and sawdust is used as bedding for the same reason. The goats have plenty of grazing space and they appreciate it. They seem to have adapted well to the climate.

BAGOT

RBST status: critical.

The Bagot is a poser of goat — very decorative, acting up to the camera and, so far, with absolutely no other useful role at all. It is handsome: there is a striking contrast between its white body and black head, beard, neck

Bagot. (*RBST*)

and shoulders. Many Bagots are not quite so clean-cut, having perhaps a white blaze or dark hindquarter patches. The coat is long and shaggy, and both sexes have a good strong pair of up-and-back horns.

The Bagots come from a semi-feral herd of decorative goats which had the run of the grounds of Bagot Park in Staffordshire for several centuries. They are probably related to the Swiss *Schwartzhal* goat, which is similar in colouring.

Although legend claims that the Crusaders who are said to have brought the original Bagots to England used them as a source of milk and meat on their journeys, today's Bagot would hardly have kept them going for a day: it is not much of a milk producer nor much of a begetter of progeny. The birth rate is low and the females are very poor mothers anyway: they have difficulty kidding and then they fail to set up a good bond between mother and offspring. With their inadequate milk supply the kids have a struggle to survive at all. After such a long confinement on one estate, they may well be thoroughly inbred. Sometimes a situation like this is in fact beneficial: in the case of the Chillingham cattle, for example, recessive weaknesses have been exposed over the generations and weeded out by natural selection. There are about fifty breeding female Bagots at present.

OLD ENGLISH

This is a neat, small goat with a short-haired coat in various colours — usually fawn or grey but also white or black, often with markings on face and legs and a dark 'eel strip' along the spine, with sometimes another across the shoulders. The neat short head tapers from a wide, flat forehead, and the ears are upright. Many of the goats have horns, which are flat at the base and incline outwards; the male's are larger than the female's. The legs are strong and quite thick, well covered with hair, and the texture of the coat in general is thick and close, often with a woolly undercoat. There are usually no tassels, though originally they appeared quite often in the old breed and were said to betray foreign blood. The nanny has a tidy, well-slung udder.

This very practical goat used to be quite common in England. There was also another British goat of a quite different type, found mostly in Ireland; it was a much coarser animal in every way, with a shaggy reddish-black coat (occasionally they were pied or white), a long, heavy and rather ugly

English Billy.

head with a prominent nose, and large, corrugated horns set close together and extending almost parallel to each other. Its legs were long, its sides flat, and it was generally somewhat gaunt — though this may have been due to its circumstances rather than its heritage. It was said to yield a lot of poor quality milk and there was a white goat of the same type in Wales.

The English goat all but disappeared during this century. There were less than a hundred left by the time of the First World War. By the thirties the number had trebled, thanks to a rescue operation and the formation of an association and a Herd Book, but the next war did not help and anyway there had been so much 'improving' with eastern and Swiss blood that the hardy, sturdy, utility native goat had lost most of those admirable qualities and was barely recognizable as a breed any more. There was a brief revival with the help of feral crosses but in the fifties it really did give up the struggle and went into hiding.

The Swiss and eastern goats had taken over, with their much better milk yields, but they had none of the hardiness and thrift of the old English, qualities which were not to be thrown away. In the late seventies a few people of great dedication began to recreate the original type — sturdily built, strong and vigorous, and capable of giving 'the best return to its owner with the least expense and trouble ... the utility goat *par excellence*,' as Holmes Pegler described it in the definitive 19th-century *Book of the Goat.*

There was enough of the old blood left for the new breeders to succeed in building up a recognizable type which certainly looks like the old English goat and which also has its hardy qualities. On the whole the new English goats are not afraid of the weather; their coats are reasonably water-resistant and they still have that woolly undercoat in the winter. They are undemanding and easy to look after, needing only a very modest ration of concentrates for an acceptable and cost-effective milk yield of perhaps a gallon a day after kidding. They are quite happy living free-range in an open field with access to a shelter and they do not need elaborate housing. There is a drawback: they are always interested in 'the other side' and boundaries need to be firmly goatproof.

The new English goat seems to be prepotent and genetically dominant, breeding true already if carefully selected for mating. There is an English Goat Breeders' Association in Somerset which is setting about re-establishing the breed in a scientific and realistic manner. Potential animals for registration are closely inspected and the criteria for acceptance are quite rigorous. The future for this most serviceable of goats is promising.

FERAL GOAT

Feral goats can still be found in Britain, mostly in Scotland (north, north-west, south-west, and the west coast islands) where there are several thousand. There are smaller populations on the English borders, in north Wales and in Ireland and no doubt a few scattered here and there elsewhere.

'Wild' goats were referred to in the 17th century but they were probably ferals, escaped from the herds that were driven from Ireland and Scotland to England. Quite a lot of goats were later abandoned when the Scottish Highlands became depopulated in the 19th century. Others were introduced for hunting or for decoration and they, too, became feral. (A feral animal, to be clear, is a domesticated species which has returned to nature to survive and to breed. There is a very specific difference between feral animals and genuinely wild species, the latter never having been domesticated.)

The feral goats of Britain are therefore based on a mixture of types, basically old native breeds but including some foreign blood. Most of them have developed long, shaggy coats in all sorts of colours and long twisted or sabre-shaped horns. Some, like the baleful black goats of Northumberland, probably have some eastern blood, and they contrast strongly with the pure white goats on Holy Island, Aran.

There is therefore a substantial caprine gene bank dispersed over several isolated populations and from a practical point of view the ferals could be valuable to goat breeders looking for new blood and old qualities. As already mentioned, the ferals are also being eyed as pasture improvers and prospective cashmere producers, and possibly as meat animals as well. The Hill Farming Research Organization's study of the ferals began with a view to using them to complement sheep on the uplands: the goats would eat the coarser vegetation, leaving the finer undersown grasses and clover for the sheep. It was realized, however, that very few farmers are likely to see this as a productive role for goats, and it was with this point in mind that HFRO began to look into the possibilities of fibre and meat production, to prove that the goats could provide cash crops as well as being pasture improvers.

On a more emotive note, there is the great pleasure of knowing that 'wild' goats still range on our uplands. Apart from deer, we have no large wild herbivores in Britain any more and the feral goats and sheep, like the 'wild' White cattle of Chillingham and the feral ponies of the Gower peninsula, serve as a substitute for the wild and evoke a certain satisfaction that man is not, after all, completely in control. Long may they range.

GOLDEN GUERNSEY

RBST status: rare.

The coat of the Golden Guernsey is distinctive for its colour, which is a soft, silky, sandy tan like a Guernsey cow. Sometimes it has white patches as well, which makes the simile even more appropriate. The coat can be short or long and flowing, especially along the back and over the hindquarters, and beneath it the skin is also 'golden'. Its build is strong but fine-boned; the neck is slender, and the face very slightly dished. There are no tassels. Its large, erect ears reach forwards with a slight upturn at the tip and most animals are horned unless they have been disbudded. Males weigh about 86–91kg (190–200lb) and females 54–59kg (120–130lb).

The origins of this affable goat are a little uncertain — perhaps a touch of Syrian, French and Maltese blood — but there have been golden goats on Guernsey since at least the early 19th century. In 1924 Miss Miriam Milbourne first noticed them among the island's scrub herds and several years later she began breeding goats for milk. She was pleased if an occasional golden kid was born but she did not select them specifically until the 1950s. By 1965 the Golden was breeding true and in 1972 an

Golden Guernsey.

association was started. The breed came to England in the late 1960s and an English club was formed.

It is a very amenable and reliable goat, with a noticeably placid and affectionate nature. It milks quietly and steadily, though moderately (average 750kg/1,650lb) on a low food intake and it yields a good butterfat percentage. More robust and hardy than other dairy breeds, it is very much a house goat, enjoying human company and happy enough in a fenced yard or on free range. As with all low-number breeds, there is always the risk of inbreeding and the pedigrees of potential partners should be carefully investigated.

WEST AFRICAN PYGMY or DWARF GOAT

The little Pygmy goats come in all sorts of colours and patterns and all sorts of shapes, but they are remarkably uniform in size and this is their distinctive feature.

They used to be called Guinea goats, after the coastal area of their origin. There were three basic varieties: the common *Capra recurva*, the *Capra depressa* from Mauritius, Madagascar and Bourbon, and a third, unnamed type found along the White Nile in Lower Egypt and along the African and Mediterranean coasts.

Pygmy goats.

Being small, kind and easy to handle, they are popular as pets and in children's pet corners on farm parks. The genetics of colour in the Pygmy have strangely never really been studied but the range of colours and markings seem to be endless and breeding can be an enjoyable pot-luck exercise.

They are quite happy to graze a paddock, given enough space, but they do need a hard yard with something to clamber about on like a pile of rocks. Although hardier than some goats, they need access to shelter from the rain at their own option, but they are usually the last goats to take cover.

The Pygmy is a prolific breeder but, being so small, it is almost impossible to hand-milk and anyway yields are very low — perhaps a couple of pints. Their smallness also counts against them as meat producers but castrated billy kids can find good homes as pets of character.

THE ROTHSCHILD GOAT

Extract from R.D. Blumenfeld's *Diary*:

> 'Oct. 8, 1900 — The Rothschild goat which ambles up and down Piccadilly every afternoon to Stratford Street nearly came to grief today. An omnibus horse slipped on the pavement and went down. The goat shied away and was nearly run over by a passing hansom. The omnibus-driver said he wouldn't have hurt the goat for worlds since it might affect the annual New Year's gift of a brace of pheasants which Leopold Rothschild sends to every driver and conductor.'

12 Other Livestock

Although there are, and were, so many breeds of cattle, sheep, pigs and goats in Britain, the search for something new, something different, is an endless one. All over the world people cast their eyes at their native wild species and wonder if they can be tamed, domesticated, befriended, controlled — used.

Other humans in other lands have domesticated their native species and the covetous British have thought that they, too, could have such animals. Over the centuries men have tried to introduce alien domesticants like bison, water buffalo, yak, llama and reindeer, not just to attract curiosity in zoos or to decorate country estates but also to be made use of — to be farmed. And they have failed. Again and again. In the 19th century, for example, a certain gentleman grazed yak and bison on the borders of Hampshire and Sussex but 'the countryside rose up against them' and they disappeared. It is not clear whether their demise was due to the alien environment and climate or to the predatory instincts of local people.

Today, farmers and land-owners are still trying, and quite serious interest is being shown in some species, one of them found in Britain in some abundance as a wild species and the others alien domesticants from other continents.

DEER

Deer have been hunted in Britain for centuries and venison has long been on the British menu. They were always potential domesticants: enclosure in parks is the first step towards control, but the most common method of obtaining venison in this country is by shooting deer for sport, rather than farming them.

Only certain species of deer are good candidates for domestication. A 'good' domesticant lives in large social groups with a strict hierarchy and an obvious leader, and the males are affiliated with female groups and are dominant to them. They mate promiscuously and they signal readiness to mate by posture or movements. Females are prepared to foster other young as well as or instead of their own. The group is adaptable to a wide range of environments, does not run too far at the sight of humans and has limited agility. It can be contained.

Poor candidates, on the other hand, live in families and territorially. The males tend to form separate groups and have to establish their dominance over a female or appease her. Pair bonding is important, and sexual readinesss is expressed by colour markings or morphological structures. The group has specialized dietary habits or needs specific habitats, is extremely wary of humans and flees a considerable distance from them, and is very agile indeed.

There are nine species of deer in Britain. Three of them are native (though native is a relative term): the Fallow, the Roe and the Red deer. The rest are introduced species, often escaped from parks and zoos in the first instance: Chinese Water deer, Muntjac, Pere David's deer, Reindeer, Sika and Wapiti.

No one is considering farming Roe deer. They are basically solitary animals (though occasionally seen in small family groups) and the bucks are territorial, defending an area of some twenty-five to thirty acres against all other bucks.

Fallow deer are rather flighty and not especially tractable, although they have been emparked for centuries. Being so timid, they are only farmed on a small scale.

Red deer, however, are being farmed in growing numbers. They are the largest of our native deer and are found in enclosed parks all over Britain. They also run on open moorland in Scotland, the Lake District, Devon and Somerset. There is a small herd in the New Forest and a few small groups of escapees here and there. The stag grows to about four feet high at the shoulder and weighs perhaps 140–160kg (300–350lb). Parkland Red deer in southern England tend to grow larger than northern and feral deer.

The coat of the stag is a glossy reddish brown in summer, and rather thicker and drab in winter. His point-tipped branching antlers increase in size annually and are shed in April with a new set maturing in time for the September rut.

Hinds are smaller and lighter in build than the stags and they do not have horns. Their young are dropped in late May, June and July after a pregnancy lasting 230–235 days. At first the calves are reddish brown with white spots but the spots fade after a few weeks.

Sika deer are also farmed, accounting for about 10% of farmed deer at the moment. It is an east Asian species which was introduced into Britain in the mid 19th century and there are feral groups in some counties. Stags reach weights of perhaps 70–80kg or 155–175lb and hinds perhaps 36–45kg or 80–100lb. Calves are dropped in May and June from a September rut. Sika bucks are sometimes put on Red hinds to produce hybrid progeny.

Wapiti bucks are occasionally used for the same purpose. They breed freely with the hinds and the crossbred calves can be as much as 40% heavier than purebred calves at thirteen months old.

There is a herd of five hundred Père David's deer on the Woburn Abbey estate in Bedfordshire. More than a score of them were exported in 1985 to China, their country of origin, where they have become almost extinct. It is hoped that the British input will help to boost numbers in the Chinese herd.

Deer 'farming'

'Farming' is not quite the right term: it is really deer management. There are only certain situations where it makes any sense at all to have a go at managing deer as a commercial enterprise rather than for sport — and the sporting estates can make quite a reasonable income from shot deer without the added work involved in farming them.

The details which follow assume that Red deer is the species being farmed.

Land is the first consideration and it saves on housing costs if the land is free-draining. Existing deer parks, down to permanent pasture, are obvious starting places: there are often economic reasons for maintaining the land as a park rather than turning it over to a more productive agricultural enterprise. In long-established parks, which have probably rarely been fertilized or limed, the usual stocking rate is likely to be from two to five per hectare, or one or two per acre, on a low-input, low-output system. Some estates run other stock in the park as well — perhaps Jacob sheep — and in that case stocking densities for the deer will of course have to be even lower. Winter feeding may be necessary because that is when the young stock are growing fast and at their hungriest. More intensive lowland enterprises stock as high as thirteen hinds per hectare and achieve calf growth rates averaging 400g (14oz) a day in July, which is when the youngstock are growing at their fastest.

Moorland is another potential setting and stocking rates naturally depend on the type of grazing. On unimproved hill land the rate might be one breeding hind per two hectares (five acres) and on improved pasture it might increase to parkland rates. However, in systems developed by the Rowett Research Institute and the Hill Farming Research Organization, sensible stocking rates have been from three to eight hinds per hectare on improved pastures enclosed by 2m or 6ft fencing, and growth rates of an average of 350g (12oz) per day were achieved among calves during July. Such an upland deer system could well be more profitable than sheepfarming on the same land.

Although housing costs can be negligible (as long as the deer have access to some kind of shelter for the worst winter weather), initial fencing and handling-area costs can be high. Secure fencing is essential: escaped deer are deemed to be wild and can be shot as game or as vermin. Boundary fences need to be well strained and at least the recommended 2m high, with posts every 15–20m (16–21yd), and droppers in between. Fallow deer can jump a two-metre fence if they panic but Red deer are less agile and less excitable. The base of the fencing must be well secured to prevent the deer from squeezing their way underneath it. Bear in mind that a slope gives a deer a good starting block in any leap for freedom.

Electric fencing can be used to good effect, especially for internal divisions.

Deer require skilled, gentle and very patient handling. They are wild animals and they can panic if pressed or restricted and in those circumstances legs are easily broken. As with so many animals, it is always best to lead them rather than drive them and they can be trained to respond to a whistle or call at feeding time in the winter. They soon learn to recognize the rattle of a feed bowl, and the occasional titbit during training works wonders.

Deer tend to be more approachable early in the morning and this should be exploited if handling is necessary. Never attempt to handle them during the rut and always carry a stick with you in that period. For the safety of people and other deer, stags' antlers are sometimes removed after the velvet has been shed in late August. Most stags are safe enough to handle in winter, spring and summer except for the occasional rogue who can never be trusted.

Avoid overcrowding. Stags have an order of dominance and if they are penned too closely they will take it out on those lower down the scale. They also tend to become more aggressive with age.

Handling pens should have an unobstructed view outwards because deer will panic if they cannot see a clear exit. Netting needs to be reinforced with breast rails near entrances and exits or alternatively (and expensively) solid timber can be used. Gateways should be about 3.5m (12ft) wide. A low, narrow creep gate is useful for drawing off hinds and calves to adjacent pens for separate handling.

Deer handle more easily in subdued light and it therefore helps to cover the entire handling area — forcing pens, races and holding pens.

An ideal group size for management is twelve to eighteen hinds with each stag (one stag can cover ten to twenty hinds). If the internal fencing is not what it might be, run the whole herd as a single unit and let them sort out their own boundaries. Stags begin to gather their harems in about mid September, and from then on they feed very little during the rut so that by mid December it is worth separating them from the hinds and giving them extra feed over the winter to restore their condition.

From late September the hinds come on heat every eighteen days and are usually mated (and conceive) in the first heat. The heat only lasts a few hours and mating normally takes place at night. Wild hinds would not normally mate until they are at least two years old but you can put a well-grown hind to the stag at fifteen to eighteen months in a more intensive enterprise.

The gestation period is about 231 days. The hind usually retires and calves without trouble. Indeed, if assistance is given she will probably desert the calf. The calf lies up for several days, with the hind returning to suckle it every six or eight hours. Then calf and hind rejoin the herd for grazing. It is possible to hand-rear a calf on a mixture of ewes' milk substitute, dextrose, cod-liver oil and eggs but it takes a fair amount of time and patience to do so successfully.

In extensive conditions calves are not weaned and they often stay with the hind even after she has dropped her next one. Under management, calves can be weaned just before the rut if required, but January weaning is preferable as it gives the hind a chance to introduce the calf to supplementary feeding.

Some farms achieve calving rates of 85–95% at yearling stage whereas sporting estates tend to find that only 60% of hinds calve successfully each year and only 50% of those calves survive the winter. With increasing experience in winter housing, feeding silage etc., several deer farmers are improving their rates each year.

Because it is still quite a young industry there can be problems in finding an abattoir which is capable of handling deer and deer farmers tend to act co-operatively in this respect. Calves can be slaughtered as early as seven to ten months if weaned early and fed intensively but normally they are taken to fourteen to sixteen months. There is a noticeable loss of appetite during the winter after the age of eighteen months and this inevitably leads to loss of weight and condition. Stock not required for breeding is usually culled at liveweights of 80–100kg (176–220lb) for stags and 70–85kg (154–187lb) for hinds.

A game-dealer's licence is required for marketing carcases to the general public. If you want to export to Europe (a big market for vension) there are strict regulations on health, hygiene and chilling facilities at the farm.

By-products from slaughtered stock include skins, antlers, tails, sinews and pizzles. There is also a market for cast antlers. At the time of writing the harvesting of velvet from a living animal is prohibited in Britain.

Whether or not a good enough market exists for farmed deer, considering the capital outlay involved in fencing and acquiring stock and considering the possible loss of the 'game' taste in farmed venison, remains to be seen. However, the demand for venison does seem to be rising quite fast. It is lean, with the lowest fat levels and cholesterol content of any red meat, and farmed venison is more tender than that of wild deer. Carcases can be butchered into all the cuts a customer is already familiar with in other meats — steaks, chops, joints, spare ribs, escalopes etc. — or used in sausages, 'veniburgers', pâté, salami and pies, or smoked, pressed or diced. In 1983, 112 deer farms in the UK produced 3,000 carcases and the British Deer Producers Association (a marketing co-operative) aims to increase production to 20,000 carcases by 1992.

LAMOIDS

There are four New World lamoids: the domesticated llama and alpaca, and the wild vicuña and guanaco. They can all inter-breed. They are all ruminants, though their stomach morphology differs from other more advanced ruminants. None of them have horns or antlers; nor do they have hooves: their feet have callous pads and claws. They are specially adapted

Llamas.

to dry environments and high Andean altitudes; for example their teeth and digestive systems enable them to make highly efficient use of sparse and fibrous vegetation, and the haemoglobin of the llama and alpaca has a greater affinity for oxygen at high altitudes than at sea-level.

The llama and the alpaca are vital to the economy of the high Andean regions. Llamas are kept at between 9,500 and 16,500 feet above sea level from Colombia to Chile and Argentina, and alpaca are at 13,000 feet or more in Peru and Bolivia. There are probably nearly seven million of them altogether.

The wild guanaco has a wider range of ecological adaptation than its three relatives. It can be found on shrublands, warm grasslands or cold grasslands and it can be at sea-level or as high as 15,000 feet. The guanaco is easily tamed as a pack animal.

The wild vicuña, however, is restricted to high altitudes (12,000 feet at the lowest) and is the least amenable to handling of all the lamoids. It has the misfortune of growing the finest wool in the world and the Incas used to have a grand round-up every three years to harvest the old males and infirm animals and to shear all the rest before releasing them. The vicuña is intractable and difficult to tame and it became very much an endangered species because people with more greed and less finesse than the very civilized Incas began killing the animals for their wool. Vicuña are now protected at the National Vicuña Reserve of Pampa Galeras in Peru, under the guidance of the World Wildlife Fund. There are now 140,000 of them and they are once again being shorn (alive!) and are spreading to other areas. British naturalist Ian MacPhail has played a major role in this success story.

Llamas and alpacas had a similar problem, though it was less catastrophic for them. They, too, have a good wool and they were very carefully and methodically farmed by the Incas, under whose benevolent management their numbers reached a maximum. But they also suffered after the Spanish invasion of 1532 and the herds were decimated, partly because their traditional grazing lands were taken over by Spanish livestock like Merino sheep and partly because they were used as a form of currency to pay hefty tribute levies. In 1567 there were 50,000 llama and alpaca in just one of many privately owned herds; five years later the entire province had less than 160,000 left.

Yet they survived and are still an essential element of Andean culture. Llamas are used mainly as pack animals (they can carry loads of 25–30kg (55–66lb) for 15–20km, or more than 10 miles, a day) and their wool is woven into ropes and saddlebags. Alpacas are kept mainly for their wool, which is made into fine cloth. Both species give a lot else besides: their skins are used for leather, their sinews for thongs, their bones for weaving tools, their dung is a main source of fuel in treeless areas and is also an essential fertilizer for the potato crop. But, surprisingly, neither animal is milked.

Alpaca wool is lustrous and very fine, containing very little kemp. There are two breeds, with different wools: the Suri, with long fibres falling down each side of the body in waves like a longwool sheep, and the Huacaya, with shorter crimped fibres like a Corriedale. The colours of the wools range from white to brown and black and are uniform across the body.

Llama wool is coarser and its colouring is not so regular in the fleece. The range is similar to the alpaca, and piebald llamas are quite common. Again there are two breeds: the Ch'aku, which is woolly, and the Q'ara, which has no wool.

Both animals also provide meat and this forms an important part of the diet in Peru and Bolivia.

Because of their importance, exports of live alpacas were prohibited in Peru in 1843. However, a few years later the Australian government commissioned Charles Ledger to transport some 'down under'. It took him four years to trek across the Andes with his livestock, and another five months at sea, but in 1858 he landed at Sydney with 274 alpaca. Within six months forty-nine young were born and within three years the herd numbered 417. They thrived in their new environment, growing much bigger and producing much more wool than in their native land, but Merino sheep distracted attention from them and the project was abandoned in 1864. Today they are once again successful in Australia.

Llamas began to be imported by the United States in the 1930s and today there are probably 5,000 there, with the largest private herd numbering 500. They have adapted well to a variety of altitudes and environments and are used as pack animals and for wool production. They have recently become fashionable as pets, and prices have gone wild.

In Britain Mr A.H. Wingfield of Ampthill, Bedfordshire, for example, bred llamas for many years, starting before the First World War. He sold them as pets, 'a number being used as uncommon, much appreciated mounts for children.' He found them to be generally hardy beasts, easy to breed in almost any climate, though bad weather conditions towards the end of 1930 resulted in the deaths of several young llamas and their dams at birth. His management system was a simple one. Large paddocks were reserved exclusively for the llamas in the breeding season, with shelters for use in bad weather, but at other times they ran freely in the park with a number of Shetland ponies (another of Mr Wingfield's hobbies). They were allowed access to all parts of the grounds and 'on occasion are to be seen in the streets of Ampthill, ridden by the head-keeper's daughter, Miss Cole, and her friends, where they are very docile in traffic and attract a good deal of attention.' Before the disastrous 1930 season, Mr Wingfield's stock of llamas had been considerably greater than the ten females and four males to which it was reduced and he had investigated the possibility of dealing with the wool as a commercial proposition. Unfortunately he found that the quantity was too small to warrant the expenditure, and he therefore abandoned the scheme.

Since those days llamas have been seen in zoos but they have much more to offer. They can utilize marginal pastureland and investigations have been made into their potential for Welsh hillfarms. The idea has been seen as a joke by some but in view of their successful adaptation in the United States it is foolish to laugh too soon. They can and do thrive in Britain. Unfortunately in 1985 a whirlwind visit by an American buyer removed nearly all the female stock in this country (they were subsequently sold on at twice the already high price paid for them here) and there are now a lot of lonesome male llamas in Britain.

Whole male llamas can be unpleasant and quite dangerous (especially when there isn't a female this side of the Atlantic!) but castrated males are delightful. They are full of curiosity and will give you a thorough going-over, sniffing you from head to toe in the friendliest manner. They may look snooty but they are in fact pleasant and affable. (Angry llamas spit their cud in your face, by the way.) They can be trained to carry children on their broad, fleecy backs, and hand-spinners are taking an interest in their wool. Despite talking to several llama owners, I cannot report on the quality of their meat, nor, in view of the American invasion, can I give you any first-hand information about the milking potential of the females.

Wool-crop llamas could very well find a role on marginal land once their products are assessed and the markets identified. They do best on dry land, though even on heavy Sussex clay they seem to have very few problems as long as they have regular walks on concrete and their feet are checked at intervals. They are subject to sheep diseases and need worming. Nutrition requirements are similar to those of cattle but they also need some browsing. They are perfectly hardy but there is a snag in Britain: they are not used to wet climates and in winter they have been known to become frozen to the ground, firmly anchored by the fleece!

They therefore need winter housing with dry straw bedding.

A well-fed llama can be mated at twelve months old but it is more traditional to wait until they are two or three years old. The females remain on heat until ovulation has been induced by copulation and it may be that, like ferrets, unmated females could eventually become ill unless ovulation is induced artificially. In any event 20% of mated females fail to ovulate; in the remaining 80% fertilization rates are high but about 40% of the embryos die in the first month of the gestation, in which case the female comes on heat again and can be re-mated.

They never have more than one calf at a time. The gestation period is a long one at 348 days (not much less in the alpaca). If males and females are kept together all the time, parturition is seasonal; in the Andes they all give birth from December to March, which is the local rainy season so that better grazing is available. Otherwise births can occur at any time of year but always take place between sunrise and early afternoon. The females come on heat again immediately after the birth but are not fertile for another ten days.

In its native land the llama is shorn every two years, yielding a fleece of about 3.5kg (7–8lb). About 20% of the fleece is made up of coarse hairs from the protective outer coat, and the final yield of short crimped fibres from the woolly undercoat is from 66% to 84% of the original weight of the fleece. Staple length is from 8–25cm and fibre diameters from 10–150 microns; the coarse hairs are the longer ones and the undercoat fibre diameters are usually about 10–20 microns. Most of them have a hollow central medulla, which makes the fibre particularly light in weight. It is used for knitwear and woven fabrics.

Yields in the UK are very variable, with claims ranging up to 3.6kg (8lb) of fibre per annum sold at £35 per kg — but this is unusually high.

Alpaca fleeces can be shorn annually in South America, where they yield 2–4kg (4–9lb) of a more consistently fine coat than the llama. Staples lengths are from 20–40cm and fibre diameters are from 22–30 microns. The fibre contains only a few coarse hairs but alpaca fibre is stiffer and stronger than wool. There are very few alpacas in the UK; their fibre is quite a lot more valuable than that of the llama (£105–£140 per kg) though the yields are similar, and the price of such stock as there is will be high.

There are also very few guanaco in Britain — perhaps a couple of hundred in zoos and as pets. They are shorn but only yield about a kilogram (2.2lb) a year, and the fibre contains no lanolin which makes hand-spinning difficult. They are much cheaper to buy than alpaca but they are more difficult to handle than the two domesticated species: they tend to be just as nosey as llamas but more nervous and it takes two men to handle them for shearing and other management. The males are very territorial and can fight each other viciously.

Vicuñas are not farmed at all in Britain, nor should they be. Although their fibre is very valuable, and the finest in the world [1–6cm, 13–14 microns, 85–550g yield p.a. in South America] they are wild animals which need plenty of space and freedom. Some people have crossed alpaca with vicuña females to improve the fleece, and the hybrids are fertile. The cross cannot be made the other way around because vicuña males are so timid that they will not mate with alpaca females.

Much more practical research still needs to be carried out to see how practicable llama and alpaca farming might be in Britain. Better feeding and management will no doubt improve embryonic survival, growth rates and perhaps fibre quality but it may be that environmental factors will affect the fibre in unexpected ways. It is thought that, with its more valuable fleece, alpaca holds out more potential than llama and that the species could adapt well to hill farms and upland areas in Britain.

HYBRIDS AND HOPEFULS

Never content with the abundant variety of the animal world, humans keep trying to create new livestock by crossing two existing types together. It can certainly be done but in most cases the offspring are sterile and cannot reproduce the 'new' animal. The mule and the hinny are typical examples.

Mule and Hinny

A mule is a cross between a jack ass and a mare, and a hinny is a cross between a stallion and a jenny. They have both been bred on a large scale worldwide since ancient times and used as draught and pack animals. British mules tended to end up doing army service in India, and the Irish specialized in hinnies.

The advantages of these hybrids are that they exhibit a high degree of heterosis: they can adapt to all sorts of adverse conditions; they can tolerate heat and withstand disease; their surefootedness is legendary, and they go on working for many years. In 1981 there were more than fourteen million mules and hinnies in the world, nearly all in the developing countries.

Mating between horse and ass is not natural; the males have to be 'trained' to the task, and fertility is usually reduced. The male hybrid offspring are always sterile and the females nearly always so. On the rare occasions when female mules have foaled (either to a jack ass or to a stallion) the second generation males are still all sterile.

Bison/Cattle crosses

The American bison (the 'buffalo' of the American West) is a massively built ruminant with a superbly insulating coat. An adult bull might stand as high as a man at the shoulder and a real whopper can weigh as much as 1,270kg (25cwt). There may be as many as 80,000 bison in North America — a tiny number compared with the thirty million that were there originally and which fed, clothed and housed their human predators.

There is still a good market in Canada and the United States for 'buffalo' meat and bison are now farmed on ranches. They are very efficient converters of forage and natural grazing, and the fat content of a bison carcase is less than that of a Hereford. They are slow to mature but the meat is heavily weighted in the more expensive cuts from the huge muscles connecting the neck and thoracic limbs.

Not surprisingly, cattle ranchers have eyed the bison's qualities and tried to inject them into their cattle. There have been three possibly successful hybrids: the Cattalo, the 'American' breed, and the Beefalo.

Three men living thousands of miles apart (in Canada, Kansas and Texas) had a go at 'taking the fur and hump of the bison and placing them upon the back of the domestic ox'. The first was Mossom Boyd of Bobcaygeon, Ontario, but his herd was dispersed. Twenty of his hybrids were acquired by the Canadian Experimental Farms Service (CEFS) in 1916 but none of them produced offspring. The CEFS continued to experiment (they also tried crossing yak with cattle) and by the 1950s they had promising results. Cattle × bison hybrid cows and quarterbred bison Cattalo outperformed domestic cattle when foraging on upland ranges in winter conditions, where the dense hairy coats protected them from the cold winds. The best results were obtained by using domestic bulls on bison cows (vice versa led to excessive amounts of placental fluids and the subsequent loss of cow and calf). First-cross hybrids were sterile in the males but usually fertile in the females, which had a 60% success rate when put to domestic bulls. Their calves were born small but grew fast and weaned at higher weights than Hereford calves. Sterility in the hybrid males was beginning to be overcome by selection when the project ceased in 1964. There is still potential for developing hardy, long-lived cattle/bison hybrid cows to produce quarterbred bison for the American meat market.

Art Jones of Portales, New Mexico, has developed the 'American' breed, adapted to the American south-west ranges. It is said to be half Brahman, a quarter Charolais, an eighth bison and a sixteenth each of Hereford and Shorthorn, but it has not yet proved itself.

In 1973 it was announced that a Californian rancher, D.C. Basolo, had a herd of five thousand 'cow–buffalo hybrids' which were claimed to be hardy, thrifty, quick to reach marketable weights of lean meat, disease-resistant and — very important — readily able to reproduce. The animals seemed to show very little trace of bison in appearance or in blood samples taken by researchers although the rancher claimed that his 'Beefalo' bulls were three-eighths bison, three-eighths Charolais and a quarter Hereford. There is an American Beefalo Association with a Herd Book and a specification that the true Beefalo is three-eighths American bison and five-eighths domestic cattle.

Yak

The bulky, hairy, bushy-tailed, grunting yak lives high up in the mountains of central Asia. There is a wild yak and a domesticated yak and they interbreed. The domestic yak comes in all sorts of colours — white, grey, black, brown, red, tawny, sometimes white-patched and sometimes piebald. It looks rather like a small, hardy breed of ordinary cattle and its greatest distinguishing features are probably its charateristic grunt and its bushy tail. It also has more ribs than domestic cattle, which give it a longer looking body. It has curved horns and a hairy udder. It is superbly adapted to living at high altitudes in cold, dry climates on very poor feed. Locally it is important as a generous provider of milk (6.5–7% butterfat), meat (dark and coarse), hair (plucked for ropes, felt and tents), leather, dung (for fuel), and muscle power for draught and pack work.

The bull can mate at any time of year, which is his misfortune as the cows are seasonal — they come on heat in the winter. The gestation period can be short compared with cattle, ranging from 224 to 284 days.

The yak can be crossed with various cattle and bison and the hybrids can live at lower altitudes (5,000–10,000ft). In the domestic cattle cross the male hybrid offspring are sterile and the females fertile. They show heterosis in weight, size and milk production; the males are very large and make good draught animals. There was recently a 'YakMac' in Scotland, which was the result of a yak bull on a West Highland cow, an appropriate combination because the two do look very similar. The youngster grew to look like an oversized Highland.

Yak fibre has traditionally been imported into this country by textile manufactuers.

Water Buffalo

The history of the domestic water buffalo goes back more than four thousand years. They were originally used as work animals and are intelligent and easy to train; they seem to like humans and are very placid and tranquil.

Apart from draught work, they are important dairy animals in many countries. The average milking buffalo in India gives a lot more milk than the average dairy cow in similar circumstances and lactations of 1,000kg (2,200lb) are common. In Italy they are machine milked twice a day and the average daily yield is 8–10kg (18–22lb). In Bulgaria they regularly attain yields of 2,000–2,500kg (4,400–5,500lb) over a 300-day lactation and have even recorded as much as 4,000kg (8,800lb). India can beat that, with an example of 5,000kg (11,000lb) in one lactation.

All buffalo milk is rich in butterfat (average 7–10%) and some individuals can produce as much as 15%. As milking animals they are obviously very useful indeed, despite recent reports in the British press that water buffalo accounted for more human deaths in Africa in 1985 than lions did! They also have outstanding potential as meat producers: slaughtered at twelve to eighteen months they can weigh 300–350kg (660–770lbs) and with a superb food conversion rate they produce it much more cheaply than cattle. The meat is lean and tender.

As their name implies, these buffalo love to wallow and they are strong swimmers. They do well in marshy areas or seasonally flooded regions and have adapted to many environments. They are thriving in several South and Central American countries, Australia, Papua New Guinea, Trinidad, Florida and Louisiana, the USSR, Iran and Iraq, Egypt, Indonesia and Malaysia, China, and all over India and Pakistan. In Europe the principal herds are in Bulgaria, Italy, Greece, Yugoslavia, Albania and Rumania and there are 122 million water buffalo in the world.

In the Middle Ages some were introduced to France, Spain, Germany and England but failed to become established. Perhaps someone could try again?

13 The Future

The climatic research unit at the University of East Anglia has come up with a long-range weather forecast for the next century, based on the growing levels of carbon dioxide in the atmosphere. They say that the earth's temperature has already risen by 5°C (9°F) since 1850 and that it will increase by another 4.5°C (8°F) by 2065. This will turn Europe and North America into drought-stricken deserts, and a 3-foot rise in sea levels will cause extensive flooding in East Anglia and Kent, exaggerated by a geological slide into the North Sea. (Fortunately the predicted 7°C rise in temperature at the North Pole is three degrees below that needed to thaw the ice-cap. Such an event would increase sea levels by another 13 feet and nobody has told us how much of Britain would keep its head above water.)

Eighty years from now, will we have livestock capable of surviving in a British desert? Quite apart from the weather forecast, think of the Sahara: much of the land on its margins was once very productive but because there is always so much pressure (and incentive) to over-utilize land for food production the desert spread and the good land became part of the wastes. That could happen here, too.

In less extreme circumstances, will we have pigs capable of foraging or making use of roughage rather than relying heavily on concentrates? When the cost of housing and heating becomes too high, will our pigs survive out of doors or will they by then all be pale imitations of their former selves?

If the day comes when we can no longer afford to pour nitrogen on to our pastures, will we have the livestock that can do well on less, with the most efficient food conversion rates for the situation? Will we have livestock hardy enough to live outside and act as walking dung-carts? When veterinary feeds become as high as those of lawyers, will we have cows and ewes that can give birth unaided? If there was another 'conventional' war could our native livestock fill the gap when we are cut off from importing frozen meat or Continental beef-boosters? And if it comes to the unthinkable will we have anything that can survive the nuclear winter?

Here is another scenario for the future, imagined by the chief agricultural adviser of a large animal-feedstuffs company.

There will be five new technical revolutions:

1. Livestock production will become even more intensive and it will spread to sheep farming.
2. There will be a dramatic move away from pedigree breeds as such. The era of the productive hybrid has already begun (pigs and chickens). Purebreds will only be needed as grandparent stock.
3. Vets will practise much more preventive medicine.
4. The area available for lowland grazing will shrink under the encroachment of other interests. Hill cattle and sheep will continue to graze uplands and marginal land but most of the remaining agricultural land will be used for cash crops rather than grass, with an emphasis on foods for direct human consumption rather than animal consumption. Animal feeds will be obtained mainly from crop residues and agricultural wastes.
5. Animal welfare and environmental considerations will be increasingly important and will give rise to an army of bureaucrats and inspectors, which will in turn make animal production very expensive indeed (in complying with the new regulations) which of course means that animal-based foods will be very expensive too.

Do you see a role in this scenario for minor breeds? During the first revolution they will surely be even more endangered. Many of them are much better suited to extensive than to intensive farming.

In the second revolution they will be much in demand (if they still exist) but their numbers will not need to be high. In the third revolution they should come into their own — so many of them are hardier and healthier than more productive animals. In the fourth they should also do well: many are hill breeds anyway and many of them are efficient at converting lower quality food into meat, milk and fibre. (The fourth revolution can already be seen at work in the 'dirt' feed-lots of the United States, where beef cattle are stocked at two hundred to the acre.)

In the fifth revolution? A big environmental factor has been omitted here: increased leisure. Time to stand and stare. At what? At acres of cabbages? At rows of soya beans? What a relief it will be to see a placid herd of white cattle grazing a park, or a bunch of horned primitive sheep living freely on an island, or a mountainside alive with cashmere-coated goats, or a comfortable pig grubbing about in a copse.

In April 1986 the Centre for Agricultural Strategy at Reading University published its report *Alternative enterprises for agriculture in the UK*. Among alternative animal enterprises it seriously considered the practical and economic possibilities for farming several of the more unusual species mentioned in this book (and others which are not). It also looked at different ways of rearing more conventional livestock.

To be realistically useful, such enterprises must be not only productive but must also find, or create, a good enough market to provide adequate returns to the producer. In the latter respect the report noted products which are currently imported at quite high levels but which could be produced at home instead, and also products for which at present there is no (or very limited) consumer demand but for which the market might soon develop, either of its own accord or with imaginative encouragement.

Excepting fur-bearing mammals, domestic poultry, fish and invertebrates, none of which are within the scope of this book, the most interesting potential enterprises seemed to be:

★ Deer farming on the uplands.
★ Goat farming for milk, fibre and meat.
★ Wallaby farming for leather and low-fat meat.
★ Alpaca and llama farming for fibre.
★ Outdoor pig farming (breeding sows).
★ Rabbit rearing for meat and fibre.
★ Reindeer (meat) for the harsher Scottish environments.
★ Fine-wool production from Merino and Merino-cross sheep.
★ Milking-ewe flocks.
★ Yak farming for hair and wool.
★ Agroforestry (silvo-pastoral systems).

These are listed here in random order with no rank of preference or practicability. Food for thought.

Combined grazing by a mixture of wild animals does less damage to vegetation *and produces more useful meat* than does the same weight of a single domestic species on the same area. Have you considered mixing wild and domestic animals to exploit a varied environment? The most obvious combination is pasture improvement by (slight cheat) feral goats which remove the coarse stuff and leave the clovers and grasses to sheep.

In Venezuela they combine capybara, cattle and fish. On sloping land they build dams to make paddock-boundary canals. Fish in the water. Capybara on the canal banks. Cattle in the paddocks.

In the Philippines they triple-crop fish, rice and vegetables. Fish and rice in the water, cabbages on ridges between the paddy fields — drain the whole complex when the rice is ripe and harvest the lot in one go.

What about the pig/tilapia/algae cycle? Pig manure for the ponds encourages the growth of algae, which feeds the tilapia, which are fed to the pigs, which . . .

At a huge Siberian research base (200,000 acres) they are studying how different animals adapt to local conditions and trying to evolve new strains for livestock farming by creating a gene pool of domestic and wild animals. Prominent among the domestic breeds on the base are Lincoln longwool and Romney sheep, Jersey cows, and West Highland and Galloway cattle. They have already crossed Jerseys with aboriginal Yakut cattle to produce an exceptionally hardy beast which can take the worst Siberian climate and yield excellent meat. The Lincolns have crossed very successfullly with wild Altai sheep.

Dr Tom Wagner of Ohio State University gave a talk in the spring of 1986 to the British Society of Animal Production. He said that very soon not only will genetic engineering improve the performance of livestock but also our cows, sheep and goats will be engineered so that they can manufacture drugs used in medicine and these will be extracted from their milk.

Watch out, livestock — minor and rare breeds especially: they are after your genes!

This book has tried to plant the seeds of the future in the minds of those who are responsible for the present and whose imaginations are fertile. There are many, many roles for minor breeds even if they are not yet recognized. Some of those roles are commercial, and some go deeper. The breeds are precious assets: do not let them sink into the sunset. Use them, or lose them. Leave a *living* legacy.

There is a phrase that is quoted so often it tends to become trite but it is entirely appropriate to the minor breeds and it will be repeated by future generations:

'Hats off to the past . . . Coats off for the future!'

Appendix I
Condition scoring

DAIRY COWS

The aim is to estimate the quantity of fatty tissue under the skin. This will give an indication of the cow's body reserves. Two areas are assessed:

(a) The tailhead area.

(b) The loin area.

Stand directly behind the cow and see that she is relaxed. Using the same hand in each case, feel the degree of fatness around the tailhead area and the loin area, and assess fatness scores for each (see below) to the nearest half point. If the tailhead score differs from the loin score by more than one point, adjust the tailhead score by no more than half a point. This adjusted tailhead score is used as the condition score.

The scores

0 = VERY POOR

There is a deep cavity under the tail and around the tailhead. The skin is drawn tightly over the pelvis with no tissue detectable in between. There is no fatty tissue in the loin area and the shapes of the transverse processes of the spine are clearly visible. The animal appears generally emaciated.

1 = POOR

Cavity present around tailhead, no fatty tissue felt between skin and pelvis there, but skin is supple. Ends of transverse processes in loin area are sharp to the touch and the upper surfaces can be felt easily. Deep depression in the loin.

2 = MODERATE

Shallow tailhead cavity lined with fatty tissue. Some fatty tissue felt under the skin. Pelvis easily felt. Ends of transverse processes in loin area feel rounded. Depression in loin.

3 = GOOD

Fatty tissue easily felt over tailhead area. Skin smooth but pelvis can be felt. Ends of transverse processes can only be felt with pressure and there is a thick layer of tissue on top. Slight depression visible in loin.

4 = FAT

Folds of soft fatty tissue at tailhead. Patches of fat apparent under the skin. Pelvis can only be felt with firm pressure. Transverse processes cannot be felt at all. No depression visible in loin between backbone and hip bones.

5 = GROSSLY FAT
Tailhead buried in fatty tissue. Skin distended. No part of pelvis or bone structure can be felt, even with firm pressure.

Ideal condition scores

Maiden heifer at service (for best conception rate): 2.5–3.5
If below 2, give extra feeding from six weeks before service.
If 4 or over, any extra feeding will *reduce* conception rate.

Cow at service (for best conception rate):

Below 1.5	52%
1.5	56%
2.0	68%
Over 2.0	72%

Cow at calving (effect on subsequent milk yield per day):

0.5 to 1.5	– 1.8kg
2.0	0
2.5 to 3.5	+ 1.1kg
4	– 1.8kg

The highest yields are obtained from cows calving at a condition score of 3.5.

SUMMARY: For best results aim for:
3.0 to 3.5 at calving.
More than 2 at first service.
3.0 to 3.5 at drying off.

BEEF CATTLE

A beef animal is in prime condition for slaughter when it is at a level of finishing that will command the best price per kilogram. You need to check the build-up of subcutaneous fat, and the most practical method is to handle the animal regularly by feeling four specific sites. Make sure the animal is relaxed, because tensed muscles feel harder and could mask the true fat levels.

(a) TAILHEAD
Use fingertips to feel the depth of fat over the pin bone. This will give a general guide to the level of finish, but note that different breeds deposit fat at this point at different rates. For any given fat level, bulls will be heavier than steers, and steers heavier than heifers.

(b) LOIN
Only assess the left-hand side of the animal, because the subcutaneous fat cover on the right side is masked by the kidney knob and channel fat. In the loin area you are assessing musculature as well as finish. Using your fingertips, spread your hand and press down so that your hand covers a wide area of firm, lean flesh. Lean feels solid; fat feels more spongy. Feel the top of the spine with the tips of your fingers to check fat covering.

(c) SHOULDER
With a flat hand and spread fingers, feel the shoulder blade and chine all over. Again, lean feels solid under your fingertips and fat feels spongy.

(d) RIB CAGE
Put a flat hand against the ribs and push it backwards and forwards. The animal's fat acts as a lubricant between the ribs and the skin. The fatter it is, the easier it will be to move your hand.

SHEEP
Body condition in sheep can be assessed at four points but the first two are the most important.

(a) Around the tail root ('dock')
(b) In the loin area: along the spinous processes of the backbone (the bits that jut up from the spine) and over the eye muscles and the tips of the transverse processes of the spine (the bits that go sideways) in the lumbar region.
(c) Along the spinous processes over the shoulder.
(d) Along the breastbone (sternum).

The fatter an animal is, the more difficult it will be to detect individual bones at the tail root, and the less prominent will be the spinous and transverse processes along the backbone. Make allowances for the thickness of the fleece! Do not press hard with your fingers because you will cause bruising.

Dock
Place your finger and thumb on either side of the tail base and feel the fat covering the vertebrae. Fat levels here will indicate the level of finish all over the body.

Loin
Press your fingers down on the spine behind the last rib and above the

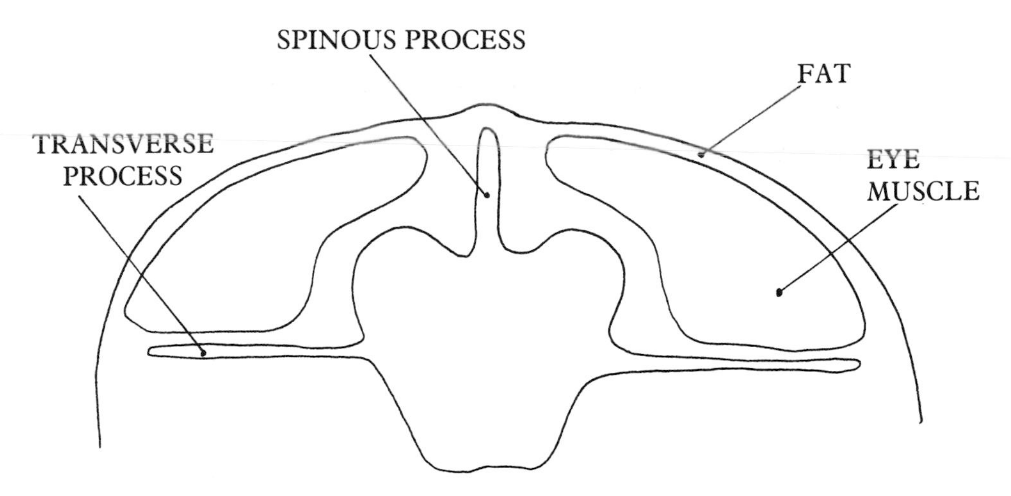

ASSESSMENT OF A LAMB'S FAT CLASS
OR A SHEEP'S CONDITION

kidneys. Locate the protruding spinous processes. At the same time use your thumb to feel the ends of the transverse processes. Decide on the degree of roundness or sharpness at the tips of the spinous processes and see whether you can pass your fingers easily under the ends of the transverses. Then evaluate the fullness of the eye muscle and the degree of fat cover over it.

Shoulder

Extend your fingers along the spine towards the head and press down gently between the shoulder-blades. Fat feels spongy, lean feels more solid.

Sternum

If you are still not sure, sit the animal up and feel the fat over its breastbone. If you are not sure even then, weigh it!

You can then assess a fat classification for the animal, from zero (on point of death from emaciation) to 5 (excessively fat).

0 Extremely emaciated and on point of death. Impossible to detect any muscular or fatty tissue between skin and bones.

1 Fat cover very thin. Individual bones very easy to detect. Processes very prominent and sharp, and easy to feel between them. Eye muscle shallow with no fat cover.
2 Fat cover thin. Processes easily felt but smooth rather than sharp. Spinous ones feel like fine corrugations. It is possible to pass your fingers under the ends of the transverses with a little pressure. Eye muscle moderate depth but little fat cover.
3 Spinous processes only slightly elevated, with smooth rounded tips. Transverses smooth and well covered, can only feel over the ends if applying quite firm pressure. Eye muscle full with moderate cover of fat.
4 Spinous processes can just be detected as a hard line between the eye muscles. Ends of transverses cannot be felt. Eye muscle full with thick fat covering.
5 Impossible to feel processes even with firm pressure. Depression between fat layers where you would normally feel the spinous processes. Eye muscle very full with very thick fat cover. There may be large deposits of fat over the rump and tail.

The body condition of the ewe at tupping determines her ovulation rate and affects lambing percentages. Score ewes six to eight weeks before tupping and make any necessary adjustments (up or down) in feeding. To achieve the highest lambing percentages, the optimum body condition at mating is 3 or 4 for lowland ewes, but scores vary markedly according to breed and environment. Hill sheep do not normally score more than about 3.

Ewes in better condition tend to produce higher lambing percentages and the lambs are more viable at birth, mortality rates are lower and the ewes milk better.

At lambing time overfat ewes are more susceptible to lambing difficulties and twin lamb disease. But if the score is less than 2.5 before lambing, the ewe needs some supplementary feeding.

Appendix II Meat and Livestock Commission Classifications

BEEF

Five factors can be taken into account in the classification of a beef carcase:

Weight
Fatness
Conformation
Sex (steer, heifer, cow, bull)
Age (optional)

Fatness

Fatness is assessed in five classes, from 1 (very lean) to 5 (very fat). Classes 4 and 5 are each subdivided into L (lower, i.e. leaner) and H (higher, i.e. fatter).

Conformation

Conformation describes the overall shape of the carcase and is, in effect, an assessment of the thickness of lean and fat covering the skeleton. There are five main classes: E, U, R, O and P. U, O and P are subdivided into upper (+) and lower (−) bands. Class E includes carcases of outstanding shape, particularly the double-muscled types. Class P includes thinly muscled carcases of inferior beef shape, usually in extreme dairy-breed types and in cows.

		FAT CLASS → Increasing fatness						
		1	2	3	4L	4H	5L	5H
CONFORMATION CLASS	E							
	U+							
	−U							
	R							
	O+							
↑	−O							
Increasing conformation	P+							
	−P							

Conformation class is expressed first. For example, a carcase in conformation class R with a fat classification of 4L is described as **R4L**.

Reducing fatness has a far greater effect on increasing meat yield than does improving conformation, but improved conformation yields a slightly higher percentage of more valuable cuts. Fat trim is waste! The yield of saleable meat as a percentage of carcase weight increases with increasing conformation and decreases with increasing fat. For example:

U+2	might yield 74.4%
U+5L	might yield 68.4%
R2	might yield 73.5%
R5L	might yield 67.5%
−O2	might yield 71.8%
−O5L	might yield 65.8%

SHEEP

The factors which can be taken into account when classifying sheep carcases are:

Weight
Fatness
Conformation
Category (age/sex group)

		FAT					→	Increasing fatness
		1	2	3L	3H	4L	4H	5
CONFORMATION	E							▒
	U							▒
Improving conformation	R							▒
	O							▒
↑	P+	▒	▒	▒	▒	▒	▒	▒
	−P	▒	▒	▒	▒	▒	▒	▒

▒ = Not eligible for SVP (Sheep Variable Premium)

Fatness

Fat classes range from 1 (very lean) to 5 (very fat). In addition, the letter **K** indicates excessive kidney knob and channel fat (over 5% of carcase weight).

Conformation
Conformation is based on a visual assessment of the thickness of flesh in relation to the skeleton. With effect from 6 January 1986 a new classification for sheep came into being. The old conformation classes were E (extra), A (average) C (poor) and Z (very poor). Any sheep in classes C or Z (or in fat class 5) was not eligible for the Sheep Variable Premium. With the new European conformation classification, class A is divided into U, R and O. C and Z are normally combined as P but can be subdivided into P+ and −P.

Conformation is largely determined by breeding. Hill lambs tend to be rather angular and leggy. Crossbreds from a meat sire can be blocky enough to rate classification as E or U.

Category
L = Lamb (born and marketed within a year beginning on the first Monday in January or born after the beginning of October in the year prior to marketing).
YS = Other clean sheep under one year old.
MS = Clean sheep over one year old (with two or more fully developed permanent incisor teeth).
Rams and ewes may be classified on request.

Weight
The adult liveweight of a breed (which is the average of mature ram and ewe weights) can be used to indicate the liveweight of lambs required to produce carcases in the target range. Some example of liveweights of breeds in this book are:

Devon Closewool	66kg (146lb)
Devon & Cornwall Longwool	95kg (209lb)
Dorset Down	77kg (170lb)
Dorset Horn	82kg (181lb)
Lincoln Longwool	91kg (201lb)
Oxford Down	100kg (220lb)
Southdown	61kg (134lb)
Teeswater	96kg (212lb)
Welsh Mountain	50kg (110lb)

The adult breed liveweight (ABL) is a reliable guide to the average fat class of batches of lambs within a breed type. Lambs that have grown well without a check and which are slaughtered at half their potential ABL will kill out at about 48% and produce carcases in fat class 3 for most breeds, though primitives and very high-performance breeds can sometimes be taken to much higher proportional weights and still be lean enough for class 2 or 3L.

As a general guide, lambs slaughtered about 10% below the predicted slaughter weight of a particular breed will mostly produce carcases of fat class 2.

To meet the demands for leaner lamb, either sell the same type of lamb at a lighter weight or sell at the same weight using a combination of larger breed types.

Ewe lambs are fatter than wethers of the same breed at the same weight. To achieve the same fat class, wethers should be killed at 5% above the average slaughter weight and ewe lambs at 10% below it.

Winter lambs grow more slowly than lambs finished off on grass and can generally be taken to slightly heavier weights and remain in the same fat class.

PIGS

The five factors which can be taken into account in classifying a pig carcase are:

Cold carcase weight	(hot carcase weight less appropriate deductions)
Backfat thickness	
Visual assessment	(all carcases which are scraggy, deformed, blemished, pigmented, coarse-skinned or partly condemned or with soft fat or pale muscle are classed Z)
Conformation	(optional; carcases with poor conformation — particularly of leg but not poor enough to be scraggy — are classed as C)
Length	(optional)

Fat

Backfat thickness is measured over the eye muscle by a probe inserted at fixed points P1, P2 or P3 level with the head of the last rib.

Pork and cutter carcases are usually measured at P1 and P3. The measurements are added and recorded in an inverted triangle. Split bacon carcases are measured at P2. (Visible backfat at the shoulder and loin can also be measured.) The P2 measurement is included in a triangle. Where applicable, the letters C or Z are marked outside the triangle. Cold carcase weight can be marked on the carcase if required.

Classification information is marked on all clean pig carcases and on young boar carcases weighing 62kg (137lb) or less.

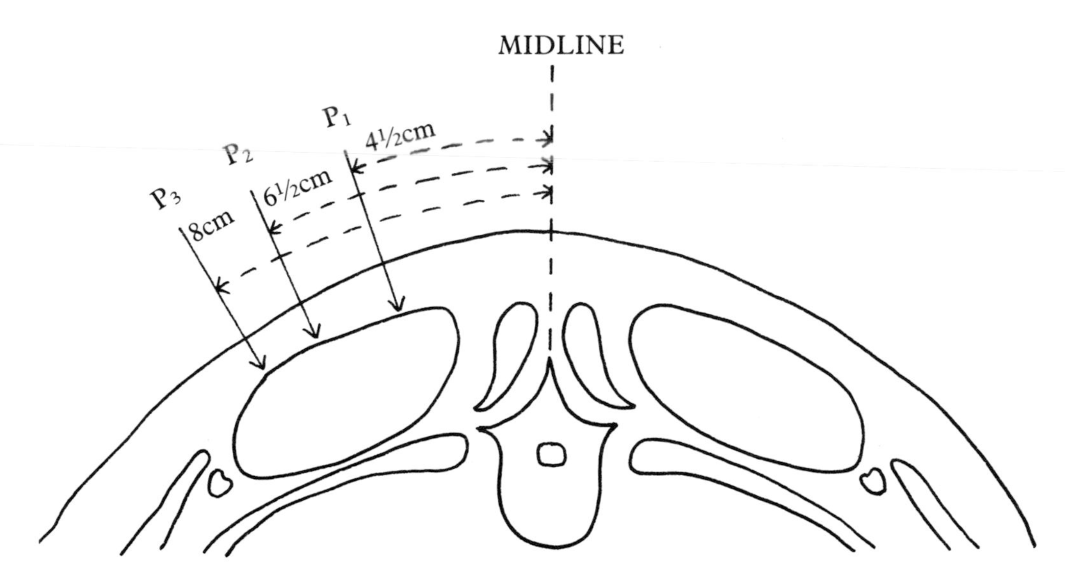

MEASURING PIG BACKFAT THICKNESS

The EEC Pig Carcase Grading Scheme is due to be implemented in all member states by 1 January 1989. Existing and new grade designations are as follows:

EEC grades		*Carcase lean meat content*
Existing	*New*	
E	E	55% or more
I	U	>50%, <55%
II	R	>45%, <50%
III	O	>40%, <45%
IV	P	40% or less
	S (special)	60% or more

In 1985 the majority of British pigs averaged the following measurements at P2:

Type of carcase	*Av. carcase weight in kg (lb)*	*Av. P2 (mm)*
Less than 60kg (130lb)	51.1 (113lb)	11.5
60–80kg (130–180lb) (mainly bacon)	66.6 (147lb)	13.9
More than 80kg (180lb)	91.6 (202lb)	22.1
All	63.4 (140lb)	13.4

The main categories of finished pigs are as follows, but the weights are only a general guide as there is some overlap between categories:

PORKER	40–67kg (88–148lb) liveweight
CUTTER	68–82kg (149–181lb) liveweight
*BACONER	83–101kg (182–223lb) liveweight**
HEAVY HOGS	102–120kg (224–265lb) liveweight

*Lowest backfat specifications.
**Ungraded pigs in this range are often described as cutters.

The propensity to lay down fat increases with age.

Appendix III The Rare Breeds Survival Trust

The Rare Breeds Survival Trust, which is a registered charity, was established in 1973. Its principal activities 'are, for the benefit of the public, to ensure the preservation of breeds and breeding groups of domesticated farm livestock of importance in the promotion of agriculture, being numerically small, and having characteristics worthy of preservation in the interests of zoological research and education.'

Several major projects were listed in an ambitious programme designed to achieve the aims of the Trust:

Survey of rare breed populations
A population survey is carried out every three years. The most recent survey was undertaken in 1985/6.

North Ronaldsay sheep project
The behaviour of North Ronaldsay sheep has been studied as a post-graduate project.

Register of congenital defects
The Trust's Technical Consultant, Lawrence Alderson, maintains a record of defects which occur in rare breeds and seeks to confirm which of these are inherited.

Breed incentive project
This is the normal medium for the provision of financial support to endangered breeds, and many of them have benefited from it.

Ease of parturition study
This important study, based on pelvic measurements, is identifying the degree of ease with which different breeds can give birth. It has already been discovered that most of the primitive breeds of sheep are much better proportioned than many major breeds in this respect. Studies of cows are nearly complete and results at the time of writing show that the Shetland and the White Park have no calving problems but that the British White has more problems than other rare breeds.

Polymorphisms
The study of blood types and chromosome structures provides informa-

tion on the relationships between the breeds and can assist in the tracing of breed origins. It has already shown that White Park cattle are not only a separate breed from British Whites but also that they are a long way apart from all our other breeds of cattle.

Linga Holm project
The Trust has acquired the island of Linga Holm, on which it manages its own flock of North Ronaldsay sheep.

Bull performance tests
Bulls of several rare breeds have been performance tested. The Trust no longer funds this project.

Polyunsaturated fats
The proportions, distribution and type of fat in a carcase are becoming more and more important. This study is now underway.

Special qualities
Many subjects are included under this heading — all of them leading to the identification and better understanding of the characteristics and qualities of different breeds.

In addition to these projects, which were launched as part of a major programme, the Trust is involved in many other activities:

Breed structure analysis
Research into the status of families and lines within breeds so that advice can be given on making best use of existing bloodlines to the benefit of the breed as a whole. The Trust can give breeders guidance on breeding programmes, mating policy, sire selection etc.

Breed registration facilities
The Trust maintains a Combined Flock Book (originally a private venture) for the registration of rare breeds of sheep such as the Boreray, Castlemilk Moorit, Cotswold, Hebridean, Manx Loghtan, Norfolk Horn, North Ronaldsay, Portland, Soay and Whitefaced Woodlands. It also provides registration facilities for 120 pig breeders, Shetland cattle, and Bagot goats. In addition it assists several breed societies with their own registration facilities.

Breeders' workshops
The Trust's Technical Consultant helps groups of breeders by attending all-day workshops which not only enable them to learn more about their

breeds and to gain practical experience but also to meet others with similar interests.

Demonstration programme
Representatives and supporters of the Trust give displays about its work at agricultural shows throughout the season.

Embryo storage study, semen bank etc.
The Trust maintains a semen bank (cattle and pigs) and is investigating embryo storage and establishing a bank of frozen fertilized eggs from selected rare breeds.

The Technical Committee is also looking at tissue culture, gene transference and other ways of ensuring the future of rare breeds.

Annual show and sale
The annual rare breeds show organized by the Trust at Stoneleigh in September is of major importance. It is essential as an event at which breeders can display their animals and see other examples of their breed, and it is also the most important annual sale of rare breeds, giving people a chance to buy new stock. The two-day event is popular with the general public, who come to it in their thousands.

The Ark
The Trust publishes a monthly magazine which is circulated to all its members and which also finds its way into libraries overseas.

Appendix IV
Useful Addresses

Note: Individual breed societies are not included here because they have a tendency to change their addresses frequently! Up to date details can be obtained, where appropriate, from the Rare Breeds Survival Trust, the British Goat Society, and the national breeders' associations for cattle, pigs and sheep.

ANIMAL AND GRASSLAND RESEARCH INSTITUTE (formerly NATIONAL INSTITUTE FOR RESEARCH INTO DAIRYING)
Church Lane, Shinfield, Reading RG2 2AQ

ANIMAL BREEDING RESEARCH ORGANIZATION
West Mains Road, Edinburgh EH9 3QJ

BRITISH AGRICULTURAL EXPORT COUNCIL
35 Belgrave Square, London SW1X 8QN

BRITISH DEER FARMERS ASSOCIATION
Cluanie-an-Teanassie, Beauly, Inverness-shire

BRITISH GOAT PRODUCERS ASSOCIATION
c/o Mrs Jas Barley, AGRI, Shinfield, Reading RG2 2AQ

BRITISH GOAT SOCIETY
Rougham, Bury St Edmunds, Suffolk, IP30 9LJ

BRITISH MILKING SHEEP ASSOCIATION
Colonsay, Hampton Lovett, Droitwich, Worcestershire

BRITISH SHEEP DAIRYING ASSOCIATION
Wield Wood, Alresford, Hampshire

BRITISH WOOL MARKETING BOARD
Oak Mills, Clayton, Bradford, W. Yorkshire BD14 6JD

CENTRE FOR AGRICULTURAL STRATEGY
University of Reading, 1 Earley Gate, Reading RG6 2AT

COLOURED SHEEP BREEDERS ASSOCIATION
Bagatelle House, Lyncombe Vale, Bath BA2 4ND

GOAT ADVISORY BUREAU
9 Pitts Lane, Earley, Reading RG6 1BX

HILL FARMING RESEARCH ORGANIZATION
Bush Estate, Penicuik, Midlothian EH26 0PY

INSTITUTE OF ANIMAL GENETICS
The King's Buildings, West Mains Road, Edinburgh EH9 3JX

INSTITUTE OF ANIMAL PHYSIOLOGY
Babraham, Cambridge CB2 4AT
MEAT AND LIVESTOCK COMMISSION
PO Box 44, Queensway House, Bletchley, Milton Keynes MK2 2EF
MEAT RESEARCH INSTITUTE
Langford, Bristol BS18 7DY
MILK MARKETING BOARD
Thames Ditton, Surrey KT7 0EL
MINISTRY OF AGRICULTURE, FISHERIES & FOOD,
Livestock Division
Great Westminster House, Horseferry Road, London SW1P 2AE
NATIONAL CATTLE BREEDERS' ASSOCIATION
106 High Street, Tring, Hertfordshire HP23 4AF
NATIONAL PIG BREEDERS' ASSOCIATION
7 Rickmansworth Road, Watford, Hertfordshire WD1 7HE
NATIONAL SHEEP ASSOCIATION
Cholesbury, Tring, Hertfordshire HP23 6PD
RARE BREEDS SURVIVAL TRUST
4th Street, National Agricultural Centre, Stoneleigh,
Kenilworth, Warwickshire CV8 2LG
SCOTTISH CASHMERE PRODUCERS' ASSOCIATION
c/o S.A.O.S., Claremont House, 18/19 Claremont Crescent, Edinburgh

Appendix V
Where to See Rare Breeds

RBST approved centres

APPLEBY CASTLE
Appleby-in-Westmorland, Cumbria CA16 6XH

ASHDOWN FOREST FARM
Wych Cross, East Sussex RH18 5JN

COTSWOLD FARM PARK
Guiting Power, Cheltenham, Glos. GL54 5UG

CROXTETH HOME FARM
Croxteth Hall, West Derby, Liverpool L12 0HB

GRAVES PARK (City of Sheffield Recreation Department)
PO Box 151, Meersbrook Park, Sheffield S8 9FL

HOLLANDEN RARE FARM ANIMALS
Mill Lane, Hildenborough, Sevenoaks, Kent TN15 0SG

PARKE RARE BREEDS FARM
Parke Estate, Bovey Tracey, Newton Abbot, Devon

RIBER CASTLE FAUNA RESERVE AND WILDLIFE PARK
Riber Castle, Matlock, Derbyshire DE4 5JU

SHUGBOROUGH PARK FARM
The Shugborough Estate, Milford, Staffordshire ST17 0XB

TEMPLE NEWSAM HOME FARM
Temple Newsam Estate, Leeds LS15 0AD

TILGATE PARK NATURE CENTRE
Crawley, West Sussex RH10 5PQ

WIMPOLE HOME FARM
Wimpole, Arrington, Royston, Herts SG8 0BW

National Trust properties with rare breeds

ARDRESS HOUSE
64 Ardress Road, Annaghmore, Portadown, Co. Armagh, N.I.

THE ARGORY
Moy, Dungannon, Co. Tyrone, N.I.

CHARLECOTE PARK
Wellesbourne, Warwickshire

HARDWICK HALL
Doe Lea, Chesterfield, Derbyshire

HOLNICOTE ESTATE
Minehead, Somerset
TATTON PARK
Knutsford, Cheshire
WEST GREEN HOUSE
Hartley Witney, Basingstoke, Hampshire

Appendix VI Imperial and Metric Conversions

WEIGHTS

1 pound (lb)	= 0.454 kg	1 kilogram (kg)	= 2.205lb
1 hundredweight (cwt)	= 50.802 kg		
1 ton	= 1.016 t	1 tonne (t)	=0.984 tons

FLUIDS

1 pint (pt)	= 0.568 l	1 litre (l)	= 1.76 pt/0.22 gal
1 gallon (gal)	= 4.546 l		

MILK MEASUREMENTS

Milk yields can be measured by volume (pints, gallons, litres) or by weight (pounds, kilograms). The correlation between volume and weight depends on the solids content of the milk. As a general guide, at 3.6% butterfat one gallon of milk weighs 10.32 pounds, or one litre of milk weighs 1.03 kilograms. This is the basis of the conversion rates used below:

1 pint (20.64 ounces)	= 0.57 litres (0.59 kilograms)
1 gallon (10.32 pounds)	= 4.55 litres (4.68 kilograms)
1 litre (1.03 kilograms)	= 0.22 gallons (2.27 pounds)
1 pound (0.97 gallons)	= 0.46 kilograms (0.44 litres)
1 kilogram (0.98 litres)	= 2.21 pounds (0.21 gallons)

LENGTH

1 inch (in)	= 2.54 cm	1 centimetre (cm)	= 0.3937 in
1 foot (ft)	= 0.3048 m		
1 yard (yd)	= 0.9144m	1 metre (m)	= 1.0936 yd
1 mile	= 0.6093 km	1 kilometre (km)	= 0.6214 miles

AREA

1 acre	= 0.4047 ha	1 hectare (ha)	= 2.4711 acres

Appendix VII
Genetics Glossary

ALLELE
One of the alternative forms of a gene occupying the same locus on a chromosome.

BACK-CROSS
Breeding of offspring to one of its parents.

FECUNDITY
A measure of the number of offspring born and reared by a dam.

FERTILITY
A measure of the ability of a female to conceive and bear offspring, or of the male to fertilize the female.

GENE
A basic unit of inheritance.

GENOTYPE
An animal's genetic make-up.

HERITABILITY
The degree to which a trait is inherited.

HETEROSIS
The additional performance (if any) shown by the first generation of crossbred progeny above the mean performance of the two parents. Often called HYBRID VIGOUR.

HETEROZYGOUS
With two unlike alleles for a specific locus.

HOMOZYGOUS
With two like alleles for a specific locus.

INBREEDING
Very close breeding, viz parent × offspring or sibling × sibling.

INBREEDING COEFFICIENT
Rate at which heterozygosity is reduced per generation; the probability that two genes at any locus in an individual are alike by descent, i.e. came from some common ancestor via both parents.

LOCUS
Point occupied by a gene on a chromosome.

NICKING
Old term used to describe one or more successful matings between families, strains or breeds.

PHENOTYPE
The outward expression of an animal's genotype.

PREPOTENCY
The ability of an animal (usually sire) to produce offspring like itself.

RECESSIVE
An allele which is masked by a dominant one and which is not normally expressed in the phenotype unless two similar recessives pair.

Appendix VIII Bibliography and References

ALDERSON, Lawrence
The Chance to Survive (Cameron & Tayleur (Books) Ltd. and David & Charles (Publishing) Ltd., 1978)
Rare Breeds (Shire Publications, 1984)
BLAKE, P.W. (ed)
Livestock Production (William Heinemann, 1985)
BOWMAN, John C.
An Introduction to Animal Breeding (Edward Arnold, 1974)
Animals for Man (Edward Arnold, 1977)
BOWMAN, John C. and AINDOW C.T.
Genetic Conservation and the Less Common Breeds of British Cattle, Pigs and Sheep (University of Reading Department of Agriculture and Horticulture, Study No. 13, 1973)
CADZOW, D.J.
The Luing Breed
CARRUTHERS, S.P. (ed)
Alternative Enterprises for Agriculture in the UK (Centre for Agricultural Studies, April 1986)
CLUTTON-BROCK, Juliet
Domesticated Animals from Early Times (Heinemann, 1981)
DALTON, Clive
An Introduction to Practical Animal Breeding (Collins, 1985)
DALTON, Clive and KILGOUR, Ronald
Livestock Behaviour (Granada Publishing, 1984)
ELWES, Henry John
Guide to the Primitive Breeds of Sheep and their Crosses (R & R Clark 1913, reprinted Redwood Burn Ltd. 1983)
ENCYCLOPAEDIA BRITANNICA, 13th edition
FORD, E.B.
Taking Genetics into the Countryside (Weidenfeld & Nicholson, 1981)
FRASER, Allan
Farming for Beef (Crosby Lockwood & Son, 1950)
FRASER, Andrew F.
Farm Animal Behaviour (Bailliere Tindall/Cassell, 1980)
FUSSELL, G.E.
The English Dairy Farmer 1500–1900 (Frank Cass & Co., 1966)

GARNER, Frank H.
The Cattle of Britain (Longmans, Green & Co., 1944)
HALLEY, R.J. (ed)
The Agricultural Notebook, 17th edition (Butterworth & Co, 1982)
HART, Edward
Showing Livestock (David & Charles, 1979)
HENSON, Elizabeth
Rare Breeds in History
HINKS, Dr John
Breeding Dairy Cattle (Farming Press, 1983)
HULME, Susan
Book of the Pig (Spur/Saiga, 1979)
MACDONALD, David (ed)
The Encyclopaedia of Mammals (Geo. Allen & Unwin, 1984)
McFARLAND, David (ed)
The Oxford Companion to Animal Behaviour (O.U.P., 1981)
MACKENZIE, David
Goat Husbandry (Faber & Faber, reprinted 1976)
MASON, I.L. (ed)
Evolution of Domesticated Animals (Longman, 1985)
MILLS, Olivia
Practical Sheep Dairying (Thorsons, 1982)
PONTING, Kenneth
Sheep of the World (Blandford Press, 1980)
ROUSE, H.
World Cattle, Vols. 1 & 2
RUSSELL, Sir John
English Farming (Wm. Collins, 1942)
RYDER, Michael L.
Hair (Edward Arnold, 1973)
Sheep and Man (Duckworth, 1983)
Sheep and Wool for Handicraft Workers (1978)
SAINSBURY, David
Farm Animal Welfare (Collins, 1986)
SCOTT, W. N. (ed)
The Care and Management of Farm Animals (Balliere Tindall/Cassell, 1978)
SMITH, F.V.
Purpose in Animal Behaviour (Hutchinson & Co., 1971)

STEPHENSON, Val
Shepherd's Calendar (A.P.P., 1981)
STOUT, Adam
The Old Gloucester (Alan Sutton Publishing Ltd., 1980)
THEAR, Katie
The Complete Book of Raising Livestock and Poultry (Martin Dunitz, 1980)
THWAITES, J.R.N.
The History of the Wiltshire Horn
URQUHART, Judy
Animals on the Farm: Their History from the Earliest Times to the Present Day (Macdonald & Co., 1983)
WATMOUGH, W.
Practical Inbreeding for the Pedigree Livestock Breeder, 6th edition (Watmoughs Ltd., 1982)
WHEATON-SMITH, Craig
Breeding Better Cows (Dairy Farmer (Books) Ltd., 1957)
WHITLOCK, Ralph
Rare Breeds (Prism Press, 1980)
The English Farm (J.M. Dent & Sons, 1983)
WILLIAMS, Ann
Backyard Pig and Sheep Book (Prism Press, 1977)
WOOD, J.G.
The Natural History of Man (1868/1870)

Booklets

ADAS:
Condition Scoring of Dairy Cows (Leaflet 612)
Dairy Herd Fertility (Ref Book 259)
Farming Deer (Leaflet 678)
Introduction to Cattle Breeding (Booklets 2403–06)
Pig Production and Welfare (Booklet 2483)
Sire and Dam Selection (Booklet 2405)
BRITISH CATTLE BREEDERS' ASSOCIATION
British Cattle
BRITISH SHEEP ASSOCIATION
British Sheep
BRITISH WOOL MARKETING BOARD
British Sheep and Wool

CENTRE FOR TROPICAL VETERINARY MEDICINE, University of Edinburgh
Draught Animal News, No. 4
COUNTRYSIDE COMMISSION
Farm Open Days
MEAT & LIVESTOCK COMMISSION
Beef Carcase Classification
Body Condition Scoring of Ewes
Group Breeding Schemes for Sheep
Lamb Carcase Production
Pig Yearbook 1986
Sheep Carcase Classification
MILK MARKETING BOARD
Dairy Facts & Figures
NATURE CONSERVANCY COUNCIL
The Capture and Handling of Deer
RARE BREEDS SURVIVAL TRUST
The Ark monthly magazine (to the contributors of which I am deeply indebted for a great deal of information)

Papers

BICHARD, Maurice
Current developments in pig breeding (Outlook on Agric. Vol. 11, No. 4, 1982)
BICHARD, M. and DAVID, P.J.
Effectiveness of genetic selection for prolificacy in pigs (J. Reprod. Fert. Supp 1. 33, 127–138, 1985)
CRAWFORD, Dr. R.D.
Assessment and Conservation of Animal Genetic Resources in Canada (Can. J. Anim. Sci. 64, 235–251, June 1984)
HODGES, John, SIMON, D.L., SMITH, Charles *et al.*
Conservation of Animal Genetic Resources (EAAP Livestock Production Science 11, 1984)
WOOD, Dr. J.D.
Factors affecting carcase composition (Span, Vol. 26, No. 1, 1983)
The influence of breed on the carcase and eating quality of pork (J. Sci. Food Agric. 30, 493–8, 1979)

Index

[* indicates table, P indicates picture]

(1) INDEX OF LIVESTOCK BREEDS AND TYPES

(2) INDEX OF PEOPLE AND PLACES

(3) GENERAL INDEX